Introduction to Oilfield Water Technology

PRENTICE-HALL INTERNATIONAL, INC., *London*
PRENTICE-HALL OF AUSTRALIA, PTY, LTD., *Sydney*
PRENTICE-HALL OF CANADA, LTD., *Toronto*
PRENTICE-HALL OF INDIA (PRIVATE) LTD., *New Delhi*
PRENTICE-HALL OF JAPAN, INC., *Tokyo*

Introduction to Oilfield Water Technology

A. G. Ostroff

Field Research Laboratory
Socony Mobil Oil Company, Inc.

Prentice-Hall, Inc.
Englewood Cliffs, N.J.

Preface

The purpose of this book is to provide the basic information necessary for intelligent and competent handling of oilfield waters. The usefulness of this information is not limited to oilfield waters, but is applicable to other industrial waters as well as waste waters. I have tried to present this information clearly and concisely. Selected references are provided which give additional information on subjects covered in this text.

Briefly described in the first chapter are the properties, problems, and methods of treatment of waters as well as discussion of the usefulness and importance of water to the petroleum industry. Chapter 2 discusses the sampling and analysis of water. The next four chapters are devoted to the principal causes of problems encountered with use and handling of water. Chapters 7 through 12 are concerned with methods of treating or conditioning water that will eliminate water problems. The last two chapters are detailed discussions of injection waters and plant waters. Some useful test procedures and sample calculations are included in the Appendix.

Duplication of material in the text has been avoided. The book is organized in the above manner so that the reader will have a good understanding of water problems and methods of corrective treatment before he reads the material on injection and plant waters.

Many people have made significant contributions to the preparation of this manuscript. However, these people cannot be held responsible for the authenticity and accuracy of the presented material. I offer my thanks to Socony Mobil Oil Company for permitting me to engage in this extracurricular project; to E. B. Elfrink for his encouragement and advice; to P.P. Reichertz, E. L. Cook, and L. G. Sharp for their help in processing the manuscript; to E. J. Bednar, J. U. Messenger, A. V. Metler, M. D. Nelson, and G. L. Smith who read the manuscript and offered helpful suggestions; to Mrs. Jerry Davis for typing the manuscript and for the assistance given her by Mrs. Katherine Welch and Mrs. Doris McWilliams; and to Miss Lucille Swindoll for preparing the figures. My appreciation is extended to P. W. Bolmer, J. B. Davis, D. S. Koons, and A. S. Odeh for their opinions on specific portions of the manuscript. I also want to thank the technical journals, book publishers, and equipment manufacturers that permitted me to use their graphs, tables, and illustrations. I very much appreciate the understanding and help of my wife, Nancy C. Ostroff, during the preparation of this manuscript.

In addition, I am very much indebted to Prof. E. R. Erikson of Augustana College (Rock Island, Ill.), Prof. Ogden Baine (deceased) of Southern Methodist University, and Prof. R. T. Sanderson of the State University of Iowa for the guidance, inspiration, patience, and understanding that they gave me during my days as an undergraduate and graduate student. Dedicated teachers of the type represented by these men have enriched the lives of all of us who have had the priviledge of association with them.

A. G. OSTROFF

Dallas, Texas

Contents

3   Scales and Sludges Deposited from Water   55

4   Water and Corrosion   95

Appendix   369

Index   401

Water and its Utilization

1

Water as a Substance

Water is one of the most abundant and important substances on earth. Its chemical formula is H_2O, which signifies two hydrogen atoms and one oxygen atom. Water is unusual in that it exists in nature as a solid, liquid, and gas. At most ambient temperatures, water is a liquid. Some physical constants of water are shown in Table 1.1.

The chemical properties of water are of interest since it is the solvent power of water that causes many oilfield problems. Chemists think of water as the universal solvent. It will dissolve virtually all inorganic substances to some extent. The solvent power of water is great because of the structure of

Table 1.1

PHYSICAL CONSTANTS OF WATER

Mol. Wt.	Den. @ 4°C	M.P. (°C)	B.P. (°C)	Critical Temp. (°C)	Critical Press. (atm)	Heat of Vaporization (cal/m)
18.016	1.00	0	100	374.1	217.7	9,720

the water molecule, its ability to act as an acid or a base, and the fact that it can function as either an oxidizing or a reducing agent.

Theoretically the angle between the hydrogen bonds to the oxygen is 90°, but because of repulsive forces it is actually 105°. This results in a polar molecule, with the oxygen end being partially negative and the end with the hydrogens partially positive. Since inorganic compounds are ionic in nature, they tend to dissolve in polar solvents. The process of solution is the breakdown of a crystal, which is only possible if the attraction of solvent molecules is nearly the same or greater than the forces holding the crystal molecule together in the solid.

Solvent action of water on sodium chloride is an example of this. Sodium chloride is an ionic compound. The negative end or oxygen atom of water attaches itself to the sodium atom, and the hydrogens or positive end to the negative chlorides. This is termed hydration, and the energy of hydration must be sufficient to overcome the crystal energy. Solubility is limited because as the amount of sodium chloride dissolved increases, the rate of reforming the crystals increases. When the rate of recrystallization equals the rate of solution, equilibrium exists and the solubility limit is reached.

The term water denotes a pure, inorganic chemical compound. When the solvent action of water dissolves a substance such as sodium chloride, a solution is formed. Physical constants of the solution, such as its boiling point and freezing point, are different from those of pure water. The substances water dissolves can contribute to the solvent power. Carbon dioxide dissolves in water and hydrolyzes to carbonic acid. This gives a solution with acidic properties which attacks and dissolves substances such as dolomite or limestone. As a result of its solvent power, liquid water does not exist pure in nature. Even dropping rain contains some dissolved gases. Thus we use the term water to refer to naturally occurring aqueous solutions of various components and concentrations.

The hydrologic cycle is a term used to describe the circulation of water on earth. It consists of evaporation of water from the sea into the atmosphere, the formation of clouds with the subsequent release of the water as rain on the land, and the return of the water to the sea by surface or subterranean routes. The hydrologic cycle is significant since it is the process by which necessary water supplies are furnished to the land for consumption by men, animals, and plants.

Water from rain or melting snow and ice either sinks into the ground, collects and flows over the surface of the earth, or evaporates. Water which collects and flows over the surface as streams, creeks, or rivers, or which collects as lakes and ponds, is termed surface water. Water which sinks into the ground to be tapped by wells or to form springs is called ground water.

Both ground and surface waters come into contact with rocks, minerals, or organic matter. Surface water flowing over these substances may dissolve or erode them. The species and concentration of impurities dissolved in water will represent the substances which the water has contacted. Surface water may carry suspended mud, sand, bacteria, vegetable matter, and colloidal matter such as clays and silica compounds. Ground water which collects in large enough quantities to be tapped by a well has been filtered by the soil and rock formations during its downward seepage. Consequently, this water usually contains little suspended or colloidal material. However, because of increased contact with soil and rock formations, this water usually acquires a higher concentration of dissolved solids. In addition to dissolved solids, ground water may contact and dissolve gases. In zones which contain both water and an atmosphere of a gas, an equilibrium will be established between the gas in the atmosphere and the gas dissolved in the water. The principal gases in contact with formation water are: nitrogen (N_2), oxygen (O_2), carbon dioxide (CO_2), methane (CH_4), ethane (C_2H_6), propane (C_3H_8), helium (He), hydrogen (H_2), and ammonia (NH_3).

Addition of oxygen or carbon dioxide to the water may increase the solvent power of the water. Usually the water becomes saturated with oxygen at the surface or in the upper soil strata. As the water filters down through the soil or rock formations, the oxygen is depleted by the oxidation of substances such as sulfides, magnetite, or organic matter. This transforms these substances into compounds that are generally more soluble in water. Carbon dioxide and water form carbonic acid, which in turn ionizes to give hydrogen ions according to the following equations:

$$CO_2 + H_2O \rightleftharpoons H_2CO_3 \qquad\qquad (1\text{--}1)$$

$$H_2CO_3 \rightleftharpoons H^+ + HCO_3^- \qquad\qquad (1\text{--}2)$$

Whereas limestone is only very slightly soluble in pure water, the carbonic acid in water containing carbon dioxide increases calcium carbonate solubility by the formation of calcium bicarbonate as illustrated by Eq. (1-3).

$$CaCO_3 + H_2O + CO_2 \rightleftharpoons Ca(HCO_3)_2 \qquad\qquad (1\text{--}3)$$

Sulfuric acid, resulting from the oxidation of sulfides, may be present in the water, as may organic acids produced by bacterial decomposition of vegetable matter. While carbonates, such as limestone and dolomite, are more readily attacked by the acid in solution, this acid may also attack other minerals.

Oxidation is an important process in the chemical attack of substances by water. Surface waters in contact with air become saturated with oxygen. Ground waters may contain oxygen from respiration of the soil or from infiltration of surface waters. Oxygen present in the water is then available to oxidize some substances, changing their composition and chemical characteristics. Oxidation of sulfides such as pyrites results in the formation of iron oxide and, under certain conditions, sulfuric acid. Sulfides in solution can be oxidized to sulfates. Oxides, ferrous ions, and manganous ions may be oxidized. Organic matter or compounds can be oxidized to carbon dioxide.

Reduction, the reverse of oxidation, is more important in petroleum formation waters that are not in contact with oxygen. The organic nature of petroleum produces a reducing atmosphere. Any required oxygen must be taken from oxygen containing oxides, nitrates, nitrites, or sulfates. Hydrogen sulfide or ammonia may result from these reduction processes. The stability of dissolved substances in given oxidation states depends upon the oxidation-reduction or redox potential existing in the water. This is influenced by the pH of the water.

Hydrolysis is another reaction by which substances, particularly silicates,

Table 1.2

ELEMENTS FOUND IN NATURAL WATER

A. *Elements Commonly Present in Natural Waters*

Boron as borate ion ($BO_3^{\equiv}$)

Calcium as calcium ion (Ca^{++})

Carbon as carbonate ion ($CO_3^{=}$) or dissolved carbon dioxide

Chlorine as chloride ion (Cl^-)

Fluorine as fluoride ion (F^-) or fluosilicate ion ($SiF_6^{=}$)

Iron as ferrous ion (Fe^{++}) or ferric ion (Fe^{+++}) or colloidal Fe_2O_3

Lithium as lithium ion (Li^+)

Magnesium as magnesium ion (Mg^{++})

Manganese as manganous ion (Mn^{++}) or colloidal Mn_2O_3

Nitrogen as nitrate ion (NO_3^-), nitrite ion (NO_2^-), or dissolved nitrogen (N_2)

Oxygen as NO_3^-, $SO_4^{=}$, $CO_3^{=}$, or dissolved oxygen (O_2)

Silicon as dissolved silicates or colloidal silica

Sodium as sodium ion (Na^+)

Sulfur as sulfate ion ($SO_4^{=}$) or sulfide ion ($S^{=}$) or colloidal sulfur

B. *Elements Occasionally Found in Natural Waters*

Aluminum (Al^{+++} or AlO_2^-)	Copper (Cu^{++})
Arsenic (As^{+++} or $AsO_4^{\equiv}$)	Iodine (I^-)
Antimony (Sb^{+++})	Phosphorus ($PO_4^{\equiv}$)
Barium (Ba^{++})	Potassium (K^+)
Bromine (Br^-)	Strontium (Sr^{++})
Cadmium (Cd^{++})	Rubidium (Rb^+)
Cesium (Cs^+)	Zinc (Zn^{++})
Cobalt (Co^{++})	

are dissolved in water. Substances subject to hydrolysis are generally salts of strong bases and weak acids. The process of hydrolysis is slow and does not decompose minerals very rapidly. Since a chemical equilibrium exists between the hydrolyzed and nonhydrolyzed material, renewal or flow of the water increases the rate of the reaction.

Based largely on the work of Clarke,[*][1] who compiled the analyses of many natural waters, Table 1.2 shows the ions that may be encountered in oilfield brines. As previously indicated, the presence of these elements depends on the particular formations which the ground water has contacted during its migration through the earth. Some of these elements are major constituents of ground waters; others are minor, while many are trace elements.

Water Sources and Types

Oilfield engineers utilize water from a variety of sources. In a general way, water from different sources can be characterized according to its salinity. Fresh water is generally obtained from rivers, lakes, streams, or comparatively shallow water sands. The salinity or concentration of dissolved salts is generally low, probably less than 2,000 ppm. Calcium, magnesium, and bicarbonate ions represent a greater per cent of the dissolved ions in fresh waters than they do in waters in contact with oil. Results of analyses of Saskatchewan River water and from an Alabama town-site water well are shown in Table 1.3. Both of these waters are extremely low in dissolved solids and suitable for human consumption.

Table 1.3

COMPOSITIONS OF SOME WATERS*

Constituent	Saskatchewan River	Ala. City	Sea Water	Marginulina Sand (Texas)	Marginulina Sand (La.)	Garner Sand (Okla.)
Carbonate	0	0	—	0	0	0
Bicarbonate	219	120	142	159	281	12
Sulfate	40	2	2,560	157	42	0
Chloride	20	11	18,980	29,573	72,782	101,479
Calcium	59	1	400	881	2,727	9,226
Magnesium	10	1	1,272	498	655	1,791
Sodium & Potassium	30	51	10,840	17,258	42,000	46,000
Iron, total	0.1	0.4	0.02	135	13	35
Barium	—	—	—	—	24	127
TDS	378.1	186.4	34,292	46,661	118,524	158,670
pH	7.7	7.6	—	6.5	6.5	5.0

*Expressed as mg/l.

*Superscript numbers refer to references grouped at the end of each chapter.

Sea water has an average salt content of 3.5 per cent. An analysis showing the ions present in greatest amounts is given in Table 1.3. In addition to these, sea water contains about 65 ppm bromine, 13 ppm strontium, and trace amounts of many other elements.[2] Salinity differences are found to exist between oceans, but the proportions of dissolved constituents remain approximately the same. Sea water is frequently used by tidewater plants for cooling water and has been used as source water for water flood projects.

Connate waters are remains of ancient seas which were buried at the same time as the igneous or sedimentary rock entrapping the water. The high salinity of some connate waters can be attributed to the formation of the sedimentary deposit from brackish waters. These waters are usually present around the edges and at the bottom of oil and gas reservoirs, and as interstitial water within the hydrocarbon-bearing zone.

In many instances, the original (connate) waters may have been replaced by migration. The water found in a formation may be either more or less saline than was the original water.

Formation waters are generally a nuisance when produced with oil and gas. Due to their usual high salinity, most states prohibit the discharge of these waters into surface waters. When pumped into water disposal wells, oilfield brines generally require some treatment in order to prevent corrosion of the disposal system or plugging of the interstices of the formation into which they are pumped.

Oilfield brines may contain several times as much dissolved salts as sea water. Concentrations of 220,000 mg/l dissolved solids are not uncommon. Sodium and chloride are the ions present in the largest amounts. Other ions present in larger than trace amounts are sulfate, bicarbonate, carbonate, calcium, magnesium, and sometimes barium. Other ions like potassium, strontium, and bromide may be present but are not generally determined in standard water analyses. Brines from Louisiana, Oklahoma, and Texas are included in Table 1.3.

Surface waters frequently carry suspended solids, causing them to be turbid. Oilfield brines from subterranean formations have flowed through porous rock which filters any suspended solids from the water. Conditions in the reservoir where these brines have been trapped are much different from those at the surface. Some brines acquire turbidity during production because of changes in conditions which influence the chemical stability of the water. Precipitation of a salt dissolved in water may result. Corrosive attack of metal pipe can result in corrosion products, giving the water turbidity.

Salts present in the brines may have been there when the water was initially trapped or dissolved by the solvent action of the water as it migrated through various rock formations. Waters in contact with chert contain some dissolved silica. Gypsum, anhydrite, and dolomite add calcium to the water.

Reduction of sulfate in the water by reducing agents or sulfate-reducing bacteria results in hydrogen sulfide. In general, the environment in which the water has been trapped or through which it migrated is reflected by the chemical substances dissolved in the water.

Uses of Water

Water is vital to the production and processing of petroleum. Major uses are for drinking, cooling, processing, boiler, and secondary recovery. Water quality requirements vary, with use being highest for boiler and potable water. Except for the brief discussion of potable water which follows, use requirements will be discussed later.

Secondary recovery represents the single biggest use of water in the oil field. A breakdown of secondary recovery projects is shown in Table 1.4. Secondary recovery accounted for more than half the 1960 production of New York, Pennsylvania, Kentucky, Indiana, Illinois, and California.[3] The number of secondary recovery projects is growing yearly.

Table 1.4
SECONDARY RECOVERY PROJECTS IN 1960[3]
(Reproduced by Permission of *Oil Gas J.*)

State	Gas Repressuring	Water	Combined Gas-Water	Miscible	Thermal	Total	1960 Production From Injection Projects (bbl)	% of Total 1960 Production
Arkansas	0	14	1	0	0	15	12,364,064	40.7
California	37	90	8	0	3	138	179,890,615	59.2
Colorado	3	20	3	0	0	26	33,267,533	71.2
Illinois	0	572	0	0	0	572	48,202,000	57.5
Indiana	0	45	0	0	0	45	7,396,536	61.7
Kansas	0	832	0	0	1	833	19,300,000	17.1
Kentucky	0	115	0	0	1	116	12,712,000	58.6
Louisiana	137	42	14	3	0	196	32,746,407	9.4
Michigan	2	66	0	0	0	68	5,254,197	33.1
Montana	1	5	0	0	0	6	13,011,419	42.9
Nebraska	2	24	0	1	0	27	5,151,390	21.9
New Mexico	1	32	1	1	0	35	7,527,337	7.2
New York	0	70	0	0	0	70	1,813,430	99.9
North Dakota	0	3	0	0	0	3	5,294,469	24.1
Ohio	0	28	0	0	0	28	205,000	4.0
Oklahoma	37	1,040	6	3	2	1,088	77,193,151	40.7
Pennsylvania	72	419	0	1	1	493	4,942,000	83.2
Texas	223	1,582	33	19	2	1,859	224,401,290	25.0
Utah	1*	2*	0	0	0	3	0	0
West Virginia	45	9	0	1	0	55	732,900	32.2
Wyoming	7	47	2	0	2	58	41,497,000	31.7
Total	568	5,057	68	29	12	5,734	732,902,738	29.6

*Pilot operations.

Water in the vapor phase is used in steam flooding to recover oil. In this secondary recovery method, steam is injected into the formation. It eventually condenses and reaches thermal equilibrium at the reservoir temperature. Heat from the steam increases the oil temperature and lowers its viscosity as well as causing thermal swelling of the oil.[4] This method requires a plentiful supply of fresh water for steam generation. Treatment of this water would correspond to that used for boiler water.

Potable Water

Water to be used for human consumption must meet certain requirements. It must definitely be free of all disease-causing organisms. Ideally, the water should be good-tasting and odor-free, but it is not always possible to adhere to these two requirements. Potable water must also be free of toxic substances and have a low dissolved-solids content. The U.S. Public Health Service standards pertaining to dissolved solids are shown in Table 1.5. Toxic substances such as arsenic and cyanide can be present in only trace amounts. Water containing as much as 1,000 ppm dissolved solids can be approved for drinking, but a 500 ppm limit is recommended.

Table 1.5

U.S.P.H.S. DRINKING WATER STANDARDS PERTAINING TO DISSOLVED SOLIDS

(From *J. Am. Water Works Assoc.*, **52** (1960), 1159)

| Substance | Limiting Concentration (ppm) | | | |
| | Recommended | | Mandatory | |
	1946	Proposed	1946	Proposed
Arsenic (as As)		0.01		0.05
Barium				1.0
Cadmium (as Cd)				0.01
Copper (as Cu)	3.0	1.0		
Chloride	250	250		
Cyanide (as HCN)		0.01		0.2
Fluoride (inorganic)		1.0	1.5	3.0
Hexavalent chromium			0.05	0.05
Iron (as Fe)	0.3*	0.3		
Lead (as Pb)			1.0	0.05
Manganese	0.3*	0.1		
Magnesium	125	50		
Nitrates		10		
Phenol		0.001	1.0	
Selenium (as Se)			0.05	0.01
Sulfate	250	250		
Zinc	15	5		
Total solids	500	500	1,000	1,000

*Iron and manganese together.

Any water can be treated to meet the requirements shown in Table 1.5. Water that requires treatment so costly as to prohibit its use as a municipal water supply could be treated for smaller groups such as drilling crews. The quality of the water determines the amount and cost of treatment. Surface waters are usually contaminated and require treatment before being used as drinking water. Ground water supplies, free of surface drainage, are better sources of drinking water. Well waters have the advantage that they usually are clearer, contain fewer bacteria, and have a more uniform mineral content than surface waters. Ground waters usually contain more hardness than surface waters.

Bacteria found in water can be divided into three general classes: natural water bacteria, soil. bacteria, and bacteria of intestinal or sewage origin. Natural water bacteria are considered nonpathogenic to humans. Most common natural water bacteria are the *Pseudomonas, Serratia, Flavobacterium*, and *Chromobacterium*. Soil bacteria are frequently found in surface waters during periods of heavy rainfall. These bacteria do not generally remain long outside their natural habitat. The more common species are *Aerobacillus, Bacillus, Crenothrix polyspora*, and *Sphaerotilus dichotomus*. Soil bacteria are not generally harmful to humans. Some bacteria encountered in the intestinal tract of men and animals are pathogenic to humans when present in drinking water. The more common ones are *Clostridium, Streptococcus, Salmonella*, and *Shigella*. *Vibrio comma* and *Endamoeba histolytica* may also be present. The presence of these bacteria is indicated by a bacterial examination of the water by a qualified microbiologist.

Before a water supply is used for drinking purposes, it should be sampled and analyzed. A mineral analysis should be made and a bacterial examination performed by a reliable laboratory. The results of these analyses determine the nature of the treatment required to make the water potable. Samples of the treated water and the raw water should be submitted every two weeks to a reliable laboratory for bacterial examination. Most state health departments will examine water for harmful bacteria at no charge. In foreign countries, it may be more of a problem to obtain a bacterial examination.

Saline Water Conversion

A source of fresh water is desalinized brackish and saline water. The cost of this water is higher than normal water selected for potable use, however, where no suitable water is available a cost of one to two dollars per 1,000 gal is not unreasonable when it may cost seven dollars per 1,000 gal to haul water. The Office of Saline Water has operated demonstration plants for converting saline water since 1961.[5] The processes used in saline water conversion may be divided into the following groups: (1) distillation with the use of fuels, (2) distillation using solar heat, (3) freezing process, (4) membrane separations, (5) chemical processes.[6]

1. DISTILLATION WITH THE USE OF FUELS

Distillation of saline water involves the removal of water from the dissolved salts. Fuels are used in this process to heat the water to a temperature where the vapor pressure is high enough to permit rapid removal of water vapor. In the *flash evaporation process*, water is heated to a temperature below the atmospheric boiling point. The pressure is then reduced to permit the water to boil. Part of the water will "flash" to vapor. The vapor is then condensed to give essentially salt-free water.

In the *vapor compression distillation process*, water vapor from an evaporator is compressed until its temperature is about 10°F higher than when originally formed. The vapor is returned to the evaporator and expanded, so that it condenses into water. The released heat is used to evaporate water.

Desalinization of sea water can be accomplished using the *multiple-effect distillation process*. Sea water is evaporated, using steam from a boiler. The evaporated water goes to a second unit where its heat is used to evaporate additional water. The process is repeated until the water obtained by additional units is not considered worth the added capital expenditure. Each unit evaporates less water than the previous one.

2. DISTILLATION USING SOLAR HEAT

The use of solar energy in the distillation of water has the advantage of eliminating the cost of fuel. However, in order to produce large quantities of water by this method, a large collecting surface is required. This method will probably find application in areas where there is a lot of sunlight, and fuels are scarce and expensive.

3. FREEZING OR CRYSTALLIZATION PROCESSES

The saline water is "flash-cooled" in a vacuum chamber to a temperature low enough to produce ice crystals in the *crystallization as ice process*. The temperature is kept above the eutectic, so that the ice crystals are pure water. However, the ice crystals occlude some brine of which they must be washed free. This is accomplished by washing the ice in a countercurrent wash chamber. Another method is the *crystallization as ice, using the refrigerant in the brine.* Refrigerant, such as isobutane, is introduced directly into the brine, freezing some of the water into ice crystals. The isobutane is vaporized from small droplets dispersed in the brine. The ice crystals must be washed free of the brine in a countercurrent wash tower.

4. MEMBRANE PROCESSES

In osmosis, the water normally flows from a dilute solution through a membrane to a more concentrated solution. The water flow is reversed in the *reverse osmosis process* of desalinization by applying sufficient pressure to the brine solution to overcome the osmotic pressure. About 350 psi is required to overcome the normal osmotic pressure differential between sea water and fresh water.[7]

In the *osmotic-ionic process*, two cation-selective membranes and two anion-selective membranes form a three-compartment cell. Feed water is placed in each compartment and the apparatus immersed in brine. The ions move from the brine to the less highly concentrated water in the outer chamber. This is electrostatically coupled with the simultaneous transfer of ions from the center chamber to the outer chamber, resulting in demineralization of the center chamber.

The *electrodialysis process* utilizes several parallel compartments separated by alternately cation- and anion-permeable membranes. Under the influence of electromotive force imposed across the assembly by electrodes, the sodium ions move toward the negative electrode, the chloride ions toward the positive electrode. This results in the water being desalinized in every other compartment.

5. CHEMICAL PROCESSES

The *gas hydrate separation process* uses a gas such as propane to contact water and form a solid hydrate. The crystals are removed from the brine, washed, and decomposed. The crystals form above the freezing point of water, so that this method requires less energy input than either freezing or distillation.

Solvents are known, namely *n*-methyl-*n*-amylamine and *n*-ethyl-*n*-butylamine which will extract water from salt solutions. The *solvent extraction process* of desalinization results in forming another solution which must be separated to remove the water.

Desalinization units are available for purchase and are in use to provide potable water in areas of the world where only sea water or brackish water exists. American Machine and Foundry has test-marketed a household unit based on electrodialysis.

Water Problems

Problems involved with the use of water are caused by the dissolved constituents. For example, pure water is not very corrosive to steel. Corrosion will proceed until the corrosion products stifle the reaction. The addition of salt to water increases conductivity and corrosion. Dissolved gases such as oxygen and carbon dioxide increase the corrosivity of the water. *Corrosion*, then, is a problem with certain waters.

Corrosion is undesirable for several reasons. Foremost, of course, is that corrosion represents destruction of equipment and replacement costs. All types of oilfield equipment exposed to water are subject to corrosion. Corrosion can cause not only a shutdown in production operations but also cause a safety hazard by weakening high-pressure equipment. Leaks in flow lines or pipelines can also result in costly damages to a farmer's property.

Corrosion products removed by turbulent water flow can deposit in processing equipment or reduce permeability in water injection wells. Damage caused by corrosion can, therefore, decrease the operational efficiency of a system.

Chemical reactions sometimes occur between some constituents dissolved in water to produce insoluble compounds. These insoluble compounds deposited by the water are called scale. *Scale formation* is a major water problem. It not only occurs in production tubing and flow lines, but in heater treaters, radiators, cooling towers, and every other piece of oilfield or plant equipment that handles water.

Scale build-up in tubing or flow lines reduces the pipe diameter and, consequently, the flow. In heat exchangers, scale acts as insulation, decreasing their effectiveness. Prevention of scale formation often requires treatment of the water to remove one of the constituents. Softening water is an example of treatment to prevent scale deposition. Certain chemical compounds which act to prevent scale formation by complexing one of the ions in the scale-forming reaction are called scale inhibitors. When practicable, these are added to scale-forming water to prevent scale deposition.

Another water problem that is becoming more serious as our population and industrial capacity grows is *water pollution*. In the early days of oil production, produced salt water could be dumped into creeks and rivers. This sometimes resulted in fish kills and making the water unfit for animal or human consumption. Today, states and the federal government have laws regulating the disposal of waste brines in bodies of fresh water. Now the field engineer must carefully consider the disposal of brine to avoid conflicts with pollution laws.

Disposal of brines or other wastes such as cooling tower blow-down water is a serious economic problem. The revenue from a barrel of oil may be three dollars. Expense in producing this barrel of oil is justified, but a barrel of waste water produces no revenue; the cost involved in its disposal must be deducted from the profit made in oil production. Disposal costs must, therefore, be held to a minimum. Operators have sometimes been forced to haul waste water, when any form of surface disposal would constitute pollution and underground disposal was not available.

Microorganisms are sometimes a problem in water-handling systems. In potable waters, the chief concern with bacteria is as a health hazard. In waterflood projects and in some plant waters, bacteria and other micro-organisms can contribute to corrosion and fouling of systems. Sulfate-reducing bacteria can generate corrosive hydrogen sulfide, resulting in corrosion of metal equipment. Corrosion products from the sulfide attack can plug or reduce permeability in injection wells. Algae growth can foul cooling towers, as well as presenting a problem in storage basins for injection water.

Use of Municipal Waste Water

Because of water shortages and the increased demand for water in our country, treated sewage is being utilized for industrial purposes. The degree of treatment required before the sewage can be used depends upon its intended use as well as the amount of treatment already applied to the sewage effluent. There is very little basic difference in treating sewage or other water supplies. Many of the rivers used as a water supply have had raw sewage dumped into them.

Municipal sewage may contain both sanitary and industrial wastes. Some industrial wastes, not normally present in sanitary wastes, may be toxic and interfere with biological treatment. Detergents may cause reclaimed water to foam, if it is used in cooling towers or spray ponds. In many cases, unwanted industrial wastes can be separated at their source from sanitary sewage. Generally, it is wise to treat a portion of the municipal waste on a pilot-plant basis before constructing a treatment plant.

Many industrial plants have utilized treated sewage in their operation.[8] Some industrial users of sewage-treatment plant effluents are shown in Table 1.6. In some instances the choice of this water was necessitated by shortages of other supplies; in others, the low cost of this water determined its choice. Texaco, Inc., and the City of Amarillo, Texas, jointly own a water treatment plant for the treatment of city sewage.[9] The treated water from this plant is used by Texaco in its refinery. Including all costs, Texaco pays 13 cents/1,000 gal. Water from an alternate source would cost 18 cents/1,000 gal. At Big Spring, Texas, an oil refinery pays 4.9 cents/1,000 gal for treated sewage effluent, whereas water from an alternate source would cost 17.5 cents/1,000 gal.[10] The cost of reclaimed water will vary with location, required water quality, and price of effluent.

Since sewage plant effluents are primarily fresh water, the dissolved solids contents are low. Some examples of a sewage treatment plant's effluent quality are shown in Table 1.7. Treatment applied to these waters before

Table 1.6

SOME INDUSTRIAL USERS OF SEWAGE-TREATMENT PLANT EFFLUENTS

(From Connel and Berg, *Sewage Ind. Wastes*, **31** (1959), 212.)

User	Source of Effluent	Use	Quantity (mgd)
Bethlemen Steel Co., Sparrows Point, Md.	Baltimore Back river treat. plant	Processing and cooling	75–118
Kaiser Steel Co., Fontana, Calif.	Plant sanitary treat. plant	Processing	0.5*
Columbia-Geneva Steel Co., Provo, Utah	Plant sanitary treat. plant	Processing	0.3*
Los Alamos Scientific Laboratory, Los Alamos, N. M.	Los Alamos treat. plant	Cooling	0.5
Grand Canyon National Park	Park treat. plant	Cooling	0.2
Southern Nevada Power Co., Las Vegas, Nev.	Las Vegas County treat. plant	Cooling	1.7
California Electric Power Co., San Bernardino, Calif.	San Bernardino treat. plant	Cooling	?†
Cosden Petroleum Corp., Big Spring, Tex.	Big Spring treat. plant	Boiler water	0.7
Texas Company, Amarillo, Tex.	Amarillo reclamation plant	Cooling and boiler water	1.5
El Paso Natural Gas Products Co., Odessa, Tex.	Odessa treat. plant	Cooling and boiler water	2.5
Champlin Refining Co., Enid, Okla.	Enid treat. plant	Cooling and boiler water	1.0
Kennecott Copper Corp., Santa Rita, N. M.	Santa Rita Treat. plant	Copper recovery	0.5*
Kennecott Copper Corp., Hurley, N. M.	Hurley treat. plants of 3 towns	Copper recovery	0.3*
Kennecott Copper Corp., Hayde, Ariz.	Hayde treat. plant	Copper recovery	?*
Bagdad Copper Co., Bagdad, Ariz.	Bagdad treat. plant	Copper recovery	?*
Inspiration Consolidated Copper Co., Inspiration, Ariz.	Inspiration treat. plant	Copper recovery	?*
Miami Copper Co., Miami, Ariz.	Miami treat. plant	Copper recovery	?*
Phelps Dodge Corp., Morenci, Ariz.	Morenci treat. plant	Copper recovery	?*
St. Anthony Mining and Development Co., Tiger, Ariz.	Tiger treat. plant	Copper recovery	?*

*As supplementary water in water reuse systems.

†Water taken from canal in which treated sewage comprises about half the total flow.

they were used as cooling waters is shown in Table 1.8. Although a sewage treatment plant's waters have been discussed for use as plant waters, they also may be used for secondary recovery projects.

It is generally recognized that certain health hazards may be encountered in treating sewage. Preventive steps are available so that personnel can be

Table 1.7

SEWAGE TREATMENT PLANT EFFLUENT QUALITY

(From Connel and Berg, *Sewage Ind. Wastes*, **31** (1959), 212.)

Constituent	Location of Plant				
	Amarillo, Tex.	Odessa, Tex.	Los Alamos, N. M.	Enid, Okla.	Las Vegas Co., Nev.
Total solids (mg/l)	—	1,012–1,564	—	700–900	856–1,026
Suspended solids (mg/l)	1–22	12–44	25	50–75	—
Chloride as Cl (mg/l)	100–115	325	—	225–300	94–154
Sulfate as SO_4 (mg/l)	65	350	—	75	329–391
Alk. as $CaCO_3$ (mg/l)	210–300	270–480	150	400–500	—
Tot. hard. as $CaCO_3$ (mg/l)	220–270	400	40	140–250	400–476
Silica as SiO_2 (mg/l)	35–75	10–40	60	30	18–33
Phosphate as PO_4 (mg/l)	10–35	75–110	15	40	6–18
Ammonia nitrogen (mg/l)	0–32	10–12	3	—	—
Nitrate nitrogen (mg/l)	0–30	—	15	—	—
BOD (mg/l)	2–66	5–29	20	70–90	10–30
pH	7–7.9	7.5–8	7	8.4	—

Table 1.8

TREATMENT REQUIRED PRIOR TO COOLING WATER USE

(From Connel and Berg, *Sewage Ind. Wastes*, **31** (1959), 212.)

Treatment	Texas Co. Refinery, Amarillo, Tex.	El Paso Natural Gas Prod. Co. Plants, Odessa, Tex.	Los Alamos Scientific Lab. Power Plant, Los Alamos, N. M.	Champlain Ref. Co. Refinery, Enid, Okla.	Southern Nev. Power Co. Power Plant, Las Vegas, Nev.
Chlorination	yes	yes	yes	no	yes
Impounding for storage and stabilization	yes	yes	—	no	yes
Cold lime softening or lime and soda ash	lime & soda	lime	—	lime	(softening contemplated)
Alum	—	yes	—	yes	—
Filtration	yes	yes	—	no	—
Sodium zeolite	no	yes	no	no	no
Hydrogen zeolite	no	yes	no	no	no
Scale and/or corrosion control chemicals	—	—	yes	yes	yes
Chlorination for slime control	yes	—	yes	bromine	yes
Other slime control chemicals	—	—	—	yes	—

protected from disease. If industrial wastes are included in the sewage, some constituents may be present which would be damaging to pipelines or other metal equipment. The presence or absence of damaging components of this kind should be determined and elimination or treatment procedures decided upon before a waste reclamation project is designed and constructed.

Water Treatment

Making water suitable for use by chemical or physical methods is termed water treatment. Suitability of water for a specific use is governed by the quality of the water and the use requirements. Rain collected in a clean container is essentially pure water and is suitable for nearly any use. Sea water is too salty to serve as drinking water but is used as plant cooling water by many tideland industrial plants.

Any water can be treated to a designated quality for a specific use. An illustration would be treatment of sea water to provide potable water. The mandatory permissible dissolved solids for potable water as shown in Table 1.5 is 1,000 ppm. Table 1.3 shows sea water containing approximately 34,292 ppm dissolved solids. The sea water must then be treated to remove a minimum of 33,292 ppm dissolved solids. Assuming that this is all that is required to make the water potable, the salt must be removed from the water or the water removed from the salt.

Passing the water through suitable ion exchange resins will remove the salt from the water. This process is very expensive for sea water and would only be used in critical situations. Distillation, also an expensive process, removes the water and leaves the salt.

Because of the expense of treatment, sea water would not be used for potable water unless no other source existed. Where there is a choice of water sources as supply for drinking, for a water flood, or any other purpose, the water requiring the least treatment is chosen. Only enough treatment is applied to the water to make it suitable for the specified purpose.

Obviously, the field engineer tries to find a flood water source that requires no treatment. This is not always possible. In addition, produced water must be disposed of and may itself require treatment. Based on analyses of the various waters available for use, treatment is specified and costs calculated. Water requiring the least or the most economical treatment is selected.

A water treatment program may consist of one single process or several, depending upon the water quality and its use. In many water floods, sedimentation is all that is necessary to remove suspended solids from the water. Others require coagulation, sedimentation, and filtration. Water for use in a boiler may only require softening, or it may require softening followed by filtration and deaeration. Flood water might require deaeration and removal of hydrogen sulfide to minimize corrosion.

The use and quality of the water determines the water treatment program. Water quality is determined from mineral analysis of the water and physical tests. Laboratory tests are used to select the necessary treatment and procedure. All phases of the treatment program are then included in the design of the water handling system.

References

[1] F. W. Clarke, *The Data of Geochemistry* (5th ed.), U.S. Geological Survey Bulletin 770 (Washington, D.C. Government Printing Office, 1924).

[2] K. Rankama and T. G. Sahama, *Geochemistry* (Chicago: University of Chicago Press, 1950), p.287.

[3] "Secondary Recovery Is Still Growing," *Oil Gas J.*, **60**, No. 2 (1962) 65.

[4] J. E. Kastrop, "The Quiet Noise over Steam Flooding," *Petroleum Management*, **36**, No. 2 (1964), 82.

[5] "Office of Saline Water's Desalinization Program," *Chem. Eng. News*, **41**, No. 3 (1963), 46.

[6] "Review of Desalinization Process," *J. Am. Water Works Assoc*, **52** (1960), 553.

[7] A. Cywin and L. S. Finch, "Federal Research and Development Program for Saline Water Conversion," *J. Am. Water Works Assoc.*, **52** (1960), 983.

[8] C. H. Connel and E. J. M. Berg, "Industrial Utilization of Municipal Waste Water," *Sewage Ind. Wastes*, **31** (1959), 212.

[9] "Texaco Uses Sewage-Plant Effluent," *Oil Gas J.*, **60**, No. 2 (1962), 92.

[10] F. E. Clarke, "Industrial Re-Use of Water," *Ind. Eng. Chem.*, **54** (1962), 18.

Analysis of Water

2

It has been previously stated that pure water is seldom, if ever, found in nature. Therefore the term water is generally interpreted to mean naturally occurring water which contains impurities such as dissolved solids or gases. Pure water is usually referred to as distilled water and, unless special precautions are taken, even this may contain trace impurities. Thus, waters differ by the amount and character of the impurities.

The particular use intended for a water determines the requirements for its chemical and physical properties. These properties are influenced greatly by the identities and amounts of the dissolved substances. The composition of the water can only be determined by chemical analysis and the physical properties by actual measurements. For a given use, the applicability of a water, as well as any treatment required, is determined by its chemical composition and physical properties.

This points up the importance of water analysis data. Like any chemical analysis, the extent and degree of accuracy of a water analysis is determined by its purpose. For most applications in the petroleum industry, a routine water analysis is sufficient. This consists of measurements pH, alkalinity, specific gravity, and specific resistivity, plus determinations of the concentration of carbonate, bicarbonate, sulfate, chloride, ferric, calcium, magnesium, and sodium ions, together with soluble silica, and total dissolved solids. If the water is for cooling tower use and chromate or phosphate inhibitors have been added, the water may be analyzed for these anions. If there is some question whether the water contains dissolved gases which may

Table 2.1
COMMON WATER ANALYSIS DETERMINATIONS

Determination	Routine Analysis	Injection Water	Cooling Water	Boiler Water	Potable Water
Alkalinity	×	×	×	×	×
Arsenic					×
Bacteriologic		○			×
Barium		○			
Calcium	×	×	×	○	
Carbonate	×	×	×	×	
Carbon dioxide		○	○	×	
Chloride	×	×	×	×	×
Chromium			○		×
Fluoride					×
Hydrogen ion (pH)	×	×	×	○	×
Hydrogen sulfide		○			
Iron	×	×	○	○	×
Lead					×
Magnesium	×	×		○	×
Manganese		○			×
Odor					×
Oxygen		○	○	○	×
Phenol					×
Phosphate			○	○	
Selenium					×
Silica	×	×		×	
Specific gravity	×	×	○		
Specific resistivity	×	×	○	×	
Strontium		○			
Sulfate	×	×	○	×	×
Sulfite		○		○	
Total Dissolved solids	×	×	×	×	×
Turbidity					×
Zinc			○		×

× Determinations usually made.
○ Additional determinations occasionally requested.

contribute to corrosion, analysis for oxygen, carbon dioxide, or hydrogen sulfide may be requested.

A complete water analysis would consist of chemical analysis for all the elements listed in Table 1.2. This would be expensive and time-consuming, since many of these elements are found in water only occasionally, or in trace amounts. A complete water analysis is usually unnecessary, because trace amounts of these elements seldom contribute to the properties of the water. Routine determinations in addition to some frequently requested determinations are shown in Table 2.1.

Uses of Water Analysis Data

A reliable water analysis is very important, since it is the initial step in solving scale, corrosion, or pollution problems. Water treatment is based on results of the analysis. Casing leaks in producing wells can be detected using results of water analyses. Compatibilities of waters for injection in secondary recovery projects can often be predicted from the water analysis data.

Water analysis data are often used to identify the source of water produced with oil and gas. Isoconcentration maps used in hydrodynamic studies are prepared from water analysis data.

Sampling Methods and Techniques

The importance of good water analysis data is readily apparent. In order to obtain useful water analysis data, a sample representative of the water in question must be obtained for analysis. Even the most precise and accurate water analysis will have little significance if the sample has been incorrectly taken and does not represent the water as it is in the system. The water analysis will represent the water sample at the time of analysis. Therefore, it is apparent that the first and most important procedure in solving a water problem is that of obtaining a representative sample of the water.

1. QUANTITY OF SAMPLE

The volume of sample required for an analysis of the water depends upon the amount of dissolved constituents in the water and the number of constituents to be determined. For example, a larger sample volume would be required to determine accurately the concentration of magnesium in Saskatchewan River water shown in Table 1.3 then in the water from the

Table 2.2

VOLUME OF SAMPLE REQUIRED FOR DETERMINATION OF THE VARIOUS
CONSTITUENTS OF INDUSTRIAL WATER

(Reprinted with permission of the American Society for Testing Materials, Philadelphia,
Penn., from "Tentative Methods of Sampling Industrial Water, D 510–62T.")

	Volume of Sample,* ml		Volume of Sample,* ml
Physical Tests		Miscellaneous:	
†Color and odor	100–500	Silica	50–1,000
†Corrosivity	flowing sample	Solids, dissolved	100–20,000
†Electrical conductivity	100	Solids, suspended	50–1,000
†pH, electrometric	100	Tannin and lignin	100–200
Radioactivity	100–1,000		
†Specific gravity	100		
†Temperature	flowing sample	Cations:	
†Toxicity	1,000–20,000		
†Turbidity	100–1,000	Aluminum, Al^{+++}	100–1,000
		†Ammonium, NH_4^+	25–500
Chemical Tests		Antimony, Sb^{+++} to Sb^{+++++}	100–1,000
Dissolved Gases:		Arsenic, As^{+++} to As^{+++++}	100–1,000
†Ammonia, NH_3	100	Barium, Ba^{++}	100–1,000
†Carbon dioxide, free CO_2	100	Cadmium, Cd^{++}	100–1,000
†Chlorine, free Cl_2	100	Calcium, Ca^{++}	100–1,000
†Hydrogen, H_2	1,000	Chromium, Cr^{+++} to Cr^{++++++}	100–1,000
†Hydrogen sulfide, H_2S	500	Copper, Cu^{++}	100–4,000
†Oxygen, O_2	250–1,000	†Iron, Fe^{++} and Fe^{+++}	100–1,000
†Sulfur dioxide, free SO_2	100	Lead, Pb^{++}	100–4,000
		Magnesium, Mg^{++}	100–1,000
Miscellaneous:		Manganese, Mn^{++} to $Mn^{+++++++}$	100–1,000
Acidity and alkalinity	100	Mercury, Hg^+ and Hg^{++}	100–1,000
Bacteria, iron	100	Potassium, K^+	100–1,000
Bacteria, sulfate-reducing	100	Nickel, Ni^{++}	100–1,000
Biochemical oxygen demand	100–500	Silver, Ag^+	100–1,000
Carbon dioxide, total CO_2 (including CO_3^{--}, HCO_3^-, and free)	100–200	Sodium, Na^+	100–1,000
		Strontium, Sr^{++}	100–1,000
Chemical oxygen demand (dichromate)	50–100	Tin, Sn^{++} and Sn^{++++}	100–1,000
Chlorine requirement	2,000–4,000	Zinc, Zn^{++}	100–1,000
Chlorine, total residual Cl_2 (including OCl^-, $HOCl$, NH_2Cl, $NHCl_2$ and free)	100–200	Anions:	
		Bicarbonate, HCO_3	100–200
Chloroform—extractable matter	1,000	Bromide, Br^-	25–100
Detergents	100–200	Carbonate, CO_3^{--}	100–200
Hardness	50–100	Chloride, Cl^-	25–100
Hydrazine	50–100	Cyanide, Cn^-	25–100
Microorganisms	100–200	Fluoride, Fl^-	25–100
Volatile and filming amines	500–1,000	Hydroxide, OH^-	50–100
Oily matter	3,000–5,000	Iodide, I^-	25–100
Organic nitrogen	500–1,000	Nitrate, NO_3^-	10–100
Phenolic compounds	800–4,000	Nitrite, NO_2^-	50–100
pH, colorimetric	10–20	Phosphate, ortho, PO_4^{---}, HPO_4^{--}, $H_2PO_4^-$	50–100
Polyphosphates	100–200	Sulfate, SO_4^{--}, HSO_4^-	100–1,000
		Sulfide, S^{--}, HS^-	100–500
		Sulfite, SO_3^{--}, HSO_3^-	50–100

*Volumes specified in this table should be considered as a guide for the approximate quantity of sample necessary for the particular analysis. The exact quantity used should be consistent with the volume prescribed in the standard method analysis, whenever the volume is specified.

†Aliquot may be used for other determinations.

‡Samples for unstable constituents must be obtained in separate containers, preserved as prescribed, completely filled and sealed against all exposure.

Garner sand. If only one or two constituents are to be determined, a small sample is sufficient, while more would be required for a standard water analysis. It is always better to have a larger sample than one that is too small.

For most water analyses, a minimum of two quarts of sample is desirable. It is recommended that the sample be collected in four one-pint containers rather than one container. It is necessary that additional samples be obtained for bacteriological examination in specially prepared sterile containers. If the water examination is of a nonroutine nature, it is advisable to consult the analyst concerning the amount of water sample required. Some sample volumes recommended by ASTM for various chemical analyses and physical measurements are shown in Table 2.2.

2. Containers for Collecting a Water Sample

Metal containers such as tin and steel cans are not used to collect water samples, since they usually corrode with resulting contamination or loss of the sample. However, glass-coated or plastic-lined metal pressure vessels may be used to collect water samples under pressure.

Sample bottles should be cleaned before use. In the laboratory, these bottles are cleaned with chromic acid cleaning mixture, alkaline permanganate solution, or concentrated hydrochloric acid. After cleaning, they are rinsed with distilled water and dried. These agents are seldom available in the field; therefore, it is recommended that the sample bottles be washed with detergent, rinsed with tap water, and, if possible, rinsed out with sample water at the time of sampling.

Glass bottles require protection against breakage in shipment by impact or freezing, while plastic bottles do not. This is often an important consideration favoring plastic bottles. A disadvantage of plastic bottles is that they are opaque and the appearance of the sample cannot be readily detected. Cylindrical shipping cartons made out of cardboard are available for bottles. These have some room for packing and give the bottles good protection against breakage.

It is recommended that, for routine water analyses, the samples be collected in clean bottles made of glass or plastic. In special cases where minute amounts of sodium or silica are to be determined, glass bottles should not be used since the water sample may slowly leach some of these elements from the glass. For most routine determinations, this is not an important consideration. Metal screw caps should not be used. Plastic caps, with plastic liners, are recommended.

3. Collecting a Production or Plant Sample

It is not feasible to discuss all the conditions under which a water sample may be taken. However, it is advisable to point out a few principles which, when applied to practice, will assure a good water sample for analysis.

The point for collection of the sample is important. It is not easy to obtain a sample of well water from the bottom of the well, so most samples are taken at the wellhead. In order to insure that the sample taken at the wellhead is representative of the water at the bottom of the well, the well should be flowed at its normal rate until the stream is uniform and does not change in appearance with continued flow. In a surface distribution system, water samples can usually be obtained at or very near the particular point of interest. If a series of water samples are to be taken, a sampling port can be installed.

The sample should be taken under conditions which normally exist in the system. If the system normally flows, the water sample should not be taken under static conditions, but when the system is flowing at its normal rate. If a water sample is taken to determine the corrosivity of a water as it flows through production tubing, the water should be sampled at the wellhead, not after the water has gone through a heater treater, or has been collected in a tank battery When water in a tank is to be sampled, it is advisable to take samples at the bottom, the middle, and the top of the tank. Often, equipment is not available for sampling the center of a liquid body, so only a surface sample can be obtained.

If a sampling port is used, a rubber hose should be attached to the swage, and the other end of the hose pushed into the bottom of the sample bottle. The bottle should be rinsed at least three times with the water before the sample is taken. After the bottle is full of sample, and ten volumes of water are allowed to overflow, the hose should be drawn out of the bottle slowly as the water continues to flow. After the hose has been withdrawn, the bottle should be capped immediately.

The purpose in capping the sample bottle immediately is to lessen the contact of the sample with atmospheric oxygen and to minimize the loss

Table 2.3

MEASUREMENTS AND ANALYTICAL DETERMINATIONS

INFLUENCED BY CONTACT WITH ATMOSPHERIC OXYGEN

(Reprinted with permission of the American Society for Testing and Materials, Philadelphia, Pa., from "Tentative Scheme for Analysis of Industrial Water and Industrial Waste Water, D1256–61.")

Alkalinity	Hydrogen sulfide
Ammonia	Manganese
Bicarbonate ion	Nitrite
Calcium ion	Oxygen
Carbon dioxide	pH
Carbonate ion	Specific conductance
Ferric ion	Specific gravity
Ferrous ion	Sulfide ion
Hardness	Sulfite ion
Hydroxide ion	Sulfur dioxide

Table 2.4

MEASUREMENTS AND ANALYTICAL DETERMINATIONS
NOT INFLUENCED BY CONTACT WITH ATMOSPHERIC OXYGEN

(Reprinted with permission of the American Society
for Testing and Materials, Philadelphia, Penn., from
"Tentative Scheme for Analysis of Industrial Water
and Industrial Waste Water, D1256–61.")

Aluminum ion	Microorganisms
Barium ion	Nitrate ion
Bromide ion	Odor
Chloride ion	Phosphate ion
Chromate ion	Potassium ion
Copper ion	Silica
Cyanide ion	Sodium ion
Fluoride ion	Solids
Iodide ion	Sulfate ion
Lead ion	Turbidity*
Magnesium ion	

*In the case of iron-bearing waters, oxidation of ferrous iron may produce turbidity.

of any dissolved gas that might be present in the water. Some analytical determinations and measurements that are influenced by contact with atmospheric oxygen are listed in Table 2.3. Determinations not influenced by contact with atmospheric oxygen are shown in Table 2.4.

Any sludge present in the sampling port should be removed by flowing before the water sample is taken. If a sample of the sludge is desired, it should be obtained before the water sample.

A record should be made of each sample taken, and a copy of that record attached to the sample in the form of a label such as that shown in Fig. 2.1. The sampling port should be identified in the event that future samples are required from that location.

A sampling tube is used for water samples that are to be analyzed for dissolved gases. The sampling tube recommended by ASTM for dissolved oxygen determinations is shown in Fig. 2.2. This tube is connected to the

Date: _____ Collected by: _____

Location of Sampling Port: _____

_____

Temp. _____ °F, Pressure _____ psi, Flow Rate _____

      Appearance of Sample: _____

Lease and Well: _____

WF or SWD Project: _____

Fig. 2.1. Water sample label.

flow line by means of a rubber tube and located so that its uppermost end is higher than the sampling port. The tube is filled so that there are no bubbles in it. The water is allowed to flow until at least ten volumes have passed through the sampling tube. The valve at the sampling port is adjusted so that the flow of water through the sampling tube can be shut off at the uppermost stopcock on the sampling tube without danger of the pressure breaking the tube. The lower stopcock is then closed and the sampling tube removed. If any gas bubbles are present in the sampling tube, the sample should be discarded and a new sample obtained.

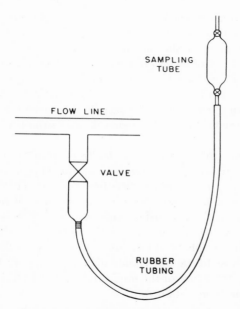

Fig. 2.2. Sampling tube for dissolved gases.

4. Collecting a Drill-Stem Test Sample

Special care should be used in taking water samples during drilling or completion operations. Drill-stem tests are subject to contamination. When drilling with muds, a certain amount of mud filtrate enters the formation, displacing the formation fluids. The mud filtrate will then be the first fluid returned in the drill-stem test.

When salt-saturated muds are used, the mud filtrate returned will be highly saline. It may contain more dissolved salts than the actual formation water. Filtrate from fresh water muds will be low in dissolved salts content. Recovery of either type of mud filtrate or mixtures of mud filtrate and formation water can be misleading if selected as a sample of formation water or other formation fluid. For a drill-stem test to be conclusive and provide a representative sample of formation water, all of the mud filtrate must be removed by flowing during the test.

Volume of mud filtrate in the formation rock can be estimated from the water loss of the mud, diameter of hole, thickness of formation, porosity of formation, and mud filtrate saturation in the invaded zone.[1] Because of capillary displacement, low permeability reservoirs are subject to deeper mud filtrate invasion and larger formation fluid displacement than higher permeability reservoirs.

When sampling water recovered from a drill-stem test, one should take the sample least contaminated with mud filtrate. In most tests this means taking the sample as close to the bottom of water recovery as possible. When several thousand feet of water are recovered, the second or third stand above the testing tool should contain representative formation water. Lower stands usually contain considerable solid material.[2] When water recoveries are less than 1,000 ft, a water sample should be taken not more than one stand above the bottom. Solid material in the sample is less harmful than mud filtrate.

Generally, it is advisable to take samples from various stands during a drill-stem test. Determination of salinities of the various samples will help in choosing the one that represents the formation water. Measurement of the resistivity of the samples will differentiate the mud filtrate from the formation water. A sample of the drilling mud should be pressed to obtain the filtrate, and the resistivity measured. Comparison of this with the resistivity values of the samples will identify any pure mud filtrate present. Samples from stands close to the tool should give the same resistivity value, which will be different from that of the mud filtrate. This indicates a sample of formation water has been obtained.

5. Time Interval Between Collection of Water Samples and Analysis

The length of time which elapses between the collection and analysis of a water sample should be as short as possible. For some analyses and physical measurements, the best results are obtained by performing immediate determinations in the field. The length of time a sample can remain stable and represent the water in question depends upon the chemical characteristics of the water itself.

The temperature of a water should be measured in the field at the time of sampling. Iron in water samples can be lost due to adsorption on the walls of the sample container or by oxidation of ferrous to less soluble ferric iron.

This is especially true if the water acquires any oxygen in the sampling process. If a water is saturated with carbon dioxide, any loss of carbon dioxide in the sampling process would change the pH-alkalinity-carbon dioxide equilibrium, possibly resulting in the precipitation of calcium carbonate. Then, the analysis would be low in both carbon dioxide and calcium content.

Samples which contain microorganisms are particularly subject to change on standing. The growth of these organisms may be retarded by keeping the sample in the dark and in a refrigerator until it can be analyzed. The following standing times are suggested as maximum limits for reliable physical and chemical analyses:[3]

Bacterially unpolluted waters	72 hours
Slightly polluted waters	48 hours
Polluted waters	12 hours

The Shell Oil Company has a trailer equipped as a water analysis laboratory. In situations where water analyses of fresh samples are critical, Shell can move the trailer into the area. This type of portable laboratory is also useful when determining a water treatment program for a secondary recovery project.

Determination of Major Components

There are several methods of analysis that can be used to determine any of the ions dissolved in water. Some analytical methods have been developed especially for water analysis. One recommended source of water analyses procedures is *Standard Methods for the Examination of Water and Wastewater*.[4] This book was prepared jointly by the American Public Health Association, the American Water Works Association, and the Federation of Sewage and Industrial Wastes Associations. Another good source of water analyses procedures is the *Manual on Industrial Water* published by the ASTM.[5] Some additional methods useful for analyzing oilfield waters have been developed by Collins *et al.* at the Bureau of Mines.[6]

Elements that are found in natural waters are shown in Table 1.2. These elements may be divided into three groups: major components, minor components, and trace components. Major components or constituents consist of the ions or salts which constitute most of the dissolved solids in waters and which contribute the most to the chemistry of the water.

1. CALCIUM

Some oilfield brines contain as much as 32,000 ppm of calcium ion.

Usually, the amount of calcium ion is exceeded greatly by the concentration of sodium ion in oilfield waters. However, in fresh water, the calcium ion generally represents a larger percentage of the dissolved solids. Calcium ion is of major importance, because it combines with sulfate or carbonate ion to form insoluble deposits.

Calcium may be determined by gravimetric or volumetric analytical procedures. Gravimetrically, calcium is precipitated as calcium oxalate, ignited to constant weight at 1100°C, and weighed as calcium oxide. Volumetrically, calcium is precipitated as calcium oxalate, dissolved with sulfuric acid and titrated with potassium permanganate. These two methods are the most accurate procedures for determining calcium. A less accurate but more rapid method consists of titrating the calcium ion with ethylenediaminetetraacetic acid using murexide as an indicator. For most routine analyses of oilfield waters, this latter titration is probably satisfactory. Calcium and magnesium can also be determined simultaneously.[7]

When gravimetric or volumetric procedures are used to determine calcium, the results should agree within 5 to 10 per cent for values below 10 ppm. Above this amount the agreement should be within 2 to 5 per cent.

2. MAGNESIUM

In natural waters, a magnesium ion content of 4,000 ppm or greater is considered high. As with calcium, the magnesium content usually represents a smaller percentage of dissolved solids in oilfield brines than in fresh waters. Again like calcium, the magnesium ion may combine with the carbonate ion to deposit a scale from the water.

Magnesium is generally determined by a gravimetric procedure, using the filtrate from the calcium determination. The magnesium is precipitated as magnesium ammonium phosphate—ignited to and weighed as magnesium pyrophosphate. Photometric and volumetric methods are available for determining magnesium, but most oilfield waters contain interfering ions which complicate the analysis. For relatively fresh waters, magnesium can be determined photometrically.

Large amounts of magnesium ion present in water interfere with the calcium ion determination and give unreliable results for both ions unless special procedures are used. The same precision and accuracy attained with calcium determinations should be expected with the magnesium determinations unless short-cut methods are used.

3. SODIUM

Formation waters generally contain high concentrations of sodium ion. In a routine water analysis, sodium is generally not determined directly by analysis but is determined by difference. Analytical determinations are made for calcium, magnesium, chloride, and sulfate ions. An *aliquot* of the water sample is evaporated to dryness and weighed. The difference between the weight of this residue and the total weight of the calcium, magnesium, carbonate, chloride, and sulfate ions is taken as the weight of sodium ions. It is apparent that any ions present but not actually determined by analysis are reported as sodium ions. Generally, this error in sodium concentration is not considered harmful, since the sodium does not form any undesirable precipitates with other ions in the water.

Sodium can be determined gravimetrically. The sodium is precipitated as sodium zinc uranyl acetate hexahydrate, washed with alcohol followed by ether, air-dried, and weighed. Sodium can also be determined using a flame photometric procedure. Determined values for sodium should be accurate to within 3 to 5 per cent. Sodium values computed from equivalents of other ions in solution may differ by as much as 10 per cent. Analyses containing computed sodium values cannot be checked, so the possibility of large errors exists. The user of the data must remember this and accept this data on the basis of the reputation of accuracy of the analyzing laboratory.

4. CHLORIDE

Chloride is another of the major ions in fresh water or formation brines. It can be determined by the Volhard method, which consists of adding a measured excess of silver nitrate to an aliquot of the water sample, and titrating the excess of silver nitrate with standardized potassium thiocynate solution. Any iodide or bromide present would be titrated as chloride. The Mohr method can also be used to determine chloride. This method consists of titrating the chloride with silver nitrate in neutral or weakly alkaline solution, using chromate as an indicator. The appearance of red silver chromate indicates the end point. As with the Volhard method, iodide and bromide ions will be titrated as chloride.

Chloride determinations are reasonably easy, so accuracy and reproducibility should be fairly good with routine laboratory work. Agreement between duplicate samples should be between 2 to 5 per cent for a concentration range of 10 to 100 ppm, and 2 to 3 per cent at concentrations above that range.

5. SULFATE

Sulfate is a major constituent, since it may be present in relatively large amounts and may combine with calcium to form slightly soluble calcium sulfate. The accepted procedure for determining sulfate is to precipitate the sulfate with barium chloride, and to weigh it as barium sulfate after ignition at 800°C.

The sulfate determination should be as accurate and precise as any routine analysis. Analyses of duplicate samples should agree within ±2 ppm.

6. BICARBONATE AND CARBONATE

The bicarbonate and carbonate ions seldom contribute appreciably to the total dissolved solids. However, these ions are extremely important in scale deposition and are therefore considered as major components. The carbonate ion is determined by titrating an aliquot of the water sample to the phenolphthalein end point with dilute sulfuric acid. To determine the bicarbonate ion, methyl orange indicator is then added, and the titration continued to the methyl orange end point. Results of duplicate samples should agree within ±1 mg/l and have an accuracy of ±2 mg/l.

Determination of Minor Components

Ions that are found occasionally in low concentrations in natural waters or plant waters are designated as minor components. These are ions which are often of interest—but not routinely determined in a water analysis.

1. BARIUM

Barium forms insoluble compounds with the carbonate and sulfate ions. Sometimes, injection waters containing sulfate but little calcium will precipitate barium sulfate which will plug the face of the injection formation. Barium is determined by precipitating the barium as barium sulfate and weighing this ignited precipitate. The accuracy and precision should be the same as for the sulfate determination.

2. CARBON DIOXIDE

Carbon dioxide is important from the standpoint of the carbonate-bicarbonate-carbon dioxide equilibrium as well as from the corrosive nature of waters containing carbon dioxide. Carbon dioxide is determined by acidifying and heating the sample in a closed system, and absorbing the liberated gas in barium hydroxide solution. The excess hydroxide is then titrated with standard acid. Dissolved carbon dioxide can also be determined using an electrode.[8] Apparatus for determining carbon dioxide in gas or in water is available.

3. CHROMATE

The concentration of chromate ion in waters which have been treated with chromate corrosion inhibitors is of interest. The chromate can be determined photometrically, using diphenylcarbazide to produce a color with the chromate ion.

4. HYDROGEN SULFIDE

The presence of hydrogen sulfide in water usually indicates that the water will have a corrosive action on metal. Hydrogen sulfide can be produced directly by sulfate-reducing bacteria, with resulting corrosion of casings and flow lines. Hydrogen sulfide is determined by calculation from the total sulfide content. If the water sample cannot be analyzed immediately for sulfide, the sulfide content should be fixed by adding a slight excess of zinc acetate solution in order to stabilize the sulfide as zinc sulfide. This information should be noted on the sample label.

5. IRON

The iron content of formation waters is usually less than 50 ppm. However, the analysis of water for iron is one method of determining whether corrosion of the metal in the system is occurring, and of following the progress of the corrosion. In order to accomplish this, it is necessary to have an iron analysis of the produced water before the corrsion begins. After acidizing, the iron content of produced water is always higher until all the acid water has been produced.

Iron is usually determined photometrically. A solution of phenanthroline is added to an aliquot of the water sample and the intensity of the orange-red complex is measured. The dissolved iron is the amount of iron in solution at the time the aliquot is taken from the water sample for laboratory analysis. Total iron represents the iron in solution and that which has precipitated in the sample bottle. Chemical Service Laboratories of Dallas, Texas, and several other companies make kits for the determination of iron in the field. The sampling procedure and source of water influence the results of the analysis. Laboratory methods can detect 0.1 ppm iron.

6. MANGANESE

The chemical behavior of manganese is similar to that of iron. Manganese is less abundant than iron, so its concentration in natural waters is normally less. Manganese also has more than one oxidation state, the most common in water being the bivalent and quadrivalent states. In natural waters the manganese concentration seldom exceeds 1 ppm.

Manganese in water is usually found in the soluble manganous form. On contact with air, manganous ion is easily oxidized to the less soluble manganic ion, which may precipitate out of solution. Manganese is determined color-imetrically by oxidizing the manganous ion to permanganate and comparing the color with a standard solution. Other laboratory methods for the analysis of manganese that are accurate to 0.05 ppm are available.

7. OXYGEN

Water containing dissolved oxygen is potentially corrosive. The recom-mended procedure for sampling water to be used in an oxygen analysis is shown in the section on sampling. Oxygen is determined by titration of an aliquot of the water sample with sodium thiosulfite, using a starch iodide indicator. Oxygen analyzers for use in gas streams or in water are available. Electrodes of other designs for the determination of dissolved oxygen in water have been used successfully.[9]

8. PHOSPHATE

The amount of phosphate present in natural water is very low or alto-gether absent. An unusually large amount of phosphate present in a natural water would be 30 ppm.[10] Phosphate compounds are frequently added to oilfield waters as scale inhibitors. Most analyses of water for phosphate are performed to determine its presence as a scale inhibitor. Phosphate can be determined by precipitating it as magnesium ammonium phosphate and weighing it after ignition as magnesium pyrophosphate. Colorimetric methods are shorter and are usually used for routine phosphate determi-nations.

9. SILICA

Quartz or crystalline silicon dioxide is abundant in nature but one of the most resistant of minerals to dissolution in water. Amorphous forms of silica such as chert are more soluble in water. Silica concentrations in natural waters usually are in the range of 1 to 30 ppm, but sometimes are as high as 100 ppm. This material is objectionable in high-pressure boiler water and some cooling waters because of its tendency to form hard silicate scales.

Water samples for silica determinations should be collected in plastic bottles, since water may dissolve some silica from the glass. Colorimetric methods are generally used to determine the amount of silica in water. Colorimetrically determined silica values in duplicate samples in the range 10 to 50 ppm are reproducible to within 2 ppm. Results of duplicates should agree somewhat more closely in the range 0 to 10 ppm.

10. SULFITE

Sodium sulfite is added to some waters in order to remove dissolved oxygen. The amount of sulfite effectively used as a scavenger can be determined by analysis of the water for residual sulfite ion. Sulfite is determined by titrating an aliquot of the water sample with potassium iodate, using starch iodide indicator.

Determination of Other Components

Most of the elements listed in Table 1.2 which were not classed as major or minor components are found in water in only trace amounts. Analysis for these components is usually limited to cases where a water is suspected of containing a sufficient amount of one of the components to warrant a recovery process.

Some of the determinations listed in Tables 2.3 and 2.4 may be routinely carried out on some waters. However, many of these such as lead, nitrite, nitrate, fluoride, copper, or odor are of limited interest in oil production.

Physical Measurements

It is important to have a knowledge of the physical as well as chemical properties of the water. Some of the physical properties can be calculated from the water analysis data. Sometimes physical measurements are used to estimate the chemical properties.

1. MICROORGANISMS

Natural waters frequently contain microorganisms such as algae, molds, or bacteria. These organisms can cause corrosion of equipment and fouling of reservoirs. Microscopic examination and microbiological tests are used to identify and count the numbers of organisms present.

2. SPECIFIC GRAVITY

The specific gravity of a water is indicative of the amount of salts dissolved in the water. A comparison of the specific gravity of two waters would approximate the relative salinity of the waters. The specific gravity is determined by weighing a given volume of the water and dividing this weight by the weight of an equal volume of distilled water. A somewhat less accurate method utilizes hydrometers to measure the specific gravity.

3. SPECIFIC RESISTIVITY

For most uses of water, the specific resistivity is not important. However, a knowledge of the specific resistivity is important for use in interpretation of electric logs. The resistivity of water can be measured or calculated from water analysis data, or estimated from charts relating resistivity to salt concentration. The measurement of resistivity and the use of similar charts also affords a rapid method for estimating the dissolved salts in plant and boiler waters.

The conductance of water in mhos is the reciprocal of the value of its resistance in ohms.

4. TEMPERATURE

The temperature of the water is the most important physical measurement. It is essential in expressing the specific gravity, specific resistivity, and pH of the water. The temperature of the water must be measured at the time of sampling, since temperature changes rapidly. The temperature is best measured with a thermometer, and the value noted on the sample label.

5. TOTAL DISSOLVED SOLIDS

The determination of total dissolved solids is especially important for cooling waters. The total dissolved-solids content predicts the build-up of solids in the water from evaporation of part of the cooling water and ultimately determines the continued usefulness of the water. This determination also serves as a check on the completeness of the water analysis. The sum of the determinations of the individual components should correspond to the total dissolved-solids value to a reasonable degree. However, in most routine water analyses, the sodium concentration is determined by difference between the total dissolved-solids content and the sum of other individual components. The total dissolved solids are determined by evaporation of an aliquot of the water sample which is free of turbidity and suspended solids. Total dissolved solids can also be computed from the weights of ions found by analysis. Computed sodium is included in this calculation. Because of formation of hydrated salts, the calculated total dissolved solid is frequently better than that actually determined by evaporation and weighing.

6. TURBIDITY

Turbidity in water indicates that suspended material is present. Turbidity measurements are useful in determining the efficiency of filters or settling basins and are also useful in indicating the completeness of processes which utilize precipitation reactions. Turbidity measurements are made by the Jackson Candle method or with a photoelectric nephelometer.

Miscellaneous Measurements

There are three other determinations which are made on water samples. These are alkalinity and acidity, hardness, and pH or hydrogen ion concentration.

1. ALKALINITY AND ACIDITY

Alkalinity and acidity are defined as the capacity of the water for neutralization. Alkalinity in water represents its ability to neutralize acid and is determined by titrating the water with dilute acid. The chief sources of alkalinity in natural waters are the hydroxide ion (OH^-), carbonate ion ($CO_3^=$), and bicarbonate ion (HCO_3^-). Other ions such as phosphate, borate, or silicate ions are seldom present in high enough concentrations to significantly affect the alkalinity.

The presence of hydroxide ions in natural waters in amounts large enough to affect the alkalinity is rare. In the titration, phenolphthalein indicator is added and the water titrated to pH 8.2, where phenolphthalein changes from red to colorless. This represents titration of the hydroxide and carbonate ions. Most oilfield waters have neither ion present. This first step in the titration is called phenolphthalein alkalinity (P.O.Alk.) and is usually expressed in ppm $CaCO_3$.

Methyl orange indicator is added and the titration continued until this indicator changes color at pH 4.5. This is called the methyl orange alkalinity (M.O. Alk.) or total alkalinity. Waters requiring more acid for titration to the phenolphthalein end point than to the methyl orange end point have hydroxide present. Even though the neutral point for water is pH 7, water buffered by the carbonate-bicarbonate system has alkalinity at pH's to 4.5.

Waters with pH below 4.5 are reported as having acidity. This may be the result of free acids such as hydrochloric or sulfuric. Mine waters frequently contain acidity; oilfield waters seldom do unless they have been returned from acidizing a well. No alkalinity exists in acid waters.

For waters over pH 4.5, alkalinity may range to 1,200 ppm, but it is generally less than 500. Acidity may range from zero to several hundred ppm in mine waters. The total alkalinity of duplicate samples should agree within 5 per cent. Acidity data is not so reliable and should be interpreted with care.

2. HARDNESS

Hardness has usually been referred to as the soap-consuming power of water. Most of this effect with soap is caused by magnesium and calcium in the water, but other alkaline earths give the same effect. Calcium and magnesium hardness represent values calculated from the concentrations of these two ions.

Carbonate or temporary hardness is that hardness which is equivalent to the bicarbonate and carbonate present. Any hardness in excess of this is termed noncarbonate hardness or permanent hardness. Hardness is usually expressed in ppm of calcium carbonate. This is obtained by multiplying the epm total hardness (calcium and magnesium concentration) by 50. Hardness is usually determined by titration with ethylenediaminetetraacetic acid rather than with a soap solution.

3. pH

The pH (or hydrogen ion) determination is very important and is usually made in all water analyses. The pH value is used in certain calculations for carbon dioxide content, hydrogen sulfide, and scale-forming tendencies. The corrosive character of water is sometimes indicated by the pH.

Water ionizes to give hydrogen and hydroxyl ions. The ionization constant is 10^{-14}, so pure water contains 10^{-7} moles of hydrogen and hydroxyl ion. The negative logarithm of the hydrogen ion concentration is the pH. For pure water the pH is 7. Values less than 7 represent acid water and above 7, alkaline water. The pH of natural water is controlled by ions and gases dissolved in the water. Most oilfield waters are buffered by the bicarbonate-carbon dioxide system that is effective in the pH range 4.5 to 8.

Colorimetric methods have been used to measure pH, but now electrometric methods are predominantly used. Glass and calomel electrodes in conjunction with pH meters give values accurate to 0.1 of a pH unit.

Expression of Water Analysis Results

There are many different methods of expressing water analysis data. Generally, the method is chosen arbitrarily by the analyst. This complicates the comparison of water analysis data from two different analysts, using two different methods or units of expressing the results of the analysis. Fortunately, conversion factors are available which enable one to convert the various units used in expressing water analysis results. Some of the more commonly used units and their conversion factors are given in Table 2.5.

Table 2.5
Conversion Factors for Water Analysis Units

To Convert from	To	Multiply by
Grains	grams	0.065
Grains per Imperial Gallon	ppm	14.25
Grains per U.S. Gallon	ppm	17.12
Grains per Imperial Gallon as $CaCO_3$	epm	0.285
Grains per U.S. Gallon as $CaCO_3$	epm	0.34
Milliliters (or cc) of dissolved CO_2	ppm	1.97
Milliliters (or cc) of dissolved H_2S	ppm	1.52
Milliliters (or cc) of dissolved O_2	ppm	1.43
ppm as $CaCO_3$	epm	0.02

1. Units

a. Parts per million

One of the commonly used units for reporting water analysis data is the part per million, abbreviated ppm. When used to express water analysis data, the part per million is a measure of proportion by weight, equivalent to a unit weight of dissolved substance per million unit weights of solution. The unit used in water analysis is the milligram, so 1 ppm is equivalent to

1 mg of solute per 1000 g of solution. For waters of low-solids content, 1 ppm is essentially equivalent to 1 mg of solute per liter of solution.

b. Equivalents per million

Another commonly used unit, the equivalent per million—abbreviated epm—is a unit chemical equivalent weight of dissolved substance per million unit weights of solution. When used in reference to water analysis data, the epm is calculated by dividing the ppm of a component by its equivalent

Table 2.6

CONVERSION FACTORS FOR CONVERTING PPM TO EPM

Cation in ppm	Multiply by	Anion in ppm	Multiply by
Ba^{++}	0.0146	Cl^-	0.028
Ca^{++}	0.050	$CO_3^=$	0.033
Mg^{++}	0.082		
Na^+	0.043	$SO_4^=$	0.021

weight, which is different for each component. A list of conversion factors used to convert parts per million into equivalents per million is given in Table 2.6.

c. Hardness units

Usually, the hardness of water is expressed as its calcium carbonate equivalent in some unit. In the United States, hardness is expressed as calcium carbonate equivalents in parts per million. When hardness is reported, the method of determining the hardness is often included. Hardness (Ca, Mg) would indicate that the hardness is the sum of the calcium and magnesium concentration, whereas hardness (soap) would mean the hardness was determined using the soap titration method.

d. Calcium carbonate equivalents

In some water analysis reports, the concentrations of the ions are ex-

Table 2.7

CONVERSION FACTORS FOR CONVERTING CACO₃

EQUIVALENTS INTO IONIC CONCENTRATION

To Convert to ppm of	Multiply ppm $CaCO_3$ Equivalents by
Ca^{++}	0.4
Mg^{++}	0.243
Na^+	0.46
Cl^-	0.709
$CO_3^=$	0.6
HCO_3^-	1.22
$SO_4^=$	0.96

pressed as calcium carbonate equivalents. Usually, the weight of the ion is converted to the equivalent weight of calcium carbonate. Some conversion factors used to convert from parts per million calcium carbonate equivalents to parts per million of the ions commonly determined in water analyses are listed in Table 2.7.

e. Part per billion

One part per billion is a unit weight of dissolved substance per billion unit weights of solution. This can be expressed as 1 microgram per 1000 grams of solution.

f. Milligrams per liter

Milligrams per liter expresses a weight-volume relationship which, over the temperature range found in most laboratories, is independent of the specific gravity. This is a practical way of expressing water analysis results, since waters are usually measured by volume rather than by weight. At low concentrations of dissolved material (less than 7,000 ppm), milligrams per liter are substantially equal to ppm.

g. Milliequivalents per liter

Milliequivalents per liter is also a weight-volume relationship and is obtained by dividing weight of the component by its milliequivalent weight. Multiplying the milligrams per liter concentration by the factors given in Table 2.6 will give the same result.

h. Hypothetical combinations

Water analysis results are sometimes expressed as hypothetical combinations. In solution, the chemical equivalent concentration of cations equals the chemical equivalent concentration of anions. When a chemist makes up a solution of calcium sulfate and sodium chloride, he knows how much of each he dissolves and can describe the solution by indicating the concentration of each salt. With natural waters, the salt content is of unknown origin. The water analyst will sometimes attempt to describe the water by matching certain anions with certain cations, and report these hypothetical combinations. *This practice is not desirable*—it may mislead an uninformed person into believing that these hypothetical combinations actually represent the water analysis.

i. Grains per gallon

Water analysis results are sometimes expressed as grains per U.S. gallon (abbreviated as gpg) or grains per imperial gallon (abbreviated as gpg Imp). One grain equals 1/7,000 of a pound, and one U.S. gallon of water weighs

8.33 pounds, compared to 10 pounds for an imperial gallon. The factor used to convert grains per gallon into parts per million is found in Table 2.5.

j. Per cent by weight

Per cent by weight is an accurate method of expressing water analysis results. This is calculated as follows:

$$\% \text{ by weight} = \frac{\text{weight of component/liter of solution}}{\text{weight of one liter of solution}} \times 100$$

2. PALMER'S CLASSIFICATION

According to Palmer[11] the fundamental character of natural waters depends upon the general properties of salinity and alkalinity. Salinity may be defined as a property given by the slightly hydrolyzable salts of the strong acids. Alkalinity is a property attributed to free alkaline bases, produced by the easily hydrolyzable salts of the weak acids.

All the positive ions may participate in producing salinity; but of the negative ions, only the anions of strong acids are significant. In natural waters, these anions are usually chloride, nitrate, and sulfate. The salinity depends on the combined activity of equal values of both positive and negative ions, and the amount of salinity is limited by the reacting values of the strong acid anions. Therefore, the salinity is obtained by doubling the total reacting value (milliequivalents) of the strong acid anions. The alkalinity is obtained by doubling the reacting values of the bases in excess of the strong acid anions.

The positive ions determined in water analysis are arranged in three natural groups:

Group (a)   Alkalies (sodium, potassium, and lithium)
Group (b)   Earths or alkaline earths (calcium and magnesium)
Group (c)   Hydrogen (acid anions)

The groups of positive ions are measured by the sum of the reacting values of the ions in the group, and in accordance with the value of the predominating groups of positive ions in the system, five special properties are designated:

(1) Primary salinity (alkali salinity). The salinity is not to exceed twice the sum of the reacting values of the alkali ions.

(2) Secondary salinity (permanent hardness). This is defined as the excess of salinity over primary salinity—not to exceed twice the reacting values of the ions of the alkaline earth group.

(3) Tertiary salinity (acidity). This is any salinity in excess of the primary and secondary salinity.

(4) Primary alkalinity (permanent alkalinity). The excess of twice the sum of the reacting values of the alkalies over salinity.

(5) Secondary alkalinity (temporary alkalinity). This is defined as the excess of twice the sum of the reacting values of the ions of the alkaline earth group over secondary salinity.

Palmer uses "primary" to refer to alkalies which are the principal soluble decomposition products of the oldest rock formations, and "secondary" to refer to alkaline earths removed from more recent formations.

Waters are classified in accordance with the numerical relationship of the value of the group of strong acid ions to the values of the groups of positive ions. The percentage values of the alkalies, alkaline earths, and strong acid anions are represented respectively by a, b, and d. Any one of the following five conditions may exist: d may be equal to a; less than a; greater than a and less than $a + b$; or greater than $a + b$. According to these conditions, waters may be divided into five classes:

Class 1
$(d < a)$
$2d$ = Primary salinity
$2(a - d)$ = Primary alkalinity
$2b$ = Secondary alkalinity

Class 2
$(d = a)$
$2a$ or $2d$ = Primary salinity
$2b$ = Secondary alkalinity

Class 3
$(d > a;\ d < (a + b))$
$2a$ = Primary salinity
$2(d - a)$ = Secondary salinity
$2(a + b - d)$ = Secondary alkalinity

Class 4
$d = (a + b)$
$2a$ = Primary salinity
$2b$ = Secondary salinity

Class 5
$(d > (a + b))$
$2a$ = Primary salinity
$2b$ = Secondary salinity
$2(d - a - b)$ = Tertiary salinity   (acidity)

Surface waters belong in the first three classes. Sea water and brines usually fall in Class 4 and waters of volcanic origin in Class 5. Palmer used no form of diagram or graphical presentation of the calculated terms. The modified Reistle plot in Fig. 2.4 shows the primary and secondary salinities represented by one type of graph.

The original purpose of Palmer's method was to facilitate comparison of data from various geologic environments. This method is not used much now, since other methods of treatment of data give similar results with less effort.

Graphic Illustrations

Reading and comparison of tabulated water analyses data is time-consuming and means little to the average reader. Graphical expression of water analyses data will often highlight important points about the analyses that the average reader might have missed from reading tables. Water analyses diagrams are an attempt to express the data graphically.

Many different water analyses diagrams are available. Not all are shown here. Some methods are more expressive of certain portions of the analysis.

These graphic illustrations are useful when large numbers of analyses must be compared. Patterns are particularly useful in detecting surface water and casing leakage in production wells.

Results of analysis of water from a secondary recovery water supply well are given in Table 2.8. This water analysis is illustrated graphically by each of the following water analysis diagrams.

Table 2.8

RESULTS OF WATER ANALYSIS No. 2036

	P.P.M.	E.P.M.	% E.P.M.	% Palmer		
Carbonate	—	—	—	PA —	TDS 155,706	
Bicarbonate	46	0.7	0.0	SA —	SP.RES.0.0631 @ 77°F	
Sulfate	7,530	158	3.0	PS 74.8	pH 6.1	
Chloride	88,300	2,472	47.0	SS 25	FREE CO: —	
				CLASS 4	HS —	
Iron, dissolved	14	0.4		ALK (CaCO$_3$)P	—	
Iron, total	14	0.4		ALK (CaCO$_3$)MO	38.50	
Calcium	8,570	428	8.1	SILICA —		
Magnesium	2,819	231	4.4	TURBIDITY —		
Undetermined	45,702	1,965	37.4	SP. GR. 1.1072 @ 77°F		

1. TICKELL'S METHOD

The Tickell method of graphically expressing water analysis data consists of plotting the per cent reaction values of the ions on six axes formed by joining the vertices of a regular hexagon. The reaction values are equivalents

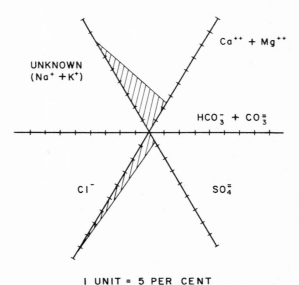

I UNIT = 5 PER CENT

Fig. 2.3. Tickel diagram of Water Analysis No. 2036.

per million, and the per cent reaction value is the number of equivalents per million of that component, divided by the total number of equivalents per million of all the components in the water, multiplied by one hundred.[12] The water analysis given in Table 2.8 is shown as a Tickell diagram in Fig. 2.3.

2. REISTLE'S METHOD

Reistle[13] graphically expressed water analysis data by plotting the ions in ppm on a vertical scale. The positive ions are plotted above a center line, and the negative ions below the line. After the ppm values are plotted, blocks are formed and colored or cross-hatched to indicate a particular ion. The width of the block has no significance. For comparison purposes, it is desirable to plot the ions in the same sequence on each graph. An illustration of a Reistle graphic presentation is shown in Fig. 2.4. The same figure shows a plot of the modified Reistle method, using reaction values or equivalents per million.[14]

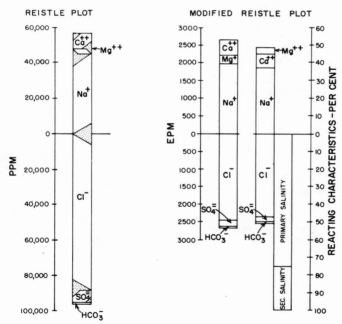

Fig. 2.4. Reistle plot of Water Analysis No. 2036.

3. STIFF'S METHOD

The Stiff method of graphically illustrating water analysis data consists of plotting the milliequivalents of the ions on a series of horizontal lines.[15]

A vertical line through the horizontal lines indicates zero. The positive ions are plotted to the left of this line and the negative ions to the right. Two scales are used. With one, the ions are plotted on a scale where one scale unit represents 100 milliequivalents of sodium or chloride ions and 10 milliequivalents of the other ions. With the other scale, one unit represents 1,000 milliequivalents of sodium or chloride ions and 100 milliequivalents of the other ions. The number of milliequivalents that each unit represents is indicated by a number beneath the symbol of the ion. The points are connected, resulting in a figure called a pattern. A Stiff pattern is shown in Fig. 2.5. This method can also be modified by plotting the concentrations on a logarithmic scale, eliminating the need to change units.

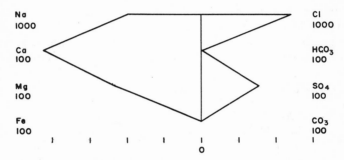

Fig. 2.5. Stiff pattern of Water Analysis No. 2036.

4. Cummer's Method

Cummer shows the per cent reaction values as horizontal bars. He also includes a bar which indicates the concentration of total dissolved solids. A Cummer bar-gram is shown in Fig. 2.6.

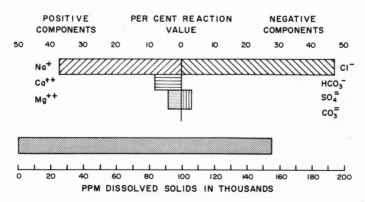

Fig. 2.6. Cummer bar-gram of Water Analysis No. 2036.

5. TELKESSY'S DIAGRAM

Telkessy plotted water analysis data in a radial form, using area to represent the percentage compositions of the ions. The milliequivalents of anions are converted to per cent of the total anion milliequivalents. The same is done for the cations. A 16-sided polygon, having an area of 200 sq mm, is constructed. Each of the sectors has an area of 12.5 sq mm, and each leg is 8.08 mm long. The cations are arranged on the right of center and the anions on the left.

The per cent of an anion calculated as per cent of the total anions in the water represents the area of a triangle in sq mm. The length of the base of the triangle L is calculated from the following equation:

$$L = \frac{\text{area}}{8.08 \times \sin 22.5°} = \frac{\text{area}}{3.09}$$

The calculated value for L is then plotted on the leg representing the anion and this point connected to the adjoining vertices of the angles of the polygon. This procedure is repeated for the other anions and cations determined by analysis. Fig. 2.7 shows a representative Telkessy diagram.

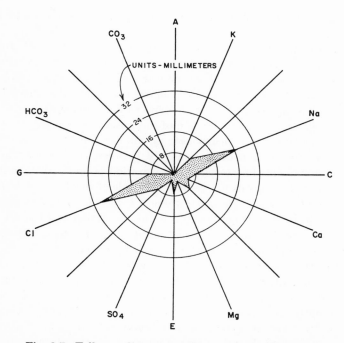

Fig. 2.7. Telkessy diagram of Water Analysis No. 2036.

6. Schoeller's Semilogarthmic Diagram

Schoeller[16] uses a semilogarithmic diagram to express water analysis data. The ions are arranged at regular intervals from left to right on the abscissa, in the order of calcium, magnesium, sodium, chloride, sulfate, bicarbonate, and carbonate. The total dissolved solids can be located at the beginning of this order and plotted as one-tenth of the concentration. The ordinate is a logarithmic scale representing the number of milliequivalents of the ions in the water.

The results of the analysis are plotted and a line drawn connecting the points representing the ions. From this diagram, Schoeller predicts the saturation of the water with respect to calcium sulfate and calcium carbonate and the pH at equilibrium. In order to determine if the water is saturated with calcium sulfate, a vertical line is drawn halfway between the sulfate and calcium ions (this line falls on the sodium line). The saturation points, represented by S, for calcium sulfate in various concentrations of sodium chloride are plotted on the vertical line in a way that $\log S = \frac{1}{2} \log$ (meq $SO_4^=$) (meq Ca^{++}). Those points are then designated as ionic strengths. Ionic strength μ is defined as

$$\frac{1}{2} (C_1 z_1^2 + \cdots C_n z_n^2)$$

where C is the concentration in moles per 1,000 grams of water, and z is the valence.

A line is drawn between the calcium and the sulfate ions. If this line crosses the vertical calcium sulfate line above the ionic strength value for a water of the same ionic strength as the water sample, the water sample is oversaturated with calcium sulfate. If the line crosses below the ionic strength value, the water is undersaturated with respect to calcium sulfate.

In order to determine the saturation of the water with respect to calcium carbonate, the calcium and bicarbonate points are joined with a straight line. A vertical line is then drawn midway between the calcium and the bicarbonate points. This line carries the saturation points corresponding to calcium carbonate for various pH values. The scale of this line is determined by $\log S = \frac{1}{2} \log$ (meq Ca^{++}) (meq A), where A is the sum of bicarbonate and carbonate ions in milliequivalents and S is the saturation of a known water with respect to calcium carbonate. The point of intersection between the vertical line and the line between calcium and bicarbonate gives the pH of equilibrium of the water analyzed. This value should be corrected for ionic strength and temperature. At 25°C (77°F), there is no temperature correction. Schoeller gives a table for temperature and ionic strength corrections, but the ionic strength corrections do not go beyond $\mu = 0.025$. Temperature corrections are not very significant at high ionic strengths. If the pH of the analyzed water is larger than the point of intersection, the water is saturated with calcium carbonate; if the pH is smaller than the point of intersection, the analyzed water is aggressive to limestone.

A third vertical line, drawn one-third the distance from the bicarbonate division to the calcium division, is used to express the carbon dioxide content of the water at equilibrium or the equilibrium pressure of carbon dioxide over the water. Mathematically, kr is determined from the following expression:

$$kr = 3 \sqrt{(\text{meq } HCO_3^-)^2 \, (\text{meq } Ca^{++})}$$

The values of kr plotted on the vertical line are obtained from the above expression for known waters and arranged on the scale according to ionic strength. The scale is adjusted so that 0.01 on the pressure scale is superimposed on the value of μ of the kr scale (the value of μ corresponding to that of the water). The point of intersection of the vertical line with a line drawn from the calcium to the bicarbonate indicates the carbon dioxide equilibrium pressure δ of the water. A Schoeller diagram is shown in Fig. 2.8.

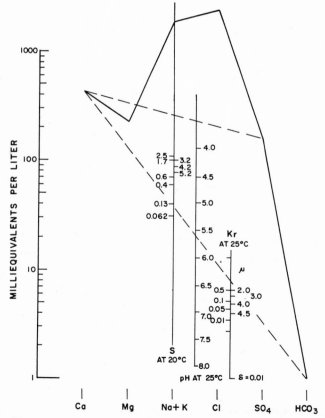

Fig. 2.8. Schoeller diagram of Water Analysis No. 2036.

7. HILL'S TRILINEAR METHOD

Hill[17] developed a method of graphing the mineral content of waters based upon arbitrary balances between cation and anion groups, similar to the Palmer classifications. The groups are further characterized by division into subtypes determined from proportionate concentrations of specific ions within cation and anion groups. If two or more waters are shown on the same plot, the total salt concentration can be shown by circles whose areas are proportional to salt concentrations rather than points.

Water Analysis 2036 is illustrated by the Hill trilinear method in Fig. 2.9. The special plotting chart used by Hill is essentially an arrangement of four equilateral triangles. These triangles are each subdivided into four smaller equilateral triangles. The Palmer groupings of primary salinity, primary alkalinity, secondary salinity, and secondary alkalinity are generally retained by Hill and designated as groups Z_1, Z_2, Z_3, and Z_4. Hill varies from Palmer by grouping the sulfate with the carbonate ion group rather than the chloride ion group. The four Z groups are termed, in order, common salt, alkali, bittern, and hardness. The perpendicular distance to any side of the cation or anion triangle represents the proportional amount of that particular cation or anion present, related to the total equivalents of cations or anions in the water.

After the point representing the cations is obtained, a line is drawn from this point parallel to line Z_2Z_1. A second line is drawn from the point

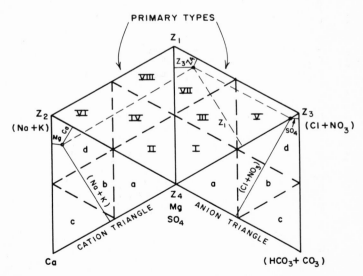

Fig. 2.9. Hill trilinear plot of Water Analysis No. 2036.

representing the anions parallel to line Z_1Z_3 and extended until it intersects the line from the cation point. Perpendiculars drawn from this third point to the sides of the triangle are proportional to the particular Z groups indicated.

More important than the relative proportions of the Z groups is the classification of the water derived from the location on the chart of this third point. Water Analysis 2036 would be classified as dVIId. The Roman numeral indicates the primary classification of the water. The presence of salts of the Z_3 group is indicated by the Roman numeral's being odd. Waters that fall in the triangle marked VII have a group Z_1 concentration that exceeds 50 per cent of the total. The first (d) representing the cation triangle indicates that the concentration of (Na$^+$ + K$^+$) is greater than 50 per cent of the cation total. The second (d) representing the anion triangle indicates that the (Cl$^-$ + NO$_3^-$) concentration is greater than 50 per cent of the total anion concentration.

Langelier[18] adapted the Hill trilinear method to the Palmer groups, wherein the sulfate ion is grouped with the chloride and nitrate rather than with the carbonates. In this adaptation, the outer shape of the diagram was modified to the shape shown in Fig. 2.10. In this modification, there are two primary classifications designated Palmer Class 1 and Palmer Class 3. Each primary triangle is subdivided into smaller triangles for the purpose of indicating the dominance of a particular ion or property. The smaller

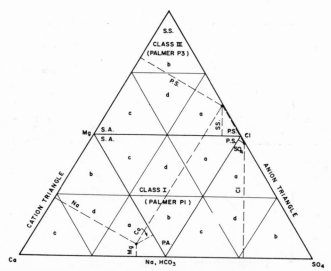

Fig. 2.10. Modified Hill trilinear plot of Water Analysis No. 2036.

triangles are lettered in alphabetical sequence with the order corresponding to (*a*) for sodium, chloride, and primary salinity; (*b*) for magnesium, sulfate, and either primary alkalinity or secondary salinity; (*c*) for calcium, carbonates, and secondary alkalinity; and (*d*) to indicate that none of the three variables is greater than 50 per cent of the total.

The modified Hill trilinear plot of water 2036 is shown in Fig. 2.10. The water has the classification *P3aaa*. This designates the water as belonging to Class *P3* in which the primary salinity is the dominant property signified by the first (*a*) after *P3*. The second (*a*) indicates that over 50 per cent of the cation equivalents are contributed by sodium, and the third (*a*) signifies that chloride contributes greater than 50 per cent of the anion equivalents.

Since water 2036 actually belongs in Palmer Class 4, it is evident that this method would not be applicable to oil field brines without additional modification. However, the method is probably satisfactory for fresh waters.

8. LANGELIER'S SINGLE-POINT METHOD

Langelier and Ludwig[18] have developed a single-point method of graphing and typing fresh waters. The method employs Cartesian coordinates, with the percentage of alkali cations plotted as the ordinate and the percentage of noncarbonate anions plotted as the abscissa. The single-point plot of water 2036 is shown in Fig. 2.11. The diagonal from the lower left-hand

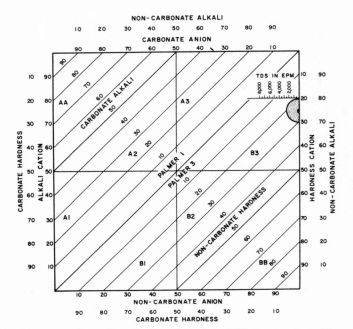

Fig. 2.11. Langelier single-point plot of Water Analysis No. 2036.

corner to the upper right-hand corner divides the diagram into two primary fields. The upper primary field, divided into areas *AA, A1, A2,* and *A3,* corresponds to Palmer Class 1. The lower primary field, divided into areas *BB, B1, B2,* and *B3,* corresponds to Palmer Class 3. According to this method of plotting, water 2036 falls in Palmer Class 3. This water would be classified as *B3–10.* The *B3* indicates the triangle into which the water falls. The *10* indicates the number of horizontal divisions in the diameter of the circle which denotes the equivalents per million of ions dissolved in the water.

The perpendicular distances from the sides of the primary triangle to the point denote the percentage values of properties which characterize the water. The diagonal scale is included in the diagram for convenience in obtaining these values.

9. LANGELIER'S SINGLE-POINT DIAGRAM OF MIXTURES

Water analysis data are used frequently to identify mixtures of two or more ground waters. Water samples from selected locations are analyzed, and the relative concentration of certain ionic constituents is used to identify the water. Three waters, *A, B,* and *C* (analyses of these waters are shown in Table 2.9) are mixed in equal proportions to form a hypothetical mixture termed *K.* The Langelier and Ludwig diagram of this mixture is shown in Fig. 2.12. A mixture of two waters would fall somewhere on a line connecting

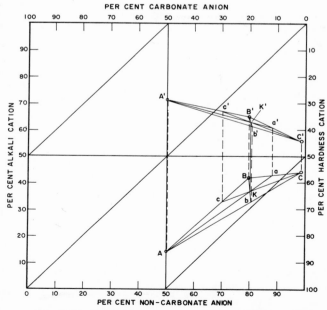

Fig. 2.12. Langelier diagram of Water Mixture *K.*

the points representing these waters. A three-water mixture would fall within a triangle formed by connecting the points representing each water.

Table 2.9
WATERS USED TO FORM MIXTURE FOR
LANGELIER'S SINGLE-POINT DIAGRAM OF MIXTURES

Constituent	Water A			Water B		
	PPM	EPM	% EPM	PPM	EPM	% EPM
Carbonate	—	—	—	—	—	—
Bicarbonate	314	5.2	25.0	1,236	20.3	10.4
Sulfate	151	3.1	15.1	1,063	22.1	11.3
Chloride	75	2.1	10.1	1,955	55.1	28.3
Calcium	61	3.0	14.5	676	33.7	17.3
Magnesium	72	5.9	28.3	280	23.0	11.8
Sodium	33	1.4	7.0	937	40.8	20.9

	Water C			Water Mixture K		
	PPM	EPM	% EPM	PPM	EPM	% EPM
Carbonate	—	—	—	—	—	—
Bicarbonate	508	8.3	0.9	686	11.3	2.9
Sulfate	1,444	30.0	3.2	886	18.4	4.8
Chloride	15,504	437.2	46.0	5,845	164.8	42.4
Calcium	3,996	199.4	21.0	1,578	78.7	20.2
Magnesium	783	64.4	6.7	378	31.1	8.0
Sodium	4,868	211.7	22.2	1,946	84.6	21.7

Waters A, B, C, and K are plotted on the chart according to the standard Langelier procedure. Points A', B', C', and K' are plotted, using the percentage values of either the calcium or magnesium as the ordinates and the strong acid anions (Cl^- and $SO_4^=$) as the abscissas. Triangles ABC and $A'B'C'$ are drawn by connecting the respective points. Lines are then drawn from each apex through K and K', respectively. The intercepts aa', bb', and cc' must fall on the same vertical lines, if K is a quantitative mixture of the three waters. The water of Fig. 2.12 fulfills this requirement, indicating that K is a quantitative mixture of A, B, and C. The fact that K is a quantitative mixture of A, B, and C can be confirmed by plotting the value of either chloride or sulfate as the abscissa and the alkali cations (Na^+ and K^+) as the ordinates. The intercepts aa', bb', and cc' should then fall on the same horizontal lines.

WATER ANALYSIS REPORT FORM

A good water analysis report form is designed to include all information pertinent to the water sample and results of the analysis. The form should also include a graphical representation of the water for rapid comparison with other waters. A report of water analysis form used by one service laboratory is shown in Fig. 2.13.

PRODUCTION PROFITS, INC.
Consultants in Petroleum Production
9130 VISCOUNT ROW
DALLAS, TEXAS

REPORT OF WATER ANALYSIS

SAMPLE NO._____

TOTAL SOLIDS_____

CLIENT_____OPERATOR_____

FIELD_____COUNTY_____STATE_____

LEASE AND WELL NO._____PROD. FORM._____

SOURCE OF SAMPLE_____DEPTH: TOTAL_____PERF._____

SAMPLE OF: PRODUCED WATER   ☐   INJECTION SYSTEM WATER ☐   OTHER ☐_____

DATE COLLECTED_____ANALYST_____

MINERAL ANALYSIS PATTERN
(NUMBER BELOW ION NAME INDICATES MEQ./SCALE UNIT)

PRECIPITATED AND SUSPENDED SOLIDS

CONSTITUENT	MG/L (PPM)
TOTAL UNDISSOLVED SOLIDS_____	
IRON OXIDE_____	
CALCIUM CARBONATE_____	
CALCIUM SULFATE_____	
MAGNESIUM CARBONATE_____	
BARIUM SULFATE_____	
SILICA_____	
ORGANIC_____	

PHYSICAL PROPERTIES

SP. GRAVITY_____

PH_____

RESISTIVITY_____OHMMETERS @ 68°

STABILITY INDEX	@ 41°F_____
	@ 86°F_____
CASO₄ SOLUBILITY	@ 41°F_____MEQ/L
	@ 86°F_____MEQ/L
MAX. CASO₄ POSSIBLE	_____MEQ/L

REMARKS:

DISSOLVED SOLIDS

CONSTITUENT		MG/L (PPM)
TOTAL SOLIDS	(CALC.)	
SODIUM	(CALC.)	
IRON	(TOTAL)	
MANGANESE		
BARIUM		
CALCIUM		
MAGNESIUM		
CHLORIDE		
BICARBONATE		
CARBONATE		
SULFATE		

DISSOLVED GASES

CONSTITUENT	MG/L (PPM)
HYDROGEN SULFIDE_____	
CARBON DIOXIDE_____	
OXYGEN_____	

Fig. 2.13. Water analysis report form.

References

[1]J. Grynberg, "DST—Success or Failure?" *Oil Gas J.*, **57**, No. 26 (1959), 106.

[2]D. F. Noad, "Water Analysis Data: Interpretation and Application," *J. Can. Pet. Tech.* (Summer 1962), p. 82.

[3]*Standard Methods for the Examination of Water and Wastewater* (11th Ed.) (New York: American Public Health Association, Inc., 1960), p. 29.

[4]*Ibid.*

[5]*Manual on Industrial Water and Industrial Waste Water* (2nd Ed.) (Philadelphia: American Society for Testing Materials, 1960).

[6]A. G. Collins, C. Pearson, D. H. Attaway, and J. W. Watkins, *Methods of Analyzing Oilfield Waters*, Bureau of Mines Report of Investigation 5819 (Washington, D.C.: Department of the Interior, Bureau of Mines, 1961).

[7]H. Katz and R. Navone, "Method for Simultaneous Determination of Calcium and Magnesium," *J. Am. Water Works Assoc.* **56** (1964), 121.

[8]G. W. Moore, C. E. Roberson, and H. D. Nygren, "Electrode Determination of Carbon Dioxide Content of Sea Water and Deep-Sea Sediment," *Geological Survey Research 1962* (Washington, D.C.: Government Printing Office, 1962), p. B-33.

[9]D. E. Carritt and J. W. Kanwisher, "An Electrode System for Measuring Dissolved Oxygen," *Anal. Chem.*, **31** (1959), 5.

[10]J. D. Hem, *Study and Interpretation of the Chemical Characteristics of Natural Water*, Geological Survey Water-Supply Paper 1473 (Washington, D.C.: Government Printing Office, 1959), p. 120.

[11]C. Palmer, *The Geochemical Interpretation of Water Analysis*, Geological Survey Bulletin 479 (Washington, D.C.: Government Printing Office, 1911), p. 7.

[12]E. G. Tickell, "A Method for the Graphical Interpretation of Water Analysis," *Report of California State Oil & Gas Supervisor*, **6**, No. 9 (1921), 5.

[13]C. E. Reistle, Jr., *Identification of Oil-Field Waters by Chemical Identification* (Washington, D.C.: Government Printing Office, 1927), p. 24.

[14]H. T. Capelle, "Water-Analysis Diagrams—Kansas Oil-Field Brines," *API Drilling and Production Practice*, (1957), p. 238.

[15]H. A. Stiff, "The Interpretation of Chemical Water Analysis by Means of Patterns," *Petroleum Transactions AIME*, **192** (1951), 376.

[16]H. Schoeller, "Geochemistry of Subterranean Waters—Application to Petroleum Formation Waters," *Revue de L'Institut Francais du Petrole et Annales des Combustibles Liquids*, **10**, No. 4 (1955).

[17]R. A. Hill, "Salts in Irrigation Waters," *Proc. Am. Soc. Civil Engrs.*, **67** (1941), 975.

[18]W. F. Langelier and H. F. Ludwig, "Graphical Methods for Indicating the Mineral Character of Natural Waters," *J. Am. Water Works Assoc.*, **34** (1942), 335.

Scales and Sludges Deposited from Water

3

The formation of scales and sludges deposited from waters is troublesome. These deposits may form in distribution lines, domestic hot-water heaters, heater treaters, various types of cooling equipment, boilers, heat exchangers, or on nearly any surface which water contacts. These deposits often prove expensive due to shutdown of equipment for removal of deposits or replacement of the equipment.

Scale and sludge are differentiated on the basis that scale is a deposit formed in place on surfaces in contact with water, while sludge may form in one place and be deposited in another. Sludges may collect in areas of a system where the flow rate is low or where there are bends in the lines, and thus build up a deposit which will reduce the flow. Sludges are usually less adherent than scales and more easily removed by mechanical methods. Scales, by the nature of their formation, are usually harder and more impermeable than sludges. One method of combating corrosion in water distribution lines utilizes the deposition of a thin layer of calcium carbonate scale on the metal surface as a protective coating.

Usually, the deposition of scale is undesirable because it is uncontrolled. Scale may build up to such an extent that flow through a pipe is reduced to a trickle. Figure 3.1 shows a section of flow line, from a secondary recovery water supply well, which was filled with deposited gypsum scale in a matter of days.

Fig. 3.1. Gypsum deposit in flow line.

The heat transfer properties of scale are generally less than those for metals. A build-up of scale on metal surfaces may act as insulation in cooling systems and boilers, causing decreased efficiency. Scale build-up in boilers can cause hot spots, in which the temperature of the metal will exceed the safe operating temperature and cause equipment failure.

Uneven scale deposition may cause pitting corrosion. If the desposited scale is particularly impermeable and the system contains dissolved oxygen, it is possible that an oxygen concentration cell may form between the scale-covered iron and the uncovered iron, resulting in pitting type corrosion beneath the scale.

There are several different kinds of scales deposited from water, and these may be formed in various ways. Boiler waters which contain calcium

Table 3.1

COMMON DEPOSITS FORMED IN WATER SYSTEMS

(Reprinted with permission of the American Society for Testing and Materials, Philadelphia, Penn., from *Manual on Industrial Water and Industrial Waste Water* (2nd Ed.).

| Name | Chemical Composition | Deposit Formation Conditions | | | Water Vapor or Steam |
		T < 100°C With or Without Evaporation	T > 100°C No Evaporation	T > 100°C Evaporation	
Acmite	$Na_2O \cdot Fe_2O_3 \cdot 4SiO_2$			×	
Analcite	$Na_2O \cdot Al_2O_3 \cdot 4SiO_2 \cdot 2H_2O$			×	×
Anhydrite	$CaSO_4$		×	×	
Aragonite	$CaCO_3$	×	×	×	
Biological					
(a) Nonspore bacteria		×			
(b) Spore bacteria		×			
(c) Fungi		×			
(d) Algae and diatoms		×			
(e) Crustaceans		×			
Brucite	$Mg(OH)_2$		×	×	
Burkeite	$Na_2CO_3 \cdot 2Na_2SO_4$				×
Calcite	$CaCO_3$	×	×	×	
Calcium hydroxide	$Ca(OH)_2$			×	
Carbonaceous		×	×	×	×
Copper	Cu			×	
Cuprite	Cu_2O		×		
Ferrous oxide	FeO		×		
Goethite	$Fe_2O_3 \cdot H_2O$	×	×	×	
Gypsum	$CaSO_4 \cdot 2H_2O$	×	×	×	
Halite	$NaCl$				×
Hematite	Fe_2O_3			×	
Hydroxyl-apatite	$Ca_{10}(PO_4)_6(OH)_2$	×	×	×	
Magnesium Phosphate (basic)	$Mg_3(PO_4)_2 \cdot Mg(OH)_2$		×	×	
Magnetite	Fe_3O_4		×	×	×
Oil (chloroform extractable)		×	×	×	×
Quartz	SiO_2				×
Serpentine	$3MgO \cdot 2SiO_2 \cdot 2H_2O$		×	×	
Siderite	$FeCO_3$				×
Silica (amorphous)	SiO_2				×
Sodium carbonate	Na_2CO_3				×
Sodium disilicate	$Na_2Si_2O_6$				×
Sodium ferrous phosphate	$NaFePO_4$			×	
Sodium silicate	Na_2SiO_3				×
Tenorite	CuO			×	
Thenardite	Na_2SO_4			×	×
Xonotlite	$5CaO \cdot 5SiO_2 \cdot H_2O$			×	

sulfate may form a scale of this composition, as steam is evaporated from the boiler. The dissolved salts are concentrated in the water until the water becomes oversaturated with calcium sulfate, which precipitates as a scale on the metal surface. Silica scale, and other scales, can be formed in boilers by the same process. The solubility of calcium carbonate decreases with increased temperature. A cooling water which is nearly saturated with calcium carbonate at room temperature may come in contact with a hot surface and, if the temperature of the water is increased to a point where the water is oversaturated, calcium carbonate may precipitate in the form of scale on the metal surface.

Scale may also form on hot surfaces from evaporation. Hot spots on the surface may form bubbles. Evaporation of the water to form the bubble leaves the salts deposited on the surface. Carbonates do not always form scale but sometimes form sludges. This sludge may bake on a hot surface to form a scale. Substances such as oil or other organic matter may act as a binder and transform sludge to scale.

Scales and sludges are formed from waters, as the waters adjust to changes in equilibrium. Calcium and magnesium carbonates exhibit a negative solubility characteristic. This is the characteristic of a decreasing solubility with increasing temperature. Therefore, a water saturated with either of these salts at a given temperature would precipitate these salts in adjusting to equilibrium, if the temperature were increased.

Chemical changes in the system can also cause scale to form. For example, the solubility of calcium carbonate is dependent on the partial pressure of carbon dioxide. A decrease in carbon dioxide partial pressure will often cause calcium carbonate scale to form in tubing and flowlines.

Calcium sulfate scale often forms when two chemically stable waters are mixed. One water may be high in sulfate content, and the other water high in calcium. Individually, the waters may be in equilibrium, but when mixed, the solubility product of calcium sulfate is exceeded and equilibrium regained by precipitation of some calcium sulfate.

In addition to scales formed from substances deposited from water, scale may form as a result of a chemical reaction between the water or some impurity in the water and the pipe itself. Corrosion products may be scales of this type. Sulfate-reducing bacteria under anaerobic conditions can cause iron scale in flowlines. The bacteria reduce sulfate and liberate hydrogen sulfide, which reacts with iron to form ferrous sulfide scale.

Scales deposited on a surface or collected sludges are seldom pure. These usually are a mixture of any sparingly soluble salts present in the water, plus any corrosion products formed on the pipe surface. This often makes it difficult to classify deposits according to a specific acid radical. The deposits may be classified generally as scale, sludge, corrosion products, and biological deposits. The more common types of deposits are shown in

Table 3.1. Deposits formed at temperatures above 100°C (212°F) are generally limited to high-temperature water heaters and boilers. The deposits formed from water vapor or steam are substances which may be present in boiler water and mechanically carried over with steam.

Calcium Carbonate

1. FORMATION

Calcium carbonate, or calcite, scale is frequently encountered in oil field operations. Calcium carbonate crystals are large, but when the scale is found with impurities in the form of finely divided crystals, the scale appears uniform. Carbonate scale can be qualitatively identified by the addition of a few drops of mineral acid. The evolution of an odorless gas indicates that carbonate is present. This does not identify the scale as calcium carbonate, since additional tests are required to identify calcium.

Deposition of $CaCO_3$ scale or sludge results from precipitation of calcium carbonate according to the following equation:

$$Ca^{++} + CO_3^= \rightarrow CaCO_3 \qquad (3\text{--}1)$$

Solubility of calcium carbonate in distilled water at 25°C (77°F), with a carbon dioxide partial pressure of 3.2×10^{-4} atm, is 0.053 g/1,000 g of water. This is a very low solubility. However, solubility of calcium carbonate is greatly influenced by partial pressure of carbon dioxide, temperature, and concentration of other salts in the solution.

When carbon dioxide comes in contact with water, it dissolves and forms carbonic acid according to Eq. (3–2). The ionization of carbonic acid is illustrated by the following equations:

$$CO_2 + H_2O \rightleftharpoons H_2CO_3 \qquad (3\text{--}2)$$

$$H_2CO_3 \rightleftharpoons H^+ + HCO_3^- \qquad (3\text{--}3)$$

$$HCO_3^- \rightleftharpoons H^+ + CO_3^= \qquad (3\text{--}4)$$

The ionization constant K_1 for Eq. (3–3) is 4.54×10^{-7} at 25°C, and the ionization constant K_2 for Eq. (3–4) is 5.61×10^{-11} at 25°C.

From the above equations, it can be seen that carbon dioxide gas dissolves in water and forms carbonic acid. The carbonic acid ionizes to form hydrogen ion and bicarbonate ion. Since the second ionization constant of carbonic acid is much smaller than the first ionization constant, the ionized hydrogen ion from the first ionization would combine with free carbonate ion in the water. The free carbonate ion shown in Eq. (3–1) would combine with this hydrogen ion to form the bicarbonate ion. It is believed that dissolved calcium carbonate does not exist in solution as calcium ions and carbonate ions but as calcium ions and bicarbonate ions.

The precipitation of calcium carbonate can be expressed by the equation:

$$Ca(HCO_3)_2 \rightleftharpoons H_2O + CO_2 + CaCO_3 \qquad (3\text{--}5)$$

By the principle of Le Chatelier, we see that by increasing the concentration of carbon dioxide, more calcium bicarbonate is formed. A decrease in carbon dioxide content in this system at equilibrium would result in the formation of calcium carbonate. Therefore, we can see that the solubility of calcium carbonate is greatly influenced by the carbon dioxide content of the water; i.e., by the partial pressure of carbon dioxide gas over the water.

The effect of carbon dioxide pressure on calcium carbonate solubility at 24°C, as determined by Miller, is shown graphically in Fig. 3.2. Starting at one atmosphere and increasing the carbon dioxide pressure to 50 atmospheres approximately triples the calcium carbonate solubility. Conversely, dropping the carbon dioxide pressure will decrease the solubility.

This phenomena occuring in some production wells or water supply wells causes calcium carbonate or calcite scale deposition. The water in the reservoir is stable with respect to calcium carbonate solubility, because a certain pressure of carbon dioxide is maintained. When the water is produced, the gas pressure decreases as the water approaches the surface. This upsets the chemical equilibrium and scale deposits.

Temperature is another factor influencing calcium carbonate solubility.

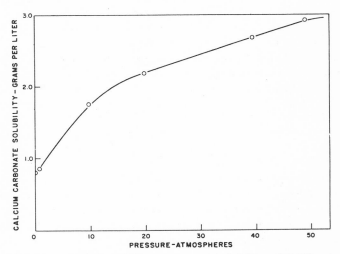

Fig. 3.2. Influence of CO_2 pressure on solubility of $CaCO_3$ at 24°C (75.2°F). (Data from J.P. Miller, "A Portion of the System Calcium Carbonate, Carbon Dioxide, Water," *Am. J. Sci.*, **250** (1952), 161.)

Fig. 3.3 shows that, as temperature increases, calcium carbonate solubility decreases. From this graph, it is readily seen that temperature changes alone can cause precipitation of calcium carbonate from saturated or nearly saturated solutions. This curve explains to some extent the scaling problems which could be encountered by injecting a water, saturated with calcium carbonate at surface temperatures, into an underground formation at higher temperatures. Also, it explains why calcium carbonate deposition is such a problem with cooling waters.

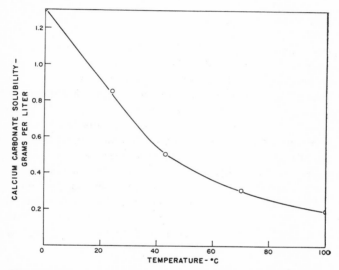

Fig. 3.3. Effect of temperature on the solubility of $CaCO_3$ at 0.987 atm of CO_2 Pressure. (Data from Miller, *Am. J. Sci.*, **250** 161.)

In oil production and water supply wells, the temperature effect acts in the reverse direction to increase calcium carbonate solubility. Generally, the temperature in the earth increases with increasing depth. Water from a reservoir will decrease in temperature as it is raised to the cooler surface. This aids in increasing calcium carbonate solubility.

A combination of factors influences carbon dioxide solubility in produced water. The lower temperature near the surface increases solubility, but the lower pressures cause loss of carbon dioxide to offset the gain from the temperature influence. In nearly all cases, the loss in carbon dioxide by pressure drop is the greater effect, so calcite scale deposits. Table 3.2 shows the combined effect of temperature and carbon dioxide pressure on calcium carbonate solubility. As temperature increases, the effect of increasing carbon dioxide pressure on calcium carbonate solubility generally decreases.

Table 3.2

CALCITE SOLUBILITY AS A FUNCTION
OF CARBON DIOXIDE PRESSURE AND TEMPERATURE*

(Reproduced from Ellis, *A. J. Sci.*, **261** (1963), 259.)

pCO$_2$ Atm.	Temperature °F								
	100	125	150	175	200	225	250	275	300
1	0.216	0.142	0.094	0.060	0.040	0.027	0.015	0.008	0.006
4	0.360	0.244	0.158	0.097	0.063	0.039	0.024	0.013	0.009
12	0.555	0.357	0.221	0.144	0.091	0.059	0.036	0.020	0.012
62	—	—	0.405	0.255	0.152	0.089	0.051	0.028	0.014

*Solubilities in g CaCO$_3$/1,000 g solution.

In a production or water well, the carbon dioxide pressure in contact with water decreases because of a pressure release and not predominantly because of a lowering of temperature. In a sealed system such as a bottom hole sampling bomb, where carbon dioxide pressure is influenced directly by temperature, calcium carbonate will not be deposited by a decrease in temperature. Pressure decrease is caused by temperature decrease. The decrease in solubility due to lowering carbon dioxide pressure is less than the increase in solubility caused by temperature decrease.[1]

The presence in the solution of salts which do not contain a common ion (calcium or carbonate ion) have an influence on calcium carbonate solubility. These salts increase the ionic strength of the solution, which exerts an effect on the activity coefficient of the calcium and bicarbonate ions. The solubility of calcium carbonate in solutions of varying sodium

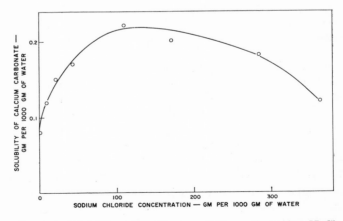

Fig. 3.4. Solubility of CaCO$_3$ in solutions of varying NaCl concentration at 25°C (77°F). (Data from Shternina and Frolova *Izv. Sektora Fiz—Khim. Analiza, Inst. Obshch Neorgan. Khim., Akad Nauk. SSSR*, **21** (1952), 271.)

chloride concentration is shown graphically in Fig. 3.4. The solubility of calcium carbonate is increased by additional amounts of sodium chloride until the concentration of sodium chloride reaches 120 g/1,000 g of water.[2] At higher concentrations of sodium chloride, the solubility of calcium carbonate begins to decrease.

Carbon dioxide pressure and temperature influence calcium carbonate solubility in salt water in the same manner as in fresh water. The effect of salt concentration and high temperatures on calcium carbonate solubility at constant pressure is shown in Fig. 3.5. The influence of dissolved sodium chloride on calcite solubility is clearly seen in this graph.

Consider the hypothetical case of a water containing 120 g of sodium chloride/1,000 g of water and saturated with calcium carbonate. The loss of small amounts of carbon dioxide or slight increases in temperature would cause calcium carbonate to precipitate. The addition of 20 per cent by volume of fresh water containing extremely small amounts of calcium ion would decrease the sodium chloride concentration to 96 g/1,000 g of water and the calcium carbonate concentration to 0.174 g/1,000 g of water. (Even though the calcium carbonate is in solution as calcium bicarbonate, it is referred to as calcium carbonate since this is the form of the precipitate.) However, in water containing this new concentration of sodium chloride, the solubility of calcium carbonate at 25°C is shown in Fig. 3.4 to be 0.212 g/1,000 g of water. Small differences in temperature or carbon dioxide content of the diluted water would, therefore, not be likely to cause calcium carbonate precipitation.

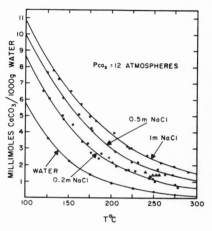

Fig. 3.5. Solubility of calcite in water and sodium chloride solutions at a carbon dioxide pressure of 12 atm. (Reproduced from Ellis, *Am. J. Sci.*, **261** (1963), 259.)

From the above brief discussion of the factors influencing calcium carbonate solubility, it is readily understood that this is a complex problem. The chief causes of scale formation are loss of carbon dioxide and temperature changes. The loss of carbon dioxide can be to some extent reflected in pH changes in the solution. The pH will also change with fairly large temperature changes.

It is important in some oilfield operations to be able to predict the tendency of water to deposit calcium carbonate. The previous discussion together with the graphs and Table 3.2 will help in this respect. Because of interest in this problem, several methods for calculating the calcium carbonate scaling tendency of water have been proposed.

2. LANGELIER SATURATION INDEX

A thin coating of calcium carbonate scale deposited on the surface of a water pipe can act as a coating to prevent corrosion. Langelier[3] developed an index for fresh waters, in the pH range of 6.5 to 9.5, that makes it possible to predict whether a given water will deposit or dissolve calcium carbonate scale. This is called the *saturation index* and is calculated from the following equation:

$$SI = pH - pH_s = pH - [(pK_2' - pK_s') + p\,Ca^{++} + p\,Alk] \qquad (3\text{--}6)$$

In Eq. (3–6), pH is the actual pH of the water; pH_s is the pH at saturation; pK_2' and pK_s' are empirical constants; $p\,Ca^{++}$ is the negative logarithm of the calcium ion concentration in moles per liter; and $p\,Alk$ is the negative logarithm of the total alkalinity, titrated to the methyl orange end point and expressed in terms of titratable equivalents per liter. The constants pK_2' and pK_s' can be calculated from thermodynamic constants. A table of $(pK_2' - pK_s')$ values for ionic strengths as high as 0.02 and temperatures to 90°C (194°F) is found in the Appendix.

A positive value for the saturation index indicates that the water is oversaturated and will precipitate calcium carbonate; a negative value indicates that the water is corrosive, i.e., will dissolve calcium carbonate scale. This saturation index serves as an indication of the tendency of the water to dissolve or precipitate calcium carbonate, but it will not indicate the capacity.

Larson and Buswell[4] modified the equation for the saturation index to include compensation for variations in temperature or salt concentration. In the equation of Larson and Buswell shown below, I is the saturation index, pH is the measured pH, (Ca^{++}) and $(Alky)$ are expressed in ppm as calcium and calcium carbonate respectively, and μ is the ionic strength of the solution. (See sample calculation in the Appendix.)

$$I = pH + \log{(Ca^{++})} + \log{(Alky)} - (pK_2' - pK_s') - 9.30$$
$$-\,\frac{2.5\sqrt{\mu}}{1 + 5.3\sqrt{\mu} + 5.5\mu} \qquad (3\text{--}7)$$

Ryznar[5] developed an equation for calculating the *stability index*. The stability index is an empirical expression, shown by Eq. (3–8), which not only indicates the scaling or corrosive tendencies of a water but gives a semiquantitative value for the amount of scale deposited or the seriousness of the corrosion tendencies. The terms of Eq. (3–8) correspond to those used in Eq. (3–7). The stability index for all waters will be positive.

$$\text{Stability Index} = 2\,\text{pH}_s - \text{pH} = 2\left[(\text{pK}_2' - \text{pK}_s') - \log(\text{Ca}^{++})\right.$$
$$\left. - \log(Alky) + 9.30 + \frac{2.5\sqrt{\mu}}{1 + 5.3\sqrt{\mu} + 5.5\mu}\right] - \text{pH} \tag{3-8}$$

A stability index of 5.5 will give an appreciable amount of calcium carbonate scale; whereas a stability index of 7.5 or higher at 140°F would be corrosive, and a stability index of 9 or higher would indicate serious corrosion. The smaller the stability index, the greater the amount of scale deposition is indicated.

The Langelier method and the above variations are only applicable to waters of ionic strength equal to or less than 0.02. This method is intended to serve only as a guide in water treatment, and experience in the use of these calculations provides the best criteria of the reliability of either the saturation index or the stability index as applied to a given system. Calculated examples of each of the indices are shown in the Appendix.

3. STIFF AND DAVIS EXTENSION OF THE LANGELIER METHOD

The Langelier saturation index has been extended empirically by Stiff and Davis[6] to apply to oilfield brines. Stiff and Davis term their index the *stability index* and represent it by *SI*. Since this is the same symbol used by Ryznar, care must be exercised to avoid confusing the two.

Stiff and Davis use the following equation to determine their stability index.

$$SI = \text{pH} - K - pCa - pAlk \tag{3-9}$$

In Eq. (3-9), K is an empirical constant used to compensate for various ionic strengths and temperatures. The values for K, pCa, and $pAlk$ are taken from graphs in the Appendix. The Appendix also contains an example of the *SI* calculated for a water. A positive index indicates scale formation, and a negative index indicates corrosion. This method is useful as a guide for predicting scaling tendencies of oilfield brines.

Magnesium Carbonate and Hydroxide Deposits

Another substance deposited from water in the form of scale or sludge is magnesium carbonate. As might be expected, the solubility of magnesium carbonate is influenced by the same factors which influence calcium carbonate solubility. According to Eq. (3-10), magnesium bicarbonate decomposes in solution to give solid magnesium carbonate, carbon dioxide, and water.

$$Mg(HCO_3)_2 \rightleftharpoons MgCO_3 + CO_2 + H_2O \tag{3-10}$$

As with calcium carbonate, the solubility of magnesium carbonate increases with increasing partial pressures of carbon dioxide over the water and decreases with decreasing partial pressures. The solubility of magnesium carbonate decreases with increasing temperature and shows similar behavior to calcium carbonate with respect to the diverse ion effect.

However, magnesium carbonate scale is not as troublesome as calcite or aragonite. The solubility of magnesium carbonate in distilled water is 0.223 g/liter, which is approximately 4 times greater than that of calcium carbonate. Since most waters which contain magnesium also contain calcium, any change in the equilibrium of the water which would tend to decrease the solubility of magnesium carbonate would also decrease the solubility of calcium carbonate, and would result in the precipitation of calcium carbonate with a subsequent decrease in the carbonate ion content. Therefore, unless the change in equilibrium was very drastic, it is unlikely that magnesium carbonate would precipitate.

An exception to the above statement could occur when waters are mixed. If one water is at equilibrium with respect to magnesium, calcium, and carbonate, and the water mixed with it contains a high magnesium content, it is likely that magnesium carbonate would precipitate before calcium carbonate. The evaporation of water to leave a more concentrated solution with respect to magnesium and carbonate may also result in magnesium carbonate scale or sludge formation.

At temperatures near the boiling point of water, any magnesium carbonate formed decomposes according to the equation

$$MgCO_3 + H_2O \rightleftharpoons Mg(OH)_2 + CO_2 \tag{3-11}$$

and the water deposits Brucite or magnesium hydroxide scale. The solubility of magnesium hydroxide decreases with increasing temperature. Waters containing calcium, magnesium, and carbonate ions tend to precipitate calcium carbonate up to temperatures of 82°C. Above this temperature, magnesium hydroxide begins to precipitate. Magnesium hydroxide scale would generally be found in boilers, heater treaters, and possibly in tubing found in high-temperature formations.

Calcium Sulfate Deposits

1. FORMATION

Calcium sulfate, or gypsum, is another solid frequently deposited by oilfield brines. Calcium sulfate usually precipitates directly on the metal surfaces of flow lines, boilers, heat exchanger tubes, etc., and consequently forms a scale rather than a sludge. The crystals of calcium sulfate are smaller than those of calcium carbonate, so the scale is generally harder and denser than carbonate scales. Sulfate scales do not effervesce when treated with acid and cannot successfully be removed by acidizing at normal temperatures. Calcium sulfate scale is more difficult to remove than calcium carbonate scale.

The precipitation of calcium sulfate from water can be expressed as:

$$Ca^{++} + SO_4^= \rightarrow CaSO_4 \tag{3-12}$$

and the solubility product is given by:

$$(Ca^{++})(SO_4^=) = K_{sp} \tag{3-13}$$

This solubility product is a number which varies with temperature and concentration of uncommon ions in the solution but is not appreciably affected by pressures encountered in oilfield operations. When the product of the calcium and sulfate ions exceeds this number, calcium sulfate precipitates until the product of the ion concentrations equals the solubility product. The solubility of calcium sulfate in distilled water is 2.09 g/liter at 25°C. This solubility is much larger than that of calcium carbonate. Ordinarily, in supersaturated waters containing both carbonate and sulfate ions in addition to calcium ions, the carbonate would precipitate first due to this large solubility difference.

The influence of temperature on the solubility of calcium sulfate in a sodium chloride solution is shown in Fig. 3.6. This graph shows that, in the temperature range of 30 to 70°C, the solubility is not appreciably affected by temperature variations. At temperatures above 82°C, the solubility decreases rapidly.[7] As indicated by Figs. 3.3 and 3.6, temperature variations will not influence calcium sulfate solubility as greatly as they will calcium carbonate

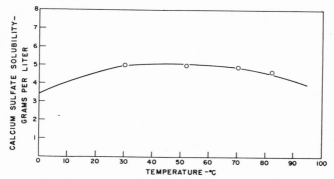

Fig. 3.6. Temperature effect on $CaSO_4$ solubility in 29.4 g/liter NaCl solution. (Data from Cameron, *J. Phy. Chem.*, **5** (1901), 562.)

solubility. An increase in temperature decreases calcium carbonate solubility, but it may increase calcium sulfate solubility.

The influence of the concentration of uncommon ions (the diverse ion effect) on calcium sulfate is appreciable, as shown in Fig. 3.7. This graph shows the variation in calcium sulfate solubility with increased sodium chloride concentration. Similar effects are shown by other salts dissolved in water. The effect of increased salt concentration is similar for both calcium sulfate and carbonate solubility.

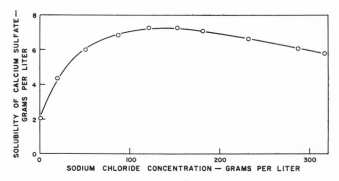

Fig. 3.7. Solubility of $CaSO_4$ in NaCl solutions at 25°C (77°F). (Data from Shternina, *Dokl. Akad. Nauk, SSSR*, **60**, No. 2 (1948), 247.)

Equation (3–12) shows that only calcium ions and sulfate ions are directly involved in the solubility of calcium sulfate, whereas carbon dioxide was involved in the solubility of calcium carbonate. Therefore, carbon dioxide partial pressure does not affect the solubility of calcium sulfate, unless carbon dioxide gas in the solution causes the dissolution of calcite or aragonite that is in contact with the water. In this case, the calcium ion concentration in the water may be raised sufficiently, depending on how nearly saturated the water is with calcium sulfate, to cause calcium sulfate to precipitate as gypsum.

Calcium sulfate exists as gypsum ($CaSO_4 \cdot 2H_2O$), sub-hydrate ($CaSO_4 \cdot \frac{1}{2}H_2O$), or anhydrite ($CaSO_4$). It is only found in nature as gypsum and anhydrite. Solubilities in water of these forms differ. Most calcium sulfate deposits in oil fields are gypsum scales because of the comparatively low temperatures at which they are deposited. In deep wells, temperatures often exceed 100°C, and anhydrite may be the stable form.

Because of depth, pressures in deep wells are high. It has recently been shown that pressure increases the solubility of calcium sulfate, but not enough to compensate for the increase in temperature of the earth as wells increase in depth.[9] Figure 3.8 shows this increase in anhydrite solubility with pressure and decrease with temperature increase. One hundred bars' pressure does not appreciably increase solubility over the increase caused by vapor pressure of water at these temperatures. It is also evident from these curves that the effect of pressure decreases as temperature increases.

The deposition of calcium sulfate from water can be caused by evaporation. Evaporation serves to remove some of the water, which means that the salt concentration in the remaining water is higher. This may be particularly true of cooling waters if some of the water evaporates. As water evaporates, the salt content is increased and may finally reach the point

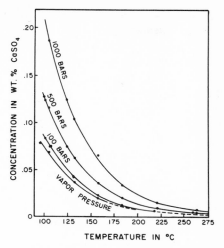

Fig. 3.8. Effect of temperature and pressure on anhydrite solubility in water. (After Dickson *et al.*, *Am. J. Sci.*, **261** (1963), 61.)

where the solubility product of calcium sulfate is exceeded, resulting in precipitation. The evolution of gases, such as methane and carbon dioxide, from waters saturated with calcium sulfate may carry off enough water vapor to cause an increase in salt concentration, resulting in precipitation of calcium sulfate.

Mixtures of waters from different water layers or sands may precipitate calcium sulfate. Water from one sand may have a high calcium ion concentration, and the water from a second sand may contain a large amount of sulfate ion. When two waters are mixed, the solubility product of calcium sulfate is exceeded, and precipitation occurs until the concentration of calcium sulfate in solution is reduced to the limit of solubility.

2. PREDICTING CALCIUM SULFATE DEPOSITION FROM WATER

Using the results of conventional water analysis, we can predict with moderate accuracy the degree of chemical stability of a brine—either by itself or when mixed with another brine of different known composition. The concentration of ions in a mixture can be calculated from the known water analyses. A method of predicting the approximate solubility of calcium sulfate in oil field brines was developed by Stiff and Davis.[10] Their method reportedly compensates for the influence of temperature, sodium ion, magnesium ion, and excess common ion on the solubility of calcium sulfate.

Barium Sulfate

1. FORMATION OF BARIUM SULFATE

One of the most insoluble substances formed from water and one that is very difficult to remove once formed on equipment is barium sulfate. It is formed by reaction between sulfate and barium ions as shown in Eq. (3–14).

$$Ba^{++} + SO_4^= \rightarrow BaSO_4 \tag{3–14}$$

The solubility of barium sulfate in distilled water at 25°C is 0.0023 g/liter. This is much less than solubilities of 2.08 g/liter for calcium sulfate and 0.053 g/liter for calcium carbonate. Barium sulfate is so insoluble that quantitative analysis methods for both barium and sulfate are based upon the precipitation of barium sulfate.

Oilfield waters containing barium are common in Kansas, Southern Oklahoma, North-Central and South Texas, and Southern California. Barium is occasionally found in brines in other sections of the country. Because of the low solubility of barium sulfate, waters containing barium

Table 3.3

SMOOTHED SOLUBILITY DATA FOR
$BaSO_4$-NaCl-H_2O SYSTEM AT VARIOUS TEMPERATURES*

(Reprinted from *J. Chem. Eng. Data*, **5** No. 4 (October, 1960), p. 514. Copyright 1960 by American Chemical Society and reprinted by permission of the copyright owner.)

NaCl (molal)	$K' \times 10^9$ (Molal)					
	25°C	35°C	50°C	65°C	80°C	95°C
0.1	1.54	2.00	2.70	3.34	3.76	3.97
0.2	2.70	3.36	4.76	5.93	7.06	7.74
0.4	4.49	5.63	7.92	10.61	13.69	16.13
0.6	6.08	7.74	11.03	15.38	20.45	24.97
0.8	7.74	9.60	13.69	20.16	26.57	33.49
1.0	9.22	11.24	16.38	24.02	32.76	42.02
1.5	12.54	15.38	22.20	32.40	44.94	62.00
2.0	15.63	19.04	27.23	39.60	56.17	78.96
2.5	18.23	21.90	31.33	44.94	63.50	93.64
3.0	20.74	24.65	34.97	49.73	70.23	107.57
3.5	23.41	27.56	38.81	53.82	76.73	120.41
4.0	25.92	30.63	42.44	58.08	82.94	132.50
4.5	28.56	34.23	45.80	63.00	89.40	144.40

*This table was determined from actual solubility measurements.

contain only a few ppm, if any, dissolved sulfate. Oilfield waters containing 50 to 100 ppm barium are not uncommon. Waters with more than 500 ppm sulfate would not contain appreciable amounts of dissolved barium.

Solubility of barium sulfate in sodium chloride solutions from 25° to 95°C has been measured.[11] These solubility data are expressed in molal concentrations in Table 3.3. Some of the molal values for barium sulfate solubility, converted to grams, are shown graphically in Fig. 3.9. These curves show that the solubility of barium sulfate increases with temperature and with foreign salt concentration. The same effect of the foreign salt was observed on the solubility of calcium carbonate and calcium sulfate. The temperature effect is opposite, since increased temperature decreased calcium carbonate and, in some temperature regions, calcium sulfate solubility.

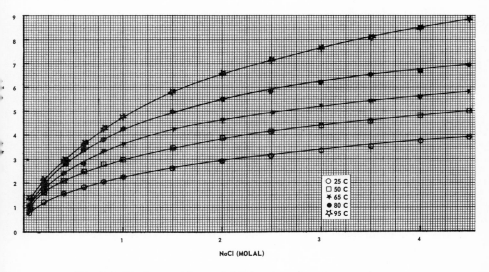

NaCl (MOLAL)

Fig. 3.9. Barium sulfate solubility at various temperatures vs. sodium chloride concentration. (Data from *J. Chem. Eng. Data*, **5**, No. 4 (October, 1960), 514. Copyright 1960 by American Chemical Society and used with the permission of the copyright owner.)

Stable waters saturated with barium sulfate at surface temperature would be stable at higher temperature existing in an oil or gas reservoir. Water saturated with barium sulfate at reservoir temperature would be unstable at lower surface temperature and deposit barium sulfate. As with other precipitation reactions from oversaturated solutions, the scale deposition would not occur instantly but would require an induction period for crystal nuclei to form. Scale would form downstream from the wellhead or in a collecting tank. This effect of increased solubility at higher temperature offers the advantage that waters stable with respect to barium sulfate at the surface can be injected without barium sulfate deposition.

2. Prediction of Barium Sulfate Solubility

Data given in Table 3.3 may be used to predict barium sulfate solubility in oilfield brines that are predominantly sodium chloride solutions. The solubility product, K'_{sp}, of barium sulfate is shown in Eq. (3–15). This is the product of the barium and sulfate concentrations in molal units.

$$(\text{Ba}^{++})\,(\text{SO}_4^=) = K'_{sp} \qquad (3\text{–}15)$$

If the product of barium and sulfate concentrations of an oilfield water of specified sodium chloride concentration is less than K'_{sp} in Table 3.3, the water is not saturated with barium sulfate. If the product is more than K'_{sp} for a specified sodium chloride concentration, barium sulfate will precipitate.

The amount precipitated or oversaturated can be estimated. If one atom of barium precipitates, one atom of sulfate must also precipitate. When x represents the molal concentration of barium sulfate precipitated, the solubility product expression becomes that of Eqs. (3–16) and (3–17).

$$([\text{Ba}^{++}] - x)\,([\text{SO}_4^=] - x) = K'_{sp} \qquad (3\text{–}16)$$

$$(\text{Ba}^{++})\,(\text{SO}_4^=) - (\text{Ba}^{++})\,x - (\text{SO}_4)x + x^2 = K'_{sp} \qquad (3\text{–}17)$$

$$x^2 - bx + c = 0 \qquad (3\text{–}18)$$

The barium and sulfate concentrations are determined by water analysis; the K'_{sp} value from Table 3.3. Equation (3–17) then reduces to Eq. (3–18), which can be solved by the quadratic equation. An example of calculating the amount of barium sulfate precipitated from an oversaturated water is found in the Appendix.

Iron Deposits

Deposits of iron compounds can be traced to two sources. One source is the water itself, which may contain dissolved iron. The second source is corrosion of iron or steel in the system, which results in formation of iron-containing corrosion products. Precipitated iron compounds from either of these sources may form scale on the surface of metal or remain in water as colloidal suspensions. Water containing colloidal ferric oxide (Fe_2O_3) has a reddish color and is usually called "red water." Water containing colloidal ferrous sulfide (FeS) has a black color and is termed "black water."

The presence of hydrogen sulfide in oil or gas production, accompanied by water, generally results in corrosion with the formation of iron sulfide scales. These iron sulfide scales may be kansite (Fe_9S_8), pyrrhotite ($Fe_{0.875}S$), and pyrite (FeS_2).[12] Oxygen-containing water can corrode the iron, resulting in the formation of hydrated ferrous hydroxide and ferric hydroxide scales or deposits. Ferrous bicarbonate scale can be formed in the corrosion of iron by water containing carbon dioxide. Often these corrosion products will be removed by the turbulent action of flowing water, resulting in particles which may plug a filter or an input well.

Formation waters rarely contain more than 100 ppm dissolved iron. Waters produced after wells have been acidized frequently contain more than this because of the dissolution of iron from the tubing or the formation. When present in solution in natural waters, iron is normally in the form of ferrous (Fe^{++}) or ferric (Fe^{+++}) ions. However, iron may also form complex ions in water and thus deviate from normal solubility considerations. The pH of the water influences the solubility of the ionic form of the iron. At pH 3 or less, appreciable amounts of ferric ion may be present, but at higher pH the formation of insoluble ferric hydroxide ($Fe(OH)_3$) limits the existence of any ferric ion to a very low concentration, practically trace amounts.

This solubility of ferrous iron may be controlled by the hydroxyl ion concentration or the bicarbonate ion concentration.[13] At pH 8, the solubility of ferrous hydroxide would permit a ferrous ion concentration of 100 ppm, and at pH 7, the theoretical concentration is 10,000 ppm. When carbon dioxide is present, the ferrous iron concentration is limited by the solubility of ferrous bicarbonate to 1 to 10 ppm between pH 7 and 8, when 25 ppm of bicarbonate are present. At pH 7 or less, the solubility of ferrous ions may be much greater, even in the presence of 100 ppm of bicarbonate ions. The solubility of ferrous bicarbonate is influenced by carbon dioxide concentration and temperature in the same manner as are the bicarbonates of calcium and magnesium.

Formation waters which contain dissolved iron can deposit it as ferrous carbonate ($FeCO_3$), ferrous sulfide (FeS), ferrous hydroxide ($Fe(OH)_2$), ferric hydroxide ($Fe(OH)_3$), and ferric oxide (Fe_2O_3). The deposition of iron compounds from a formerly stable water is dependent upon the presence and concentration of sulfide ions, and carbonate ions (in solution as bicarbonate), dissolved oxygen, pH of the water, and the oxidation-reduction balance of the water.

When formation water containing ferrous and bicarbonate ions contacts air, ferric hydroxide can be formed, as shown in Eq. (3–19).

$$2Fe^{++} + 4HCO_3^- + H_2O + \frac{1}{2}O_2 \rightleftarrows 2Fe(OH)_3 + 4CO_2 \quad (3\text{--}19)$$

This reaction commonly occurs in sample bottles when iron-containing waters are sampled and an air space is left in the top of the bottle. It is difficult to obtain a water sample without exposure of the water to air; consequently, it is advantageous to determine the iron content at the time of sampling.

Deposition of iron compounds from water can also result from bacterial action. *Gallionella ferruginea* are aerobic bacteria which extract ferrous iron from iron-containing waters and deposit it as ferric hydroxide. Waters which contain carbonic acid and pass through iron-containing geologic strata often contain *Gallionella*, as do water wells pumping water from river gravel beds or from old glacial fills.

The chemistry of iron dissolved in water or iron compounds in contact with water is more complex than that of the other compounds mentioned. This is mainly caused by the two common oxidation states of iron—ferrous (Fe^{++}) and ferric (Fe^{+++}). The two oxidation states form compounds of different solubilities with the same anions. For example, ferric hydroxide is practically insoluble above pH 4, whereas 100 ppm of ferrous iron from ferrous hydroxide could be in solution at pH 8. Ferrous iron is readily oxidized to ferric iron in oxygen-containing waters. This generally results in the precipitation of hydrated mixed iron oxides. Dissolved iron may also precipitate as insoluble sulfides or carbonates. The chemistry of dissolved iron is further complicated by the existence of soluble iron-organic complexes and iron-hydroxo complexes such as $FeOH^+$, $FeOH^{++}$, and $Fe(OH)_2^+$.

The oxidation state of the dissolved iron is important in oilfield waters. A change in the oxidation state may result in the deposition of iron compounds. If iron compounds or minerals are present in the producing formation, what affect will the flood water have on these? Will iron compounds near the well bore be dissolved, only to be deposited some distance from the well bore and reduce permeability or cause plugging?

One approach to this problem has been the formation of stability field diagrams based on the oxidation-reduction potential-hydrogen ion concentration-iron relationship of the water. The oxidation-reduction or redox potential (Eh) is obtained from the Nernst equation

$$Eh = E° + \frac{0.059}{n} \log \frac{A_{ox}}{A_{red}} \tag{3–20}$$

where $E°$ is the standard electrode potential of the couple, n is the number of electrons involved in the oxidation, A_{ox} the activity of the oxidized form, and A_{red} the activity of the reduced form. Using this equation and equations for solubility products of the compounds involved, a stability field diagram such as that shown in Fig. 3.10 can be drawn.[14] Calculations for this diagram were made using values measured at 25°C.

In Fig. 3.10 the outside ordinate represents the bicarbonate ion activities and the outside abscissa the pH of the water. The inside ordinate and abscissa represent ferrous iron activity. The activities of ferric iron (Fe^{+++}) are represented by a scale between the ferrous iron (Fe^{++}) activity and pH scales. The heavy lines from the top which slant to the left are limits of the fields of precipitation of ferrous carbonate-ferric hydroxide and represent *Eh* values. Heavy lines from the top slanting to the right are limits of the fields of the precipitation of ferrous carbonate-ferrous sulfide. These also represent *Eh* values. Light diagonal lines from the top to the right represent maximum ferrous iron concentrations in the area of ferrous carbonate precipitation. Ferrous ion concentrations in the areas of ferrous sulfide and ferric hydroxide precipitation are obtained by drawing vertical lines downward from the points where these diagonals intersect the $FeCO_3$-FeS and $FeCO_3$-$Fe(OH)_3$ boundaries. The thin vertical lines represent maximum ferric ion concentrations in the area of ferrous hydroxide precipitation. Ferric ion concentrations in the $FeCO_3$ area are obtained by drawing diagonal lines from the points of intersection of the Fe^{+++} lines and $FeCO_3$ lines parallel to the Fe^{++} lines. Lines drawn vertically downward from where these lines intersect the FeS-$FeCO_3$ boundary represent Fe^{+++} concentration in the FeS area.

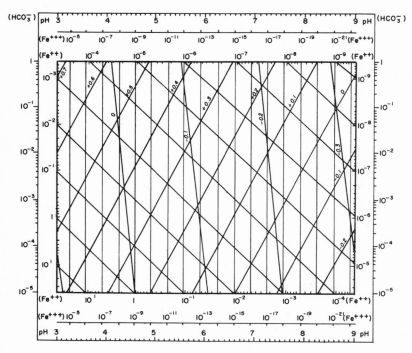

Fig. 3.10. Iron stability field diagram. (From Schoeller, *Rev. Inst. Franc. Petrole Ann. Combust. Liquids*, **10** (1955), 181.)

The lower left-hand corner of this iron stability field diagram represents low pH values and low bicarbonate ion concentrations. Therefore, the iron solubility is high. Conversely, at the upper right-hand corner, the bicarbonate concentration and pH are high, so the iron concentration is low. The iron concentration varies between these extremes.

Waters in contact with reducible hydrocarbons would normally be expected to have low redox potentials. Fig. 3.11 shows an example of the possible iron concentrations when $Eh = 0$. The left-hand area represents solid ferrous sulfide (FeS), the center ferrous carbonate ($FeCO_3$), and the right-hand section represents solid ferric hydroxide. In this figure, only $Eh = 0$ lines are shown, and some of the lines representing ferrous and ferric concentration have been omitted to clarify the example. The heavy solid lines which represent $Eh = 0$ also define the fields of precipitation. Thin solid lines represent maximum ferrous ion concentration and thin broken lines maximum ferric ion concentration. These concentrations are in terms of activities, where the activity equals the molal concentration times the activity coefficient. This is only representative at 25°C (77°F).

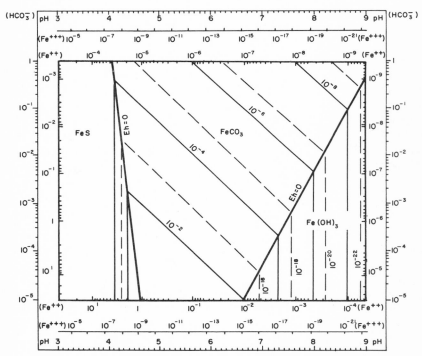

Fig. 3.11. Ferrous and ferric ion concentrations when $Eh = 0$. (From Schoeller, *Rev. Inst. Franc. Petrole. Ann. Combust. Liquids,* **10** (1955), 181.)

At present, these iron stability field diagrams are a laboratory and theoretical approach to studies of waters containing dissolved iron or for waters going into formations containing iron minerals. They provide an insight into the factors which control iron concentrations and possible deposition in formation waters. If we can accumulate more information on the Eh of subterranean waters, we can better understand the relationship between the redox potential and constituents in the water.

Water in contact with air will dissolve oxygen. The Eh of water in contact with air is generally in the range of 0.35 to 0.50.[15] Formation water in contact with oil would normally have an Eh lower than 0.35. Carefully measuring a mixture of injection water and formation water would give an Eh value for the mixture. Knowing the pH, Eh, and bicarbonate ion concentration, and using an iron stabiliby diagram, the maximum concentration of iron in the mixed water could be estimated. Using measured pH, Eh, dissolved iron concentration and bicarbonate ion concentration, the Eh of a formation water can be estimated.

Silica Deposits

Natural waters are occasionally found containing as much as 100 ppm silica. Silica may be present as colloidal, amorphous silica, and as the hypothetical monosilicic acid (H_4SiO_4). For most uses, the silica content of the water is not an important consideration. However, in modern high-pressure boilers, silica deposits can be a real problem. The various silica scales shown in Table 3.1 all form above 100°C (212°F) and have been found in boilers. Boilers are ideal places for scale formation due to the constant evaporation of water, resulting in the concentration of salts in the remaining water. With a slightly soluble salt, the solubility product is soon exceeded and a deposit formed. These silica scales all have relatively low solubilities.

Silica scales form in boilers, and are often formed on steam turbine blades due to carry-over of silica by the steam. These silica scales resemble porcelain and are not soluble in acid.

Biological Deposits

Algae, fungi, and bacteria are living organisms that may cause fouling in lines and equipment. Most algae require carbon dioxide and sunlight for their growth. They may be particularly active in cooling towers. Dislodged algae growths can cause serious obstructions in lines, on screens, or on the surface of formation rock.

Plugging of injection wells by bacterial growth is not uncommon. However, oilfield waters usually do not contain the necessary nutrients to produce large bacterial growths. Biofouling problems in water-handling systems are generally caused by a chemical change in the water or the addition of a bactericide that results in killing the organisms. The dead cells then accumulate on the formation face or in some location of restricted water flow.

Sampling Water-Formed Deposits

Since water-formed deposits are seldom homogeneous but vary in composition at different parts of the system, it is important that the field sample be collected as near the site of formation as possible without any physical or chemical alteration. This is not always possible, since the greatest scale formation may occur in an inaccessible part of the system. However, a sample should be removed from an accessible location closest to the point of difficulty. Samples taken at different parts of a system should be submitted to the laboratory separately and without mixing.

1. REMOVING DEPOSITS

Sludges, loosely adhered scale deposits, and biological deposits are easily removed using a scraper, knife blade, spoon, or a piece of wood. Hard, adherent scale deposits are more difficult to remove for sampling. Sometimes it is possible to dislodge brittle scale by mechanical or thermal shock; that is, by a mechanical blow or by heating the metal and scale and suddenly chilling the scale with cold water. Due to the nature of these deposits, a limited amount of water will not affect them for analytical purposes.

If possible, some of the scale should be sampled with the underlying surface intact. If a piece of pipe or tubing can be cut from the system, this should be done. The section can then be cut longitudinally with a shaper or dry saw and squeezed in a vise to dislodge the deposit. In order to avoid contamination of the sample, no cutting oil should be used. Care should be exercised in order to avoid contamination of the sample by any deposits on the exterior of the pipe. Often, it is not possible, practical, or desirable to remove the scale in the field. In these cases, a portion of the pipe containing the scale sample should be submitted directly to the laboratory.

Where it is not practical to remove a section of the pipe, and mechanical or thermal shock fails to dislodge the scale, the deposit may be removed by chiseling or sometimes by cutting with a knife. If possible, insert the knife or chisel between the scale and underlying surface and chip off large fragments of the scale. Whether using mechanical shock or a chisel, care should be exercised to avoid damaging the equipment.

The sampled deposit should be carefully collected, so as to avoid contamination by foreign matter. Dry deposits can often be caught, as they are removed, in a clean envelope. If wet, a clean bottle will serve as a satisfactory container. Samples of slimes or biological deposits should be collected using sterile instruments and containers. Some of the mother liquor should remain in contact with these samples during sampling and shipment. These latter samples should be kept refrigerated during storage and shipment.

2. Quantity of Sample

The amount of deposit required varies with the desired type of laboratory investigation. A complete laboratory examination may require up to 100 g (about $\frac{1}{4}$ lb) of deposit, whereas a routine chemical analysis is possible with only a 10 g sample. Informative data may be obtained on smaller samples by using X-ray diffraction methods. It is better to have an excess of sample rather than too little.

3. Labeling and Shipment

Sample labels should show the date of sampling, the location, the method of sample removal, the time expired during deposition, any known water analysis data, the temperature of the system upstream and at the point of deposition, history of scale removal, and any changes in water or fluid that has flowed through the system. Dry samples of deposit can be shipped in moisturetight glass or plastic containers. Sections of pipe with the sample still intact should be protected from dirt and mositure by a plastic wrapping or some other form of wrapping, such as an old inner tube turned inside out, and shipped in a wooden box. Biological samples should be protected from freezing. If no analysis data are available on the water, a water sample should be included in the shipment.

4. Analysis of Water-Formed Deposits

A reliable analysis of water-formed deposits can serve as a clue to proper water treatment procedures. The water treatment can then be designed to eliminate the undesirable accumulation of deposits in the system. For this reason, reliable methods should be used to identify the deposits. The extent of the analysis depends upon the composition of the scale or sludge. It is relatively simple to identify a single-constituent scale or sludge. However, as has previously been stated, pure deposits seldom occur, and usually the deposit consists of several constituents. It is possible that the constituent present in the largest amount is not responsible for the undesirable characteristics of a scale—a minor component may be responsible for binding the deposit together in the form of a scale.

The initial examination begins with a visual inspection of the deposit. The sample is described in terms of color, size, hardness, magnetism, and odor. If the deposit appears to be a crystalline inorganic material, microscopic investigation may offer a clue to its identity. This may be followed by instrumental analysis methods such as X-ray diffraction or spectrographic procedures. Spot tests sometimes reveal the presence of certain ions. A chemical analysis can be performed in order to determine the exact chemical composition of the deposit. It requires a combination of these methods to describe accurately the combinations of elements in a deposit.

The identification of biological deposits necessitates the use of a biological microscope and certain techniques of identification. The identification procedures used to determine the general classification (algae, molds, or bacteria) of the biological material are relatively simple, but in many cases it requires a trained microbiologist to determine the actual specie of the organism.

A procedure of chemical analysis for quantitatively determining the composition of water-formed deposits is given in the Appendix. Application of the above mentioned instrumental and/or spot tests for qualitative identification of constituents may shorten the quantitative analysis.

Scale Prevention by Water Treatment

Scale formation can be prevented by treating the water to remove the undesirable dissolved solids. Treatment procedures vary with the nature of the undesirable solids, volume of water to be treated, and use of the water. Some procedures that are satisfactory for treating small volumes of water are too expensive for use where large volumes are treated.

Softening the water by the lime and soda ash process removes ions that cause calcium carbonate, calcium sulfate, barium sulfate, strontium sulfate, and ferrous carbonate scales. Ion exchange can also be used to remove scale-forming ions. Distillation not only removes all scale-forming ions, but corrosive gases as well. Hot or cold lime-soda ash-magnesia processes can be used to remove silica. By aerating water to remove iron, formation of iron deposits can be prevented. These methods are all discussed in detail later.

Use of Chemicals To Prevent Scale

The successful methods used to prevent the deposition of scale from scale-forming waters involve the removal of the anion or cation of the scale, or the prevention of scale formation by the addition of a chemical scale inhibitor to the water. The addition of chemicals as scale inhibitors prevents scale formation by tying up the scale-forming cation (usually calcium, iron, or barium) in solution. This can be accomplished by using a chemical capable of chelating, complexing, or otherwise inhibiting the scale-forming cation. This process is generally referred to as sequestration, defined as the formation of soluble complex of metal ions in the presence of anions that would normally cause the cation to precipitate. Many chemicals are known to form soluble complexes with iron, calcium, magnesium, and barium. The cost and effectiveness of a sequestering agent ultimately determines its applicability for large-scale use in preventing scale formation.

Condensed Phosphates

Perhaps the oldest and most widely used sequestering agents are the inorganic polymetaphosphates. The original polymetaphosphates used in scale prevention were sodium salts of metaphosphoric acids. More recently dimetallic phosphates have been used. These molecularly dehydrated phosphates are clear, glassy solids made by fusing sodium-calcium, sodium-magnesium, or sodium-zinc phosphates. Because of their slow rate of dissolution in water, these dimetallic phosphates offer advantages in feeding that the more readily dissolved sodium metaphosphates do not have. For example, a chemical feeder charged with a dimetallic phosphate would feed the desired concentration of phosphate over a longer time period than one charged with an equal weight of a sodium metaphosphate.

When using phosphates for scale control, it is not necessary to complex all the scale-forming anion. For example to soften a water containing 200 ppm of calcium carbonate hardness would require 1,100 ppm of sodium hexametaphosphate, while 2 ppm of sodium hexametaphosphate will prevent the precipitation of calcium carbonate scale. This is called the "threshold" treatment.[16]

In the threshold treatment, the water is not softened by the addition of the polyphosphate. In fact, small-scale nuclei are formed, such as minute particles of calcium carbonate or calcium sulfate. The phosphate adsorbs on the surface of the crystal nuclei and prevents growth of the crystal and scale deposition. This property of the polyphosphates makes their use for scale control economically attractive.

1. SOLUBILITY OF POLYPHOSPHATES

The first four polyphosphates listed in Table 3.4 are fairly soluble in fresh waters and brines. The last three listed are dimetallic phosphates and dissolve more slowly. These dimetallic phosphates are of recent development and are called "controlled-solubility" phosphates. Actually, it is not the solubility of the controlled-solubility phosphates that makes their use attractive for scale prevention, but their low solution rate.

The solution rate of these dimetallic phosphates is dependent upon chemical composition, physical particle size, temperature, and nature of

Table 3.4
SOME POLYMETAPHOSPHATES USED FOR
PREVENTING SCALE FORMATION

Name of Phosphate	Formula
Tetrasodium pyrophosphate	$Na_4P_2O_7$
Sodium triphosphate	$Na_5P_3O_{10}$
Trisodium tripolyphosphate	$Na_3P_3O_9$
Hexasodium hexametaphosphate	$Na_6P_6O_{18}$
Sodium-calcium phosphate	$Na_2O \cdot CaO \cdot P_2O_5$
Sodium-magnesium phosphate	$Na_2O \cdot MgO \cdot P_2O_5$
Sodium-zinc phosphate	$Na_2O \cdot ZnO \cdot P_2O_5$

the brine.[17] The effect of changes in chemical composition on the solution rate of a dimetallic phosphate is shown in Fig. 3.12. In this particular system, increasing the calcium oxide content decreases the solution rate.

As with other soluble substances, the solution rates of these controlled-solubility phosphates are influenced by their particle size or surface area exposed to the water. The effect of surface area is shown in Fig. 3.13. It is apparent from this figure that crushing the pieces of dimetallic phosphate so as to obtain smaller sieve sizes greatly increases the rate of solution. It is possible to adjust the solution rate of sodium-calcium phosphate by varying both the particle size and the chemical composition. This is particularly helpful in fracturing applications where the particle size is necessarily small. Here, the solution rate can be decreased to the desired level by increasing the amount of calcium oxide.

The solution rate of the controlled-solubility phosphates is also influenced by temperature. The change in solution rate with temperature is shown in Fig. 3.14. It is readily seen that increases in temperature result in a greater solution rate. The solution rate increases 35 per cent for a 10°F rise in temperature.

The nature of the brine also has an effect on the solution rate of controlled-solubility phosphates. As shown in Fig. 3.15, increases in the chloride content of a brine greatly increase the solution rate. This rate increases about

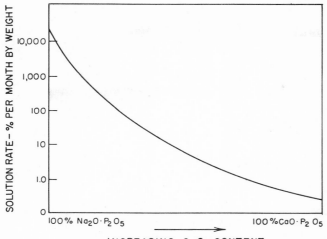

Fig. 3.12. Solution rate of the controlled-solubility phosphate system $Na_2O \cdot CaO \cdot P_2O_5$ as a function of chemical composition. (Reprinted by permission of *J. Petrol. Technol.* from B. Sloat, "Controlled Solubility, Phosphates: A versatile Solution to Oil Field Scale Problems," Paper 1317-G presented at 34th Annual Fall Meeting, Society Petroleum Engineers, Dallas, Texas, October 4–7, 1959.)

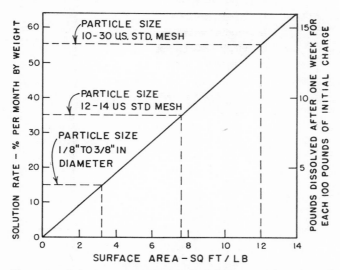

Fig. 3.13. Solution rate of $Na_2O \cdot CaO \cdot P_2O_5$ as a function of surface area. (Reprinted by permission of *J. Petrol. Technol.*, from B. Sloat, "Controlled Solubility, Phosphates: A Versatile solution to Oil Field Scale Problems," Paper 1317-G presented at 34th Annual Fall Meeting, Society Petroleum Engineers, Dallas, Texas, October 4–7, 1959.)

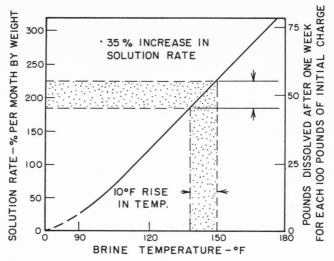

Fig. 3.14. Influence of temperature on the solution rate of sodium-calcium phosphate. (Reprinted by permission of *J. Petrol. Technol.*, from B. Sloat, "Controlled Solubility Phosphates: A versatile Solution to Oil Field Scale Problems," Paper 1317-G presented at 34th Annual Fall Meeting, Society Petroleum Engineers, Dallas, Texas, October 4–7, 1959.)

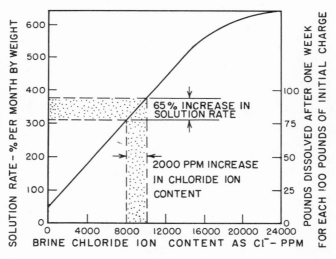

Fig. 3.15. Influence of chloride ion concentration on the solution rate of sodium-calcium phosphate at zero hardness. (Reprinted by permission of *J. Petrol. Technol.*, from B. Sloat, "Controlled Solubility Phosphates: A Versatile Solution to Oil Field Scale Problems" Paper 1317-G presented at 34th Annual Fall Meeting, Society Petroleum Engineers, Dallas, Texas, October 4–7, 1959.)

65 per cent for every 2,000 ppm increase in chloride content. This effect does not increase so rapidly at chloride concentrations greater than 15,000 ppm. Up to 5,000 ppm, increases in the hardness content of the brine greatly reduce the solution rate. This effect at constant chloride concentration and varying hardness is shown in Fig. 3.16. A hardness of 5,000 ppm as calcium carbonate compensates for the increase in solution rate due to 25,000 ppm of chloride ion.

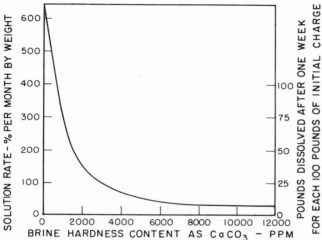

Fig. 3.16. Solution rate of sodium-calcium phosphate as a function of hardness content at 25,000 ppm chloride content. (Reprinted by permission of *J. Petrol. Technol.*, from B. Sloat, "Controlled Solubility Phosphates: A Versatile Solution to Oil Field Scale Problems," Paper 1317-G presented at 34th Annual Fall Meeting, Society Petroleum Engineers, Dallas, Texas, October 4–7, 1959.)

It is possible to overtreat by dissolving an excess of the controlled-solubility phosphate in the water. If the dissolved-solids content of the brine is high enough, some precipitation of the phosphate will occur. However, the concentration of controlled-solubility phosphate necessary for threshold treatment is less than the amount that is necessary to cause precipitation. In preparing phosphate solutions for batch treatment, precipitation of phosphate can occur if the tolerance of the brine used for making up the solution is exceeded.

2. REVERSION OF POLYPHOSPHATES

The polyphosphates and dimetallic phosphates used for scale prevention are metaphosphates or dehydrated phosphates. In solution, these dehydrated phosphates undergo hydrolysis or reversion to the hydrated orthophosphates. Fortunately, the chain and ring phosphates have slow rates of hydrolysis at room temperature in neutral solution. The rate of reversion is influenced by temperature, pH, concentration, enzymes, the nature of the brine or water, and the particular phosphate.

The effects of temperature, pH, and phosphate composition on the reversion of phosphates can be illustrated by considering sodium tripolyphosphate and sodium hexametaphosphate. For a test period of 22.2 hours at 150°F, sodium tripolyphosphate had 30 per cent reversion at pH 5, 8 per cent at pH 7, and 1 per cent at pH 9.[18] In the same test, sodium metaphosphate had a 2 per cent reversion at pH 5, compared with 30 per cent for the sodium tripolyphosphate. On increasing the temperature to 190°F, the sodium tripolyphosphate underwent 100 per cent reversion at pH 5 and the sodium metaphosphate 42 per cent in the same time period and at the same pH. The reversion of the sodium metaphosphate dropped to 18 per cent at pH 9 and 190°F.

Certain enzymes catalyze the reversion of these phosphates.[19] This enzymatic reversion of metaphosphate by microorganisms, such as bacteria in the water, seems to be less with the sodium-zinc phosphate. The rate of reversion of the phosphates to the orthophosphate is also increased by higher concentrations of the phosphate and higher ionic concentrations in the brine. The effects of these factors are of much less magnitude than those of pH and temperature.

If an excess of a soluble phosphate is dissolved in a brine, a white precipitate may form. This is not necessarily caused by reversion of the phosphate but is probably reprecipitation of the phosphate. This is particularly likely when brines are used to make up concentrated feed solutions of soluble phosphates. It is less likely to occur when using controlled-solubility phosphates.

The factors governing the reversion of metaphosphates indicate that consideration should be given to environmental conditions and choice of phosphate. The risk of reversion and subsequent calcium phosphate precipitation in the openings and voids of injection formations exists when treating injection waters with these phosphates. However, this has been successfully accomplished. Generally, hanging a basket of controlled-solubility phosphate in the water supply tank will effectively prevent scale formation. In the case of production wells, the reversion would probably occur at the surface without causing serious difficulty.

3. Use of Polymetaphosphates

Scale formation on downhole tubing and pumps may be prevented by dropping some controlled-solubility phosphate down the annulus, or passing part of the produced water through a feeder containing the phosphate and then recycling it down through the annulus.[20] Normally, 2 to 10 ppm of phosphate in the produced water will be sufficient to prevent scale formation. The important thing is that the produced water should *come in contact* with the phosphate. If the bottom of the hole is far below the producing zone and the produced water does not contact the solid particles of controlled phosphate, the treatment will not be fully effective. In some instances, it may be practical to hang a wire basket on the bottom of the tubing string for the purpose of holding controlled-solubility phosphates. This is only practical if the basket can be filled from the surface.

Controlled-solubility phosphate placed in the bottom of the hole will not effectively reduce scale formation within the producing formation near the well bore. This can sometimes be accomplished by using controlled-solubility phosphate in fracturing. It may apply to primary producing wells as well as secondary recovery wells.

A case history of using controlled-solubility phosphates in fracturing may serve as an illustration. This particular well was a producing well in a secondary recovery operation.[21] Fracturing with sand increased production, but it declined rapidly. The reservoir was fully pressured, and water was being continuously injected. It was decided that scale was forming in the formation adjacent to the well bore. The formation was fractured with oil, sand, and 12 to 40 mesh phosphate. The production increased and for a longer period of time than previously observed for fracturing with sand alone. When water analysis for dissolved phosphate indicated the injected phosphate had dissolved, production had declined and the treatment was repeated.

In fracturing operations, the sodium-calcium phosphate had a low enough dissolution rate to provide some lasting power and had a high enough concentration to give threshold treatment. An oil-base media was preferred, because it does not dissolve any of the phosphate. Acids should never be used, since they promote the reversion to the orthophosphate which combines with calcium in the water to form insoluble calcium phosphate.

Sodium hexametaphosphate has also been used to stabilize iron and manganese in water. The hexametaphosphate must be well mixed in the water before iron or manganese are oxidized and start to precipitate. Usually, 2 parts by weight sodium hexametaphosphate are added to 1 part of combined iron and manganese. A minimum of 2 ppm sodium hexametaphosphate is added, even if total iron and magnanese is less than 1 ppm.[22]

The sodium hexametaphosphate does not prevent oxidation of the iron and manganese. It apparently forms an almost colorless complex of iron phosphate, which is a well-dispersed colloidal suspension. The water does not form the characteristic rusty color which usually occurs when dissolved iron is oxidized. The same mechanism prevents the formation of black water from manganese oxidation.

Ethylenediaminetetraacetic Acid

In recent years, organic chelating agents have been discovered for nearly every metal ion. One of these chelating agents, ethylenediaminetetraacetic acid (referred to as EDTA), or its sodium salts has found application in water softening and as a scale inhibitor. EDTA forms stable soluble complexes with magnesium, calcium, strontium, barium, and other divalent metals. When these metal ions have formed this soluble complex with EDTA, they cannot combine with the carbonate and or sulfate ions in the water to form scale.

EDTA has an advantage over the polymetaphosphates, since EDTA does not undergo a reversion or hydrolysis and is stable in acid solution and at elevated temperatures. However, EDTA does not give the threshold effect that is obtained with the polymetaphosphates. Therefore, the amount of EDTA required depends upon the amount of calcium, magnesium, or barium ion present in the water. To prevent scale formation, it would not be necessary to complex all of the scale-forming cations, but only enough to reduce the concentration so that the solubility product of the particular scale is not exceeded.

The amount of EDTA necessary to complex 1 ppm of calcium ion depends upon which sodium salt of EDTA is used and the amount of hydrated water molecules. Some data on the amounts of various EDTA salts necessary to complex 1 ppm of calcium and the solubility of the EDTA salt in water are shown in Table 3.5. It is evident that, as the molecular weight of the complexed cation increases, the amount of EDTA necessary to complex 1 ppm of the cation decreases.

Table 3.5

CONCENTRATION OF EDTA AND ITS SODIUM SALTS NECESSARY
TO COMPLEX 1 PPM CALCIUM ION, MAGNESIUM ION, AND BARIUM ION

	Solubility g/100 cc H_2O @ 79°F	pH of Water Solution	ppm Necessary To Complex 1 ppm of Alkaline Earth Metal		
			Mg^{++}	Ca^{++}	Ba^{++}
Ethylenediaminetetraacetic acid	0.02	2.3	12.0	7.4	2.1
Disodium ethylenediaminetetra-acetate dihydrate	11.1	5.0	15.4	9.5	2.7
Trisodium ethylenediaminetetra-acetate monohydrate	57.0	8.4	15.6	9.6	2.8
Tetrasodium ethylenediaminetetra-acetate dihydrate	103.0	10.3	16.9	10.4	3.0

The relative strengths of the complexes formed between EDTA and some cations are shown in Table 3.6. The larger the log K value, the more stable the complex formed. The data in Table 3.6 show that, if these ions were all present in water and EDTA added, the iron would be complexed first. If additional EDTA were available, calcium would be complexed, and then magnesium, strontium, and barium. The complexes formed between EDTA and the divalent metals are stronger than those formed with the polyphosphates. As shown in Fig. 3.17, the maximum chelating or complexing efficiency of EDTA is attained at pH 8 and remains nearly constant at higher pH.

Table 3.6
RELATIVE STRENGTHS OF SOME EDTA STABLE COMPLEXES WITH METAL IONS

Metal Ion	Mg^{++}	Ca^{++}	Sr^{++}	Ba^{++}	Fe^{++}	Fe^{+++}
Log K*	8.69	10.70	8.63	7.76	14.23	25.10

*K = Equilibrium formation constants for 1:1 chelates.

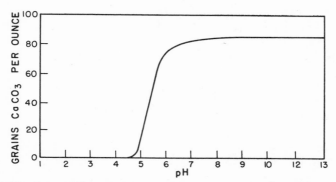

Fig. 3.17. Effect of pH on chelating power of EDTA. (From A.E. Martell and M. Calvin, *Chemistry of the Metal Chelate Compounds*, (Englewood Cliffs, N.J.: Prentice-Hall, Inc., 1952, p. 494.)

EDTA is more expensive than some of the polyphosphates such as sodium hexametaphosphate. This is a limiting factor in its use. However, EDTA is used in boiler waters and some plant waters where the volumes are much smaller than in water floods. EDTA may be used in conjunction with less expensive scale-prevention chemicals. For example, a mixture of 1 to 25 lb of tetrasodium ethylenediaminetetraacetate dihydrate and 1 to 5 lb of hexametaphosphate for treating 125,000 gal of boiler feed water has been disclosed.[23] It is believed that the EDTA salt retards the reversion of the hexametaphosphate, so that a synergestic effect is obtained by the combination.

Iron-Sequestering Agents

Citric acid and gluconic acids and their sodium salts have found use as sequestering agents for iron. These compounds, like EDTA, form a soluble complex with ferric iron. The free acids are not effective as sequestering agents, but as the pH of the solution is raised, their effectiveness increases. The effect of pH on the iron-sequestering power of sodium gluconate, sodium citrate, and sodium tetraphosphate is shown in Fig. 3.18. The figure shows that the proper pH is particularly important when using sodium citrate.

Both the citrate and the gluconate radicals sequester calcium ion. The chelating capacity is influenced by pH, as shown in Fig. 3.19. This figure also shows that more moles of gluconate or citrate than of EDTA or tetraphosphate are required to chelate calcium.

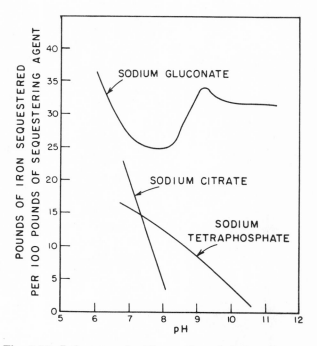

Fig. 3.18. Influence of pH on the chelating power of some iron-sequesterants. (Reprinted from P.B. Crawford, *Producers Monthly*, **21**, 12 (March 1957).)

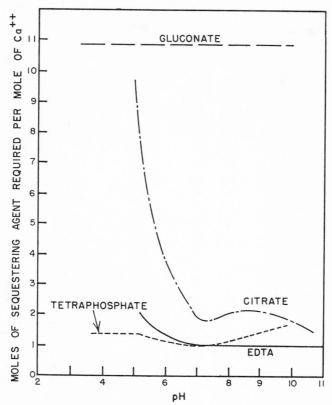

Fig. 3.19. Influence of pH on the chelating power of some calcium sequesterants. (Reprinted from S. Chaberek and A. E. Martell, Organic Sequestering Agents, (New York: John Wiley & Sons, Inc., 1959, p. 312)

Removal of Scales

Removal of scales deposited from water is usually expensive and time-consuming. It is much better to prevent scale deposition by chemical or water treatment methods than to depend upon scale removal methods. Scales are often deposited in systems before a scale problem is recognized, and it becomes necessary to remove this scale if the equipment is to be salvaged.

The initial step in scale removal is to determine the composition of the scale and the extent of the problem. Chemical composition of the scale is determined by obtaining scale samples and submitting them to chemical analysis. Laboratory tests can also be applied to determine the effectiveness of various scale removal agents and techniques.

Calcium carbonate scale is the simplest to remove. It is acid soluble and dissolves readily in 5, 10, or 15 per cent hydrochloric acid. Iron and most other metals are attack by hydrochloric acid and must be protected by the addition of 0.2 to 1.0 per cent acid corrosion inhibitor. Since the reaction between acid and carbonate produces carbon dioxide gas, precautions must be taken to release the produced gas pressure from closed systems.

In production wells and some flow lines, scale will often be covered with paraffin deposits or oil films that prevent a scale removal agent from contacting and reacting with the scale. Sometimes the addition of a surfactant to the acid will be sufficient to assist the acid in penetrating to the scale. In other cases it may be necessary to resort to a pretreatment such as flush with a paraffin solvent or hot oil wash.

Most iron sulfide and oxide scales are acid soluble and can be removed by treatment with corrosion-inhibited hydrochloric acid. The reaction between the acid and sulfide produces poisonous hydrogen sulfide gas. Personnel should be protected from this gas. Citric acid is effective in removing iron oxides because of a combination of effects. Its acidity attacks the scale, and the citrate ion forms a soluble compound with the dissolved iron.

Magnetite deposits can be removed from boilers by means of citric acid and ammonia treatment. Approximately 2.5 lbs of citric acid react with 1 lb of magnetite. A 1 to 3 per cent citric acid solution is made, and the pH adjusted between 3 and 5 with ammonia. The temperature of cleaning should be about 150° to 200°F. The cleaning time varies with thickness of deposit, but four hours is about average. As the colorless ammonium citrate solution dissolves iron, it becomes pale yellow-green, changing to olive drab when the ammonium citrate is spent. The pH may rise to 6 or 6.5.

Calcium sulfate does not react with acids as carbonate does, so it is not as readily removed by acid treatment. However, the solubility of calcium sulfate is greater in 5 per cent hydrochloric acid than it is in water, and this aids in dissolving this scale. Laboratory tests have shown that a 10 per cent solution of sodium hydroxide will remove up to 12.5 per cent of its weight of gypsum scale.

Solutions of EDTA and the polyphosphates have also been promoted as scale solvents. Five per cent aqueous solutions of the tetrasodium salt of EDTA have been used to remove calcium sulfate scale from the heating surfaces of evaporators. The primary disadvantage of the method is the cost of the EDTA. However, some saving can be realized when using EDTA for scale removal if the EDTA solution is regenerated.[24] The scale is removed with high pH EDTA solution. The calcium is precipitated out in a separate tank by adding sulfuric acid to bring the pH to 4.5. After the calcium settles out, the supernatant solution is transferred to another tank, and the pH adjusted to 10 or 11 with sodium hydroxide. This solution is then ready to be used again.

References

[1]A. J. Ellis, "The Solubility of Calcite in Sodium Chloride Solutions at High Temperatures," *Am. J. Sci.*, **261** (1963), 259.

[2]E. B. Shternina and E. V. Frolova, "The Solubility of Calcite in the Presence of CO_2 and NaCl," *Izv. Sektora Fiz.-Khim. Analiza, Inst. Obshch. Neorgan. Khim., Akad. Nauk SSSR*, **21** (1952), 271.

[3]W. F. Langelier, "The Analytical Control of Anti-Corrosion Water Treatment," *J. Am. Water Works Assoc.*, **28** (1936) 1500.

[4]T. E. Larson and A. M. Buswell, "Calcium Carbonate Saturation Index and Alkalinity Interpretations, *J. Am. Water Works Assoc.*, **34** (1942), 1667.

[5]J. W. Ryznar, "A New Index for Determining Amount of Calcium Carbonate Scale Formed by Water," *J. Am. Water Works Assoc.*, **36** (1944), 472.

[6]H. A. Stiff and L. E. Davis, "A Method for Predicting the Tendency of Oil Field Waters To Deposit Calcium Carbonate," *Trans. AIME*, **195** (1952), 213.

[7]F. K. Cameron, "Solubility of Gypsum in Aqueous Solutions of Sodium Chloride," *J. Phys. Chem.*, **5** (1901), 562.

[8]E. B. Shternina, "Tentative Calculation of Solubility of Calcium Sulfate in Aqueous Salt Solutions," *Dokl. Akad. Nauk SSSR*, **60**, No. 2 (1948), 247.

[9]F. W. Dickson, C. W. Blount, and G. Tunnell, "Use of Hydrothermal Solution Equipment To Determine the Solubility of Anhydrite in Water from 100° to 275°C and from 1 Bar to 1000 Bars Pressure," *Am. J. Sci.*, **261** (1963), 61.

[10]H. A. Stiff and L. E. Davis, "A Method for Predicting the Tendency of Oil Field Waters to Deposit Calcium Sulfate," *Trans. AIME*, **195** (1952), 25.

[11]C. C. Templeton, "Solubility of Barium Sulfate in Sodium Chloride Solutions from 25°C to 95°C," *J. Chem. Eng. Data*, **5** (1960), 514.

[12]F. H. Myer, O. L. Riggs, R. L. McGlasson, and J. D. Sudbury, *Corrosion*, **14** (1958), 109t.

[13]T. E. Larson and R. M. King, "Corrosion of Water at Low Flow Velocity," *J. Am. Water Works Assoc.*, **46** (1954), 1.

[14]H. Schoeller, "Geochemistry of Subterranean Waters—Applications to Petroleum Formation Waters," *Rev. Inst. Franc. Petrole Ann. Combust. Liquides*, **10** (1955), 181.

[15]J. D. Hem, "Stability Field Diagrams as Aids in Iron Chemistry Studies," *J. Am. Water Works Assoc.*, **53** (1961), 211.

[16]G. B. Hatch and O. Rice, "Threshold Treatments of Water Systems," *Ind. Eng. Chem.*, **37** (1945), 710.

[17]B. Sloat, "Controlled Solubility Phosphates—A Versatile Solution to Oil Field Scale Problems," Paper 1317-G presented at 34th Annual Fall Meeting, Society Petroleum Engineers, Dallas, Texas (Oct. 4–7, 1959).

[18]J. Green, "Reversion of Molecularly Dehydrated Sodium Phosphates," *Ind. Eng. Chem.*, **42** (1950), 1542.

[19]J. R. Van Wazer, *Phosphorus and Its Compounds*, **1** (New York: Interscience Publishers, 1958), p. 453.

[20]A. B. Featherston and R. G. Mihram, "Minimization of Scale Deposits in Oil Wells by Placement of Phosphates in Producing Zones," *J. Petrol. Technol.*, **11** (March, 1959), 29.

[21]R. C. Earllougher and W. W. Love, "Sequestering Agents for Prevention of Scale Deposition in Oil Wells," *J. Petrol. Technol.*, **9** (April, 1957), 17.

[22]G. L. Illig, Jr., "Use of Sodium Hexametaphosphate in Manganese Stabilization," *J. Am. Water Works Assoc.*, **52** (1960), 867.

[23]J. E. Edwards and ICI, British Patent 568000 (1945).

[24]S. Chaberek and A. E. Martell, *Organic Sequestering Agents*, (New York: John Wiley & Sons, Inc., 1959), p. 338.

Water and Corrosion

4

Corrosion

Corrosion can be defined as the destructive attack of a metal by a chemical or electrochemical reaction with its environment. The air oxidation of hot steel forming an iron oxide coating is an example of chemical attack. Corrosion of this type seldom occurs in the oil field. The second type, electrochemical corrosion, occurs at a solid-liquid interface. This occurs in nearly every instance where oilfield waters contact steel equipment.

In order to have electrochemical corrosion, it is necessary to have an (1) anode; (2) cathode; (3) electrolyte; and (4) external connection. Remove any one of these and corrosion will cease. This is the principle of corrosion mitigation; to remove one of the four components necessary for the corrosion reaction.

The anode and cathode are called electrodes. The anode is the electrode at which oxidation occurs or where electricity leaves the metal and enters the electrolyte. For iron, the anode reaction is shown in Eq. (4–1), where iron is oxidized to the ferrous ion.

$$Fe = Fe^{++} + 2e^- \qquad (4\text{–}1)$$

$$H^+ = \frac{1}{2}H_2 - e^- \qquad (4\text{–}2)$$

Reduction occurs at the cathode. An example is the reduction of hydrogen ion, shown in Eq. (4–2).

The electrolyte of interest here is water. Its function is not only to carry corrosive materials to the surface but to provide a medium of electron transfer utilizing ions. Any connection, excluding the electrolyte, between the anode and cathode is an external connection. Anodes and cathodes both exist on steel surfaces. The body of the steel serves as an external connection. The severity of corrosion depends upon the potential generated between the anode and cathode.

A good example of corrosion is a dry cell. The center carbon electrode is the cathode. A zinc case serves as anode. These electrodes are separated by an electrolyte that is essentially ammonium chloride solution. When an external connection in the form of a flashlight bulb is attached, corrosion occurs as zinc goes into solution, and the bulb glows. The greater the flow of electricity through the cell, the greater is the amount of zinc that corrodes. The relationship between the amount of zinc corroding and the flow of current is quantitative.

Forms of Corrosion Damage

1. UNIFORM OR THINNING CORROSION

In this form of corrosion attack, the entire surface of the metal is corroded, and the metal thickness reduced by a uniform amount. This would occur with a homogeneous metal when no difference in potential existed between any points on the surface. The anode in galvanic corrosion could undergo thinning.

2. PITTING CORROSION

This is the most common type of attack that occurs with heterogenous metals such as steels and other alloys. It is a localized attack, where the rate of corrosion is greater at some areas than at others. This is caused by differences in potential between different points on the metal surface. A break in an oxide film protecting a metal surface can cause pitting attack.

3. INTERGRANULAR CORROSION

This form of corrosion occurs with alloys when a difference in potential exists between the grain boundary and the grain. The smaller grain boundary acts as the anode. This type of corrosion is particularly serious with aluminum alloys containing copper and austenitic stainless steels containing carbon.

4. GALVANIC CORROSION

Galvanic corrosion occurs where two different metals or alloys come in contact. The severity of galvanic corrosion depends upon the difference in potential between the two metals, and the relative size of the cathode and anode areas. The galvanic series for metals and alloys in sea water is shown in Table 4.1. Active metals are at the top of the series. Coupling a metal near the top with one near the bottom will cause galvanic corrosion of the more active metal.

If the area of the active metal is very large compared with the area of the less active metal, corrosion will not be so severe. Polarization will also modify the amount of current flowing during the corrosion reaction.

A comprehensive discussion of corrosion theory is beyond the scope of this book. The reader is referred to three excellent books in this field by Uhlig[1,2] and by Evans.[3] Our chief interest is the substances dissolved in water and the properties of water that cause corrosion which can be removed or altered by water treatment.

Water in the Corrosion Process

The presence of water is essential to the low-temperature corrosion process. However, pure water containing no dissolved substances is only very mildly corrosive to iron. Since iron is anodic to hydrogen in pure water, the iron corrodes to produce hydrogen gas and ferrous hydroxide, which raises the pH of the water. The attack proceeds until the solubility of ferrous hydroxide is exceeded and the ferrous hydroxide deposits on the metal surface in the form of a film, smothering the corrosion reaction.

Table 4.1

GALVANIC SERIES FOR METALS IN SEA WATER

(From Jellinek, *Chem. Eng.* (Aug. 25, 1958), p. 126.)

Active or Anodic End

Magnesium
Zinc
Alclad 3S
Aluminum 3S
Aluminum 61S
Aluminum 63S
Aluminum 52
Low steel
Alloy steel
Cast iron
Stainless steels (active)
    Type 410
    Type 430
    Type 304
    Type 316
Ni-resist
Muntz metal
Yellow brass
Admiralty brass
Aluminum brass
Red brass
Copper
Aluminum bronze
Composition G bronze
90/10 Copper-nickel
70 + 30 Copper-nickel-low iron
70 + 30 Copper-nickel-high iron
Nickel
Inconel
Silver
Stainless steels (passive)
    Type 410
    Type 430
    Type 304
    Type 316
Monel
Hastelloy C.
Titanium

Noble or Cathodic End

Water containing impurities or dissolved substances can be corrosive or noncorrosive, depending on the nature of the dissolved substances. Chromates and phosphates are dissolved in water to inhibit or reduce corrosion. Other substances such as salts, acids, hydrogen sulfide, carbon dioxide, and oxygen can increase the corrosivity of the water. Generally, the water encountered in oilfield operations contains one or more of these substances which increase its corrosivity.

In addition to the impurities which are commonly found in water, temperature and velocity also influence the corrosivity of water. Seldom is a corrosion problem encountered where only one of these contributing factors is present. Generally, the problem is complex because of these various influences and the manner in which they may interact with each other.

Influence of Dissolved Oxygen

Oxygen dissolved in water is probably the most troublesome corrosion-producing substance. The solutility of oxygen in water is shown in Table 4.2. The product of corrosion of iron by oxygen-containing water is a mixture of iron oxides, usually hydrated, and generally referred to as rust. The following equations illustrate this in the simplest form and in water containing only dissolved oxygen.

$$Fe + 2H^+ \rightleftharpoons Fe^{++} + 2H° \tag{4-3}$$

$$2H° + \frac{1}{2}O_2 \rightleftharpoons H_2O \tag{4-4}$$

$$2Fe^{++} + \frac{1}{2}O_2 + H_2O \longrightarrow 2Fe^{+++} + 2OH^- \tag{4-5}$$

The action of the oxygen is twofold—it depolarizes the cathode, and it oxidizes the ferrous ions to ferric ions, which form the insoluble (above pH = 3) ferric hydroxide. If the formation of ferric hydroxide occurs out of contact with the metal, there is no stifling of the reaction by this corrosion product. In a closed system, this reaction will continue until the dissolved oxygen is used up and the ferrous hydroxide smothers the reaction.

However, in a system in contact with the air, the oxygen supply is continually replenished. The rate of corrosion, in this case, is generally restricted by the transport of oxygen from the air through the water to the metal. While the rate of corrosion may not be as high as that produced by the attack of acids, the inexhaustible supply of air assures that the reaction may continue for a long period of time. The corrosion rate of steel in water has been found to be approximately proportional to oxygen content up to 5.5 cc/liter.[4,5] The corrosion rate is lower at higher oxygen concentrations. This may be explained by the fact that at low oxygen concentrations, the corrosion product formed is not as impermeable to oxygen diffusion as that formed at higher oxygen concentrations. Hydrated ferrous hydroxide is formed first in both cases. However, at high oxygen concentrations, the ferrous compounds are oxidized at a rate sufficiently rapid to precipitate the hydrated ferric hydroxide next to the metal as a protective film.

In waters containing high salt concentrations, corrosion is proportional

Table 4.2

SOLUBILITY OF OXYGEN IN FRESH WATER AND IN SEA WATER OF STATED
DEGREES OF SALINITY AT VARIOUS TEMPERATURES WHEN EXPOSED TO
WATER-SATURATED AIR AT A TOTAL PRESSURE OF 760 MM HG. DRY AIR
IS ASSUMED TO CONTAIN 20.90 PER CENT OXYGEN*

(Calculated by G. C. Whipple and M. C. Whipple from measurements of C. J. J. Fox. Reprinted from *Standard Methods for the Examination of Water, Sewage, and Industrial Wastes* 1955 (10th Ed.), with permission of American Public Health Association, Inc.)

	Chlorides in Sea Water (parts per million)					Difference per 100 ppm Cl	Dissolved Oxygen in Chloride-free Water	
	0	5000	10000	15000	20000	ppm	C°	ppm
°C	Dissolved Oxygen in Parts per Million by Weight					ppm	C°	ppm
0	14.62	13.79	12.97	12.14	11.32	0.0165	30	7.6
1	14.23	13.41	12.61	11.82	11.03	0.0160	31	7.5
2	13.84	13.05	12.28	11.52	10.76	0.0154	32	7.4
3	13.48	12.72	11.98	11.24	10.50	0.0149	33	7.3
4	13.13	12.41	11.69	10.97	10.25	0.0144	34	7.2
5	12.80	12.09	11.39	10.70	10.01	0.0140	35	7.1
6	12.48	11.79	11.12	10.45	9.78	0.0135	36	7.0
7	12.17	11.51	10.85	10.21	9.57	0.0130	37	6.9
8	11.87	11.24	10.61	9.98	9.36	0.0125	38	6.8
9	11.59	10.97	10.36	9.76	9.17	0.0121	39	6.7
10	11.33	10.73	10.13	9.55	8.98	0.0118	40	6.6
11	11.08	10.49	9.92	9.35	8.80	0.0114	41	6.5
12	10.83	10.28	9.72	9.17	8.62	0.0110	42	6.4
13	10.60	10.05	9.52	8.98	8.46	0.0107	43	6.3
14	10.37	9.85	9.32	8.80	8.30	0.0104	44	6.2
15	10.15	9.65	9.14	8.63	8.14	0.0100	45	6.1
16	9.95	9.46	8.96	8.47	7.99	0.0098	46	6.0
17	9.74	9.26	8.78	8.30	7.84	0.0095	47	5.9
18	9.54	9.07	8.62	8.15	7.70	0.0092	48	5.8
19	9.35	8.89	8.45	8.00	7.56	0.0089	49	5.7
20	9.17	8.73	8.30	7.86	7.42	0.0088	50	5.6
21	8.99	8.57	8.14	7.71	7.28	0.0086		
22	8.83	8.42	7.99	7.57	7.14	0.0084		
23	8.68	8.27	7.85	7.43	7.00	0.0083		
24	8.53	8.12	7.71	7.30	6.87	0.0083		
25	8.38	7.96	7.56	7.15	6.74	0.0082		
26	8.22	7.81	7.42	7.02	6.61	0.0080		
27	8.07	7.67	7.28	6.88	6.49	0.0079		
28	7.92	7.53	7.14	6.75	6.37	0.0078		
29	7.77	7.39	7.00	6.62	6.25	0.0076		
30	7.63	7.25	6.86	6.49	6.13	0.0075		

*Under any other barometric pressure, P, the solubility may be obtained from the corresponding value in the table by the formula:

$$S' = S \frac{P}{760} = S \frac{P'}{29.92}$$

in which S' = Solubility at P or P'

S = Solubility at 760 mm or 29.92 in.

P = Barometric pressure in mm and

P' = Barometric pressure in in.

The second decimal place in the above table is not accurately known. The average difference from the mean of five different investigators represents 0.07 ppm. Until further data are obtained, however, the second decimal place has been retained in the table.

to the amount of oxygen dissolved in the water.[6] As the salt concentration in the water increases, the solubility of oxygen decreases and, consequently, the corrosion rate is reduced. This is shown in Fig. 4.1, where data of greatest corrosion rates represents solutions of lowest sodium chloride concentrations and therefore highest oxygen saturation values. The corrosion rate shows a maximum at 5.2 cc/liter of oxygen or 0.5 mole sodium chloride. In waters containing low salt concentrations, the corrosion is governed by the conductivity of the water.

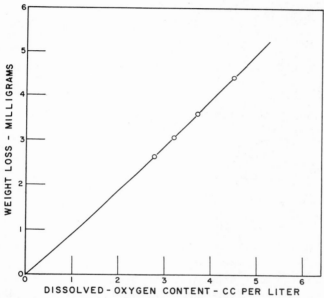

Fig. 4.1. Corrosion in sodium chloride solutions containing dissolved oxygen. (Data from Evans and Hoar, *Proc. Roy. Soc.* (*London*), *Ser. A.*, **137A** (1932), 343.)

Corrosion can also be caused by differential aeration cells, which are concentration cells caused by differences in oxygen concentration between two parts of the system. This results in a difference in potential between the portion of high oxygen concentration and that of low oxygen concentration. The area of corrosion can be demonstrated by considering two oxygen electrodes in an aqueous solution. The left-hand electrode has an oxygen partial pressure of 0.2 atmospheres and a potential E_1, and the right-hand electrode has an oxygen partial pressure of 0.02 atmospheres and a potential E_2.

$$E_1 = -0.4 - \frac{0.059}{4} \log \frac{0.20}{\text{OH}^{-4}} \tag{4–6}$$

$$E_2 = -0.4 - \frac{0.059}{4} \log \frac{0.02}{OH^{-4}} \qquad (4\text{-}7)$$

$$\Delta E = E_2 - E_1 = \frac{0.059}{4} \log \frac{0.20}{0.02} = +0.015 \qquad (4\text{-}8)$$

Since the above cell potential, ΔE, is positive, the free energy for the reaction will be negative, indicating that the reaction will be spontaneous. Thus, the right-hand electrode, which has an oxygen partial pressure of 0.02 atm, will be the anode. Therefore, corrosion occurs in differential aeration cells at the area of low oxygen concentration.

Corrosion of iron which occurs at a water-air interface can be attributed to differential aeration. Oxygen from the air is available to the meniscus area formed at the water line. As oxygen is depleted at levels beneath the water line, the meniscus area becomes cathodic to the immersed iron. In hard waters, the alkaline cathodic reaction products precipitate calcium and magnesium compounds, which deposit on the iron and shield a part of it from the aerated solution. Since this shielded area is deprived of oxygen, corrosion occurs here at the water line.

Influence of Dissolved Carbon Dioxide

Carbon dioxide dissolved in water can contribute to the corrosion of steel. Corrosion caused by water containing dissolved carbon dioxide is characterized by clean, uniformly thinned surfaces below the water line. The rate and amount of corrosion is dependent upon the salts dissolved in the water, the carbon dioxide content, the oxygen content, the temperature, and the composition of the steel. Carbon dioxide is present in water as: (1) the carbon dioxide in carbonate ions; (2) the carbon dioxide necessary to convert the carbonates to bicarbonates; (3) the amount of carbon dioxide necessary to keep the bicarbonates in solution; and (4) any excess carbon dioxide. This excess carbon dioxide is referred to as "aggressive" carbon dioxide, and is the most corrosive form.

For equal concentrations, carbon dioxide dissolved in water is not as corrosive as oxygen dissolved in water. At 60°C, a solution containing 4 ml of dissolved oxygen is seven times as corrosive as one containing the same volume of dissolved carbon dioxide.[7] In distilled water with only oxygen present, the corrosion rate of mild steel (0.15 per cent carbon) increases two-fold between 60°C and 90°C; whereas the corrosion rate increases by 2.6 fold in the same temperature range with only carbon dioxide dissolved in distilled water. The increase in corrosion rate can be attributed to increased diffusion rates of the dissolved gases with increased temperature. The greater increase in corrosion rate in the carbon dioxide solution with increased temperature is caused by a decrease in the acidity—or finite carbon dioxide concentration—required at the metal surface for hydrogen evolution. This makes the carbon dioxide more effective.[8]

In corrosion caused by carbon dioxide dissolved in water, the following reaction applies where carbon dioxide reacts with water to form bicarbonate but not carbonate:

$$2CO_2 + 2H_2O + 2e^- \longrightarrow 2HCO_3^- + H_2 \tag{4-9}$$

The depolarizing reaction of oxygen at the cathode is

$$2O_2 + 4H_2O + 8e^- \longrightarrow 8OH^- \tag{4-10}$$

Comparison of these reactions indicates that, on the basis of electrons, oxygen dissolved in water should be roughly four times as corrosive as an equal molar amount of carbon dioxide.

When dissolved in water, carbon dioxide acts as an acid, so that the acidity of the solution and the corrosion rate are increased by increasing the partial pressure of the carbon dioxide. Corrosion resulting in hydrogen gas evolution may occur at pH 6 with carbon dioxide, whereas pH 4 is required with highly ionized hydrochloric acid.[9] This can be explained by the fact that carbonic acid is a slightly ionized acid and therefore would require a greater amount of carbonic acid, or more total acidity, to obtain pH 6 than the amount of hydrochloric acid necessary to obtain pH 4. The rate of corrosion is influenced by the partial pressure of carbon dioxide. This is illustrated in Fig. 4.2. The rate of corrosion increases rapidly with increased carbon dioxide pressure to 200 psia. There is a lesser increase to 300 psia, while greater pressures result in no further appreciable change.

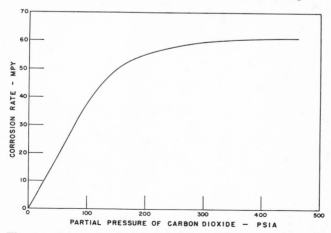

Fig. 4.2. Corrosion of steel in distilled water containing CO_2 at various partial pressures. (Plotted from data of Rhodes and Clark, *Ind. Eng. Chem.*, **28** (1936), 1078.)

Water that contains both dissolved oxygen and carbon dioxide is more corrosive to steel than water which contains only an equal total concentration of one of these gases. For example, in a solution containing 10 cc of carbon dioxide per liter, the corrosion rate is 8 mils per year (mpy); in a solution containing 0.67 cc of dissolved oxygen per liter, the corrosion rate is 4 mpy. A solution containing the above amounts of each of these dissolved gases has a corrosion rate of 17 mpy, which is greater than the sum of the corrosion rates of the individual gases.[8] This effect occurs at low oxygen concentrations and may be related to the nature of the corrosion products. At high oxygen concentrations, the adherent film formed by corrosion on the surface of the metal is essentially unaffected by the carbon dioxide, whereas at low oxygen concentrations, the carbon dioxide interferes with the formation of the corrosion film, resulting in an increased corrosion rate.

It has been mentioned previously that dissolved carbon dioxide influences the solubility of magnesium and calcium carbonates. These salts sometimes precipitate on the surface of metal pipe and form a protective coating. Water containing aggressive carbon dioxide will not deposit this protective coating. Salts dissolved in the water may act as buffers, thereby preventing the pH from reaching a low enough value to produce serious corrosion.

In waters containing high ratios of carbon dioxide to oxygen, corrosion is accompanied by the evolution of hydrogen; the corrosion *rate* is governed by the acidity and by the composition and physical structure of the steel. At low ratios, oxygen depolarization controls the reaction and all low-alloy composition steels corrode the same. Different investigators[8,10,11] have found a difference in corrosion rates of different low-alloy steels in aqueous systems containing only dissolved carbon dioxide.

Influence of Dissolved Hydrogen Sulfide

Hydrogen sulfide, like carbon dioxide, is not corrosive in the absence of moisture. Water containing dissolved hydrogen sulfide is corrosive. Hydrogen sulfide is very soluble in water and, when dissolved, behaves as a very weak dibasic acid, yielding an acid solution in distilled water. Generally, when hydrogen sulfide exists at the bottom of an oil or gas well dissolved in a brine, there is no oxygen or other oxidizing agent with it. Under these conditions, the dissolved hydrogen sulfide will attack iron and *nonacid-resistant* alloys. When the brine is pumped to the surface, oxygen from the air dissolves in the brine giving a water which may even be corrosive to *acid-resistant* alloys. Dissolved oxygen will slowly oxidize the hydrogen sulfide to give water and free sulfur according to the equation:

$$H_2S + \frac{1}{2}O_2 \rightarrow H_2O + S \qquad (4\text{--}11)$$

The rate of corrosion of mild steel in distilled water containing dissolved hydrogen sulfide varies with the concentration of dissolved gas. Fig. 4.3 shows this variation with hydrogen sulfide concentrations ranging from 2 to 2,640 ppm at a constant temperature.[12] The corrosion rate increases rapidly up to a hydrogen sulfide content of 150 ppm, remains nearly constant in the range 150 to 400 ppm, and diminishes rapidly as the concentration of hydrogen sulfide approaches 1,600 ppm. From 1,600 ppm to 2,640 ppm, the corrosion rate remains fairly constant, indicating that high concentrations of hydrogen sulfide may act to inhibit the corrosion reaction. The use of polysulfides in aqueous systems to prevent blistering and fissuring has been disclosed.[13] Polysulfides *are not* recommended for use in acid solutions.

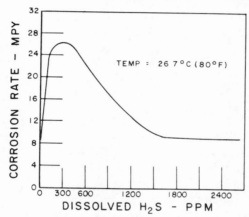

Fig. 4.3. Corrosion rate of mild steel in distilled H_2O containing varying concentrations of H_2S. (From Watkins and Wright, *Petrol. Eng.*, **25**, No. 12 (1953), B50. Reprinted with permission of *Petrol. Eng.*)

The corrosion rate in water containing dissolved hydrogen sulfide is also influenced by the presence of dissolved salts and dissolved carbon dioxide. A series of three curves showing the corrosion rates of 1020 steel in distilled water containing dissolved hydrogen sulfide, in brine containing dissolved hydrogen sulfide, and in brine containing both dissolved hydrogen sulfide and carbon dioxide is shown in Fig. 4.4. The corrosion rates in the brine solutions are higher than those in distilled water, and the brine containing hydrogen sulfide gives the highest corrosion rate. The differences in corrosion rates are attributed to the corrosion products formed in the different solutions.[14] In the distilled water system, kansite (Fe_9S_8) formed only a moderately protective tarnish until more protective pyrrhotite ($Fe_{0.875}S$)

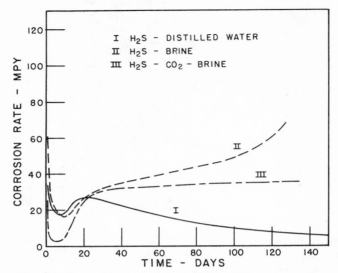

Fig. 4.4. Corrosion rates in hydrogen sulfide-water systems. (Modified after Myer, Riggs, McGlasson, and Sudbury, *Corrosion*, **14** (1958), 109t, and reprinted with permission of *Corrosion*.)

and pyrite (FeS_2) scales formed. Since only kansite scale formed in the brine systems, the corrosion rate continued to increase.

The corrosion rate is also influenced by the composition of the steel exposed to water-containing hydrogen sulfide. This difference is pronounced between different alloys but may also be evident between different compositions of essentially the same alloy. A 10 mpy difference has been found in the corrosion rates of two copper-bearing mild steel samples exposed to water saturated with the same mixture of oxygen, carbon dioxide, and hydrogen sulfide.[11] This indicates the possibility of incurring an error in comparing the corrosivity of two environments on the basis of corrosion of steel tubing or flow lines without considering the composition of the steels.

Influence of Dissolved Salts

Salts dissolved in water have a marked influence on the corrosivity of the water. At extremely low concentrations of dissolved salts, different anions and cations show varying degrees of influence on the corrosivity of the water. The anions most commonly found in water are chloride, sulfate, and bicarbonate. The effect on the corrosivity of distilled water to steel resulting from the addition of these ions is shown in Fig. 4.5. In the concentration range shown in this graph, the sulfate ion has a greater effect on the corrosivity of the water than the chloride ion, and the bicarbonate ion shows inhibitive tendencies. In solutions containing bicarbonate ion along with either chloride or sulfate ion at concentrations up to 100 ppm, the bicarbonate ion showed increasing inhibition with increasing concentration but did not entirely prevent corrosion.[15]

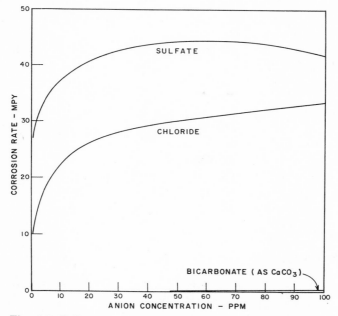

Fig. 4.5. Influence of sulfate, chloride, and bicarbonate on the corrosion of steel. (Data from Hatch and Rice, *J. Am. Water Works Assoc.*, **51** (1959), 719.)

The influence of the anion on corrosivity also depends upon the metal in question. Waters containing sulfate ion would not seriously corrode lead because of the formation of lead sulfate on the surface of the lead. The corrosion rate of stainless steel is greater in 0.1 mole potassium chloride than in 0.1 mole potassium sulfate because of the greater penetration of the protective oxygen or oxide coating by the chloride ion.[6] The order of decreasing penetrating power of anions has been given as: chloride > bromide > iodide > fluoride > sulfate > nitrate > monohydrogen phosphate.[16]

Water solutions containing equal concentrations of salts of the same anion but different cations show different degrees of corrosivity to mild steel. With alkali metal chlorides, the corrosion rate is greatest in potassium chloride solutions, less in sodium chloride solutions, and lowest in lithium chloride solutions.[17] The order of decreasing corrosiveness of cations has been given as: ferric > chromic > ammonium > aluminum > potassium > sodium > lithium > barium > strontium > calcium > manganese > cadmium > magnesium.[17]

Generally, the corrosivity of waters containing dissolved salts increases with increasing salt concentration until a maximum is reached, and then the corrosivity decreases. This may be attributed to increased electroconductivity because of the increased salt content, until the salt concentration is great enough to cause an appreciable decrease in the oxygen solubility, resulting in a decreased rate of depolarization.[18] The dissolved salts may also decrease the protectivity of any corrosion products which form, and thus increase corrosion. This is demonstrated, for the case of a hydrogen sulfide-brine solution, in Fig. 4.4.

Influence of pH

The chemical nature of the electrolyte is an important external factor governing the rate of corrosion, and the pH is an important characteristic of the electrolyte. The influence of pH on the rate of corrosion of water solutions containing oxygen from the air is dependent upon the metal corroded. Diagrams illustrating the influence of pH on the rate of corrosion of some metals are shown in Figs. 4.6 and 4.7. The corrosion rates of the noble metals, gold and platinum, are shown in Fig. 4.6 to be unaffected by the pH of the water. In the same figure, the characteristic curve showing effect of pH on the corrosion of aluminum, zinc, and lead is shown. Here the metals show a large increase in corrosion rate in both acidic and basic solutions.

The shape of this curve may be explained by the fact that aluminum, zinc, and lead are amphoteric metals or ampholytes. That is, the metals form hydroxide precipitates that are insoluble in water solutions approximating a neutral pH, but they dissolve in solutions that are sufficiently alkaline or acidic. In the neutral pH range where these metals form insoluble hydroxides, the hydroxides will deposit on the surfaces of the metals, resulting in coatings which will retard corrosion. In highly acid water solutions, these metal ions form soluble salts; consequently, the protective films are removed and corrosion progresses. In highly alkaline water solutions, soluble complex compounds are formed, such as sodium zincate (Na_2ZnO_2) and sodium aluminate ($NaAlO_2$)—again destroying the protective films and permitting corrosion to proceed unchecked.

A third type of pH-corrosion rate diagram illustrating the effect of pH on the corrosion rate of iron, nickel, cadmium, and magnesium is shown in

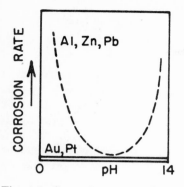

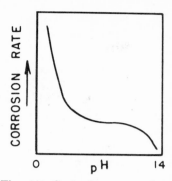

Fig. 4.6. General curves showing corrosion rates versus pH for aluminum, zinc, lead, gold, and platinum. (From Akimov, *Corrosion*, **15** (1959), 455t, and reprinted with permission of *Corrosion*.)

Fig. 4.7. General curve showing corrosion rate versus pH for iron, nickel, cadmium, and magnesium. (From Akimov, *Corrosion*, **15** (1959), 455t, and reprinted with permission of *Corrosion*.)

Fig. 4.7. This curve shows the formation of soluble compounds in a region of high acidity, and the formation of less soluble and somewhat protective films in the neutral region. In contrast to the amphoteric metals, these metals form hydroxides, which are insoluble in highly alkaline environments and thus form protective films at high pH values. The solubility curve of ferrous hydroxide as a function of pH is similar in shape to the curve in Fig. 4.7.

In the pH range 4 to 9.5, the iron surface is in contact with an alkaline-saturated solution of hydrated ferrous oxide, and corrosion progresses as oxygen diffuses through this barrier.[19] The rate at which this layer of hydrated ferrous oxide is formed depends upon the dissolved-oxygen content. If the acidity is due to a highly dissociated acid (such as hydrochloric), hydrogen evolution will occur in the corrosion of iron at pH 4 or less. The hydrated ferrous oxide will be dissolved at this low pH, resulting in direct contact between acid and iron. Carbonic acid solutions react with iron at pH 6 or less, resulting in hydrogen evolution. Since hydrogen evolution is probably the product of direct attack on the iron by the acidity of the solution and since carbonic acid is a weakly dissociated acid, it appears that total acidity is as important a factor as pH.

A relatively dilute alkaline solution affords corrosion protection to iron, but a highly alkaline solution does not. In a water solution of 4 per cent sodium hydroxide, the corrosion rate of iron is very low, and the potential of the iron on the hydrogen scale is approximately 0.1 volt.[19] At extremely high concentrations of sodium hydroxide, the potential drops to an active value, and iron corrodes, forming soluble sodium ferrite ($NaFeO_2$).

Influence of Temperature

The effect of temperature changes on the corrosion rate in waters is more complex than the simple chemical principle that an increase in temperature increases the reaction rate. An increase in the temperature of a corroding system has four main effects: (1) the rate of chemical reaction is increased; (2) the solubility of gases in the water is decreased; (3) the solubility of some of the reaction products may change, resulting in different corrosion reaction products; and (4) viscosity is decreased, and any thermal differences will result in increased circulation.[20]

Generally, corrosion rate increases with increasing temperature. This is particularly true when corrosion is due to the presence of mineral acids in water, resulting in hydrogen evolution. However, in waters which are corrosive due to the presence of dissolved oxygen, the corrosion rate increases with increasing temperature only until the temperature becomes high enough to cause an appreciable decrease in the oxygen solubility. Further temperature increase beyond this value results in a decrease in the corrosion rate for open systems, where the oxygen is free to escape. In a closed system, the oxygen cannot escape and the corrosion rate continues to increase with increasing temperature. These effects are shown in Fig. 4.8.

In waters containing calcium or magnesium bicarbonates, temperature increases result in the evolution of carbon dioxide and increased corrosion. At the same time, calcium or magnesium carbonates may deposit on the

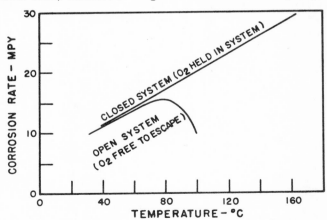

Fig. 4.8. Effect of temperature on corrosion in oxygen-containing water. (From F. N. Speller, *Corrosion Causes and Prevention*, New York: McGraw-Hill Book Co., 1951. Used by permission.)

metal surface, resulting in the formation of a protective coating. Some of the carbonate ion may also combine with ferrous ion, forming ferrous carbonate in the corrosion product.

If the temperature increase is not uniform over the metal system, the hotter areas tend to be anodic to the colder areas.[21] This may result in pitting corrosion. Zinc is normally anodic to steel in water and is sometimes used as a sacrificial material in the cathodic protection of steel. However, this may change with increased temperature. In the temperature range 60° to 90°C, the zinc may become the cathode, resulting in corrosion of the steel.[22]

Influence of Velocity

The flow of water over a metal surface influences the corrosion rate chiefly through the effects of water movement on the other factors governing corrosion. In stagnant waters or waters at zero velocity, the general corrosion rate is usually low, but localized or pitting corrosion may occur. Generally, some motion in a corrosive system causes greater uniformity and results in a thinning type of corrosion rather than pitting. Some flow or motion is also desirable when corrosion inhibitors are used, so that the inhibitors may be effectively distributed. Turbulence may occur at high velocities, and the turbulence may result in nonuniform conditions that lead to pitting corrosion. At high velocities, the film of corrosion product may be removed as it forms, resulting in corrosion of the bare metal surface. Systems which contain areas of high and low velocity may experience deposition of sludges or suspended solids in areas of low velocity. These sludge deposits can restrict oxygen diffusion, resulting in corrosion under the deposits. In oxygen-free systems, the area subject to the highest velocity becomes anodic to the area subject to lowest velocity, and corrodes.[23] When dissolved oxygen is present, an oxygen concentration cell is formed, and the area of low velocity (receiving less oxygen) becomes the anodic area.

In systems containing oxygen, the replenishment of oxygen to the metal surface may be slow and the corrosion product relatively porous. Corrosion rates increase with velocity in such systems, until the oxygen replenishment rate is high enough to provide a protective film of ferric hydroxide, and then the corrosion rate tends to decrease. If the velocity is further increased, the corrosion rate may increase because of the mechanical removal of the corrosion products.

Extremely high velocities may give rise to low-pressure areas where vapor bubbles may form; on collapse, these can cause cavitation erosion at areas of higher pressures. Impingement attack may occur, under turbulent

flow conditions, if the water carries debris and air bubbles. The forward
ends of the corrosion pits may be undercut because of the impingement of
the air bubbles. Mechanical erosion can result from waters carrying suspended sand or other particles at high velocities.

The influence on the initial corrosion rate of the velocity of water flow
through steel pipe has been studied by Speller and Kendall.[24] Some of their
results are shown in Fig. 4.9. At 80°F, the corrosion rate increased with
increasing velocity until a nearly constant value was attained, which did not
change appreciably with further velocity increases. At higher temperatures,
the corrosion rates in the one-quarter-inch and one-half-inch pipes continued
to increase with increasing velocity. This indicates that the steel surface
cannot always be passivated by increasing the supply of oxygen to the steel
surface. This may depend on the original condition of the surface.

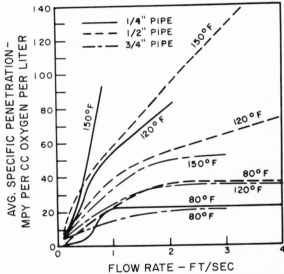

Fig. 4.9. Effect of velocity of flow on the initial rate of cor-
rosion of steel pipe. (Reprinted from Speller and Kendall,
Ind. Eng. Chem., **15** (1923), 134, and used by permission of
Ind. Eng. Chem.)

It is evident from Fig. 4.9 that the initial rate of corrosion increases
more rapidly as the velocity increases in the small-diameter pipes—possibly
due to the effect of turbulence. This investigation demonstrates that the
initial corrosion rate can be reduced in some instances by simply using
oversized pipe to decrease both velocity and turbulence.

Preventing Corrosion of Water-Handling Systems

There are several different methods available for preventing or minimizing corrosion of metal in contact with water. In some instances, more than one of these methods will eliminate corrosion. The choice is then made on the basis of economic considerations. Usually the method costing the least in money and manpower, yet giving adequate protection, is chosen. Sometimes only one method of corrosion prevention is suitable, so the cost of corrosion must then be balanced against the cost of treatment.

Corrosion should always be considered in the design of a water-handling system. A little thought and a minimum of effort during the various stages of design may save many dollars and extend the life of the system. The choice and location of metals used should be considered. Provisions should be made during the design for the application of a corrosion prevention method, if the need arises. Poor planning has often caused the use of a corrosion mitigation method that was much more costly than one that could have been used, had the system been adequately designed.

Methods of Measuring Corrosion

Before initiating a corrosion prevention program, it is necessary to determine if corrosion is present, the cause of corrosion, and the rate or severity of corrosion. In order to determine the effectiveness of a corrosion prevention method, the rate of corrosion should be measured before and after application of prevention measures.

1. VISUAL

Visual observation or inspection is the oldest and the most widely used method of detecting corrosion. Everyone has seen rust and knows the appearance of corroded iron. Corrosion in water wells and flow lines is often detected by red or black water. Corrosion may be so severe that leaks appear.

Visual observation has the disadvantage that the corrosion rate cannot be accurately determined using this method. In pipelines, buried flow lines, and wells, it is not possible to see the exposed metal, so some other method must be used.

2. WEIGHT LOSS SPECIMENS

Corrosion rates can be measured by exposing pieces of metal similar to that in the system to the corrosive environment. These specimens are carefully cleaned and weighed before exposure. The time of exposure is measured. When the specimens are removed, they are cleaned and weighed. From their loss of weight and the length of time they have been exposed, their corrosion rate is determined. Corrosion rates are usually measured in mils per year (mpy) penetration. Other units of rate are sometimes used. A procedure for cleaning steel-corrosion weight-loss specimens and calculating the corrosion rate is found in the Appendix.

The appearance of the weight-loss specimen after exposure may indicate the cause of corrosion. For example, a black sulfide coating shows the presence of hydrogen sulfide in the system. Ferric oxide indicates oxygen is present. Carbon dioxide corrosion can sometimes be detected by ferrous carbonate deposits on the specimen.

3. ELECTRICAL RESISTANCE CORROSION PROBES

Electrical resistance corrosion probes can also be used to determine corrosion rates. The operation of these probes depends upon measuring the change in resistance of a metal specimen as it corrodes in a corrosive environment. The resistance of the exposed specimen is usually compared with the resistance of a reference specimen. Resistances are measured potentiometrically, by a Wheatstone or other bridge method.

These probes are available in a variety of metals and alloys. Probes can also be obtained for use at various temperatures and pressures. Portable measuring instruments, designed especially for use with these probes, are commercially available.

4. DETERMINATION OF DISSOLVED IRON

Analysis of water for dissolved iron is sometimes used to estimate the rate of corrosion. Ideally, the iron content of the water should be measured before corrosion begins, so that some comparison can be made between the iron concentration before and after corrosion. This is not always possible, especially in the case of production wells. It is essential that the iron content of the water be measured before a corrosion prevention program is initiated. A reduction in dissolved iron concentration after the treatment is started indicates a decrease in the rate and amount of corrosion.

It should be emphasized that, with any method used to measure corrosion rates, a low rate does not necessarily mean freedom from corrosion problems. Often the rate or over-all thinning will be very low, but conditions may exist for pitting corrosion. Unfortunately, this is best observed by visual observation and is sometimes only apparent after a pit has penetrated the pipe wall.

Prevention of Corrosion by Water Treatment

Corrosive agents can sometimes be removed from water by using water treatment methods. The use of these methods depends on the amount of water to be treated, concentration of the corrosive agent, use of the water, and cost of treatment. All methods of treatment mentioned here are discussed more fully in later chapters.

1. DE-AERATION

Oxygen can be removed from water by de-aeration. De-aeration is frequently applied to boiler-feed water used for boilers operating at high temperature. At temperatures existing in these boilers, even small amounts of oxygen present a serious corrosion problem. De-aeration is also used on some water flood supply waters in which the presence of oxygen presents a critical problem.

2. DEGASIFICATION

Degasification is a general term applied to the removal of dissolved gases such as carbon dioxide and hydrogen sulfide. These dissolved gases are either removed entirely or their concentrations reduced to such a value that they do not contribute significantly to corrosion. In instances where sour water is the only available supply for injection water, it is necessary to remove hydrogen sulfide. Otherwise, corrosion may form iron sulfide that will eventually plug the formation rock in the injection well.

3. WATER SOFTENING

In addition to removing calcium and magnesium ions, the lime and soda ash process for water softening removes dissolved carbon dioxide. The pH of most waters softened by this method is increased. This may also contribute to reducing corrosion.

Prevention of Corrosion by Addition of Inhibitors

Corrosion inhibitors are chemical substances that are added to the corrosive environment to reduce or eliminate corrosion. By the addition of corrosion inhibitors to water, a simple and inexpensive solution to the corrosion problem is often found. Otherwise, the solution to the corrosion problem may require extensive modification and replacement of equipment or installation of water treatment equipment.

There are a wide variety of chemical substances used as corrosion inhibitors. Both inorganic and organic compounds are used. The conditions of the environment and type of corrosion govern the choice of inhibitor. Usually, the choice of inhibitor is based on the experience of the corrosion engineer and some trial-and-error testing.

Some typical inorganic corrosion inhibitors are shown in Table 4.3 and

Table 4.3
SOME TYPICAL INORGANIC CORROSION INHIBITORS

(From Gatos, *Corrosion*, **12** (1956), 235. Reprinted with permission of *Corrosion*.)

Inorganic Inhibitors	Approximate Conc., %	Corrosion Environment	Metallic System
Borax	2–3	alcohol antifreeze mixtures	automobile cooling system
Calgon	small amount	water systems	steel
Disodium hydrogen phosphate	0.5	citric acid	steel
Potassium dichromate	0.05–0.2	tap water 68–194°F	iron-brass
Potassium dihydrogen phosphate + sodium nitrite	small amount + 5%	sea water	steel
Potassium permanganate	0.10	0.3N NaOH solution	aluminum
Sodium benzoate	0.5	0.03% NaCl solution	mild steel
Sodium carbonate	small amount	gas condensate wells	iron
Sodium chromate	>0.5	cooling water	electrical rectifier systems
Sodium chromate	0.07	$CaCl_2$ brine	Cu, brass
Sodium dichromate	0.025	water	air-conditioning equipment
Sodium dichromate + sodium nitrate	0.1 + 0.05	water	heat-exchange devices
Sodium hexametaphosphate	0.002	water, about pH = 6	lead
Sodium metaphosphate	small amount	ammonia	mild steel condensers
Sodium nitrite	0.005	water	mild steel
Sodium nitrite	20% of sea water	sea water-distilled water mixtures	mild steel
Sodium orthophosphate	1	water, pH = 7.25	iron
Sodium silicate	small amount	sea water	Zn, Zn-Al alloys
Sodium silicate	0.01	oil field brines	steel pipes

typical organic corrosion inhibitors in Table 4.4. Generally, the organic inhibitors form films on the metal surface, protecting the metal from attack. These are termed safe inhibitors, since the addition of an amount too small to prevent corrosion will not cause an increase in corrosion. Some inorganic compounds, like the chromates, are anodic inhibitors or passivators.[25] An insufficient concentration of these can cause concentration of corrosion attack or pitting. Inhibitors can sometimes be added that will increase the protective properties of corrosion products.[26,27]

Table 4.4
SOME TYPICAL ORGANIC CORROSION INHIBITORS
(From Gatos, *Corrosion*, **12** (1956), 235. Reprinted with permission of *Corrosion*.)

Organic Inhibitor	Approximate Conc., %	Corrosion Environment	Metallic System
Benzanilide	0.2	lubricants	Cd-Ni, Cu-Pb bearings
Formaldehyde	small amount	oil wells	oil well equipment
Formaldehyde	0.05	sour crude oil	Diesel engines
Dioctyl ester of sulfosuccinic acid	0.05	refined petroleum oils	pipelines
Erythritol	small amount	K_2SO_4 solution	mild steel
Ethylaniline	0.5	HCl solutions	ferrous metals
Mercaptobenzothiazole	1	HCl solutions	iron and steel
Morpholine	0.2	water	heat-exchange systems
Oleic acid	small amount	polyhydric alcohols	iron
Phenyl acridine	0.5	H_2SO_4 solutions	iron
Pyridine + phenylhydrazine	0.5 + 0.5	HCl solutions	ferrous metals
Quinoline ethiodide	0.1	1N H_2SO_4	steel
Rosin amine-ethylene oxide	0.2	HCl solutions	mild steel
Tetramethylammonium azide	0.5	aqueous solutions of organic solvents	iron and steel
Thiourea	1	acids	iron and steel

Many commercially prepared corrosion inhibitors used in the oil field contain surface active agents. When these are added to a system for the first time, they remove loose deposits of corrosion products. Precautions should be taken to prevent these deposits from accumulating in equipment or in injection wells in order to prevent plugging.

Many times the simple addition of a corrosion inhibitor will solve a corrosion problem. There are still some corrosion problems that are not solved by inhibitors alone. One example of this is a salt water injection system, containing small amounts of dissolved oxygen. Organic corrosion inhibitors will reduce over-all corrosion, but they will not prevent pitting corrosion. It becomes necessary to remove the oxygen as well as to add an inhibitor.[28]

Prevention of Corrosion by Cathodic Protection

Cathodic protection consists of applying an electric current to the surface of the metal to be protected, in such a way that it will become a cathodic area. The current is applied externally, so that a net positive current enters all areas of the metal, including those that were previously anodic. Cathodic protection is applied to protect steel, brass, lead, copper, and aluminum against corrosion when these metals are immersed in water.

Protective currents are obtained from several different sources. Sacrificial anodes such as magnesium and zinc provide a protective current when coupled to steel. The current is obtained at the expense of the anode, which corrodes. Theoretically, any metal coupled to one below it in Table 4.1 will act as a sacrificial anode. The direct current necessary for protection can also be obtained by rectifying alternating current and applying it with an impressed current anode.

The current density required for cathodic protection depends on the metal, the environment, and the rate of corrosion. Applied current density must always exceed the current density equivalent to the corrosion rate. Generally, the current density required for protection is determined from potential measurements of the protected metal. Steel is usually protected if its potential is -0.85 volt versus the copper-copper sulfate half-cell. The order of magnitude of current densities required for the protection of steel in various environments is shown in Table 4.5. The specific current density for protection in these environments would have to be determined by actual measurement.

Current density required for protection may decrease with time after the initial application of cathodic protection. For example, in sea water

Table 4.5

ORDER OF MAGNITUDE OF SOME PROTECTIVE CURRENTS FOR STEEL

(From Jellinek, *Chem. Eng.*, Sept. 22, 1958, p. 168.)

Environment	Amp./Sq. Cm.
Well-cured halogen-free concrete	7×10^{-8}
Sterile, anerobic neutral soil water	5×10^{-7}
Halogen-containing concrete	5×10^{-7}
Aerated neutral soil water	4×10^{-6}
De-aerated hot water	4×10^{-6}
Moving fresh water	6×10^{-6}
Moving sea water	1.5×10^{-5}
Oxygen-saturated hot water	1.5×10^{-5}
Anaerobic soil with active sulfate-reducing bacteria	5×10^{-5}
Hot sulfuric acid	4×10^{-2}

a deposit referred to as "cathodic chalk" forms on the cathodic metal, reducing the current demand.[29]

Cathodic protection is particularly useful in protecting the submerged areas of water tanks and filters. Since only the areas below the water line are protected, other methods must be used to protect metal above the water line. Cathodic protection has an advantage over coatings in protecting sand filters, since coatings will not stand sand abrasion during backwashing operations.[30]

Prevention of Corrosion by Coatings

Corrosion can be prevented by removing or separating the corrosive environment from the metal. This is the principle of coatings applied for corrosion protection. Paint and galvanizing are examples of coatings that have been used for many years.

The choice of coating is dependent on the temperature, pressure, and corrosive agent. Coatings are applicable to almost any environment, if the cost is not prohibitive. Some metal coatings, like zinc on steel, or aluminum alloys clad to aluminum, actually offer cathodic protection when the base metal is exposed. With most other coatings, a break in the coating that exposes base metal causes serious corrosion. Corrosion in the form of pitting concentrates at these breaks and often perforates the metal.

Coatings can be divided into three general categories:

1. METALLIC COATINGS

Most metal coatings are applied by dipping the article into a molten bath of the metal or by electroplating the coating from aqueous solution. Some coatings are also applied by metal spraying. Metal coatings can be classified as (1) noble or (2) sacrificial. A noble metal coating such as chrome plating protects by its own resistance to corrosion. Sacrificial coatings such as zinc and cadmium cathodically protect the base metal. Some metallic coatings and methods of application are shown in Table 4.6.

2. INORGANIC COATINGS

Inorganic coatings are represented by vitreous enamels, cement lining, phosphate coatings, and oxide coatings. Vitreous enamels or glass coatings are very corrosion-resistant but somewhat brittle. Cement coatings are very popular for lining water flow lines.

Table 4.6

METALLIC COATING AND METHODS OF APPLICATION

(From Jellinek, *Chem. Eng.*, Oct. 20, 1958, p. 165.)

	Coating-Metal Requirements	Coating Characteristics	Metals Used
Hot Dipping Short-time immersion into bath of molten coating metal.	low melting point alloying capability	alloy layers (not pure metal) adherent, moderately uniform thickness difficult to control	Al, Zn, Sn, Pb, alloys
Cementation Powdered coating metal alloyed with base metal at temperature below melting point.	alloying capability	alloy throughout hard, brittle, porous poor corrosion resistance	Al, Zn, Cr, W, Si, Mo
Cladding Veneering and alloying of two or more metals under pressure; rolling of duplex ingots.	rolling characteristics like base metal alloying capability	pure metal surface impervious controlled thickness	Cu, Ni, stainless steels, noble metals
Electroplating Electrodeposition of coating metal at cathode from solution or fused salt bath.	workable deposition potential adhesion to base metal	pure, uniform, impervious no alloying unstressed controlled thickness, hardness	Ag, Au, Cd, Co, Cr, Ni, Pb, Sn, Zn, Cu, alloys
Metal Spraying Atomization of molten metal in hot gas stream. Wire or powder may be melted in gun by flame or arc.	nonrefractory not easily oxidized	porous laminated structure harder, less dense than cast metal no alloying with surface applicable to structures	Al, Cu, Fe, Pb, Sn, Zn, alloys
Vapor Plating Surface condensation of metal vapors by pyrolysis of metal compounds, cathode sputtering, vacuum evaporation.	vaporizability	costly crystalline, fine grain very thin readily applied to nonmetals	Mo, W, Cr, Al, Au, Ag, Ni

3. ORGANIC COATINGS

Organic coatings are the most widely used means of protecting against corrosion. These coatings represent a large variety of materials that can be classified as paint, enamel, lacquer, and plastic linings. In recent years, plastic linings have found frequent usage in protecting tubing, flow lines, and tanks from corrosion. The surface preparation and application of these coatings is very important in the success of the coating.

Prevention of Corrosion by Use of Plastics

Since World War II, the use and number of plastics available has greatly increased. Fiberglass-reinforced plastics that can withstand pressures as high as 1,200 psi are available in the form of pipe. Some practical indices for various plastics versus corrosion are shown in Table 4.7.

Generally, plastics are used in applications where temperatures and pressures are low. Plastic pipe is frequently used for flow lines with particularly corrosive oilfield brines. Many of the plastics shown in Table 4.7 are also used as coating materials.

Prevention of Corrosion with Metals

Metals resistant to corrosion are available for virtually all corrosive environments encountered in the oil field. The limitation on the use of many of these metals, such as platinum and gold, is their cost. There are many other metals and alloys, whose cost is only slightly more than steel, that are resistant to corrosion in specific applications.

The choice of a metal to resist corrosion in a specific application is governed by the nature of the corrosive environment, use of the equipment, and cost. In the oil field, the greatest use of corrosion resistant metals is for pumps and meters. Here, the amount of metal required is not large and the ability to resist corrosion necessary. Whenever a metal other than steel is used and is joined to steel lines, it is important to take precautions to avoid galvanic corrosion.

Table 4.1 shows the galvanic series for metals in sea water. This can be used as a guide for selecting metals for use in other saline waters. Metals at the bottom of the series are more resistant to salt water corrosion than those

Table 4.7

Practical Indices for Plastics Versus Corrosion*

(From Seymour, *Modern Plastics Encyclopedia*, 1962 (Bristol Conn.: Plastics Catalog Corp., 1962), p. 45. Reprinted with permission.)

	Relative Cost†	Relative Resistance to Physical Damage	Relative Resistance to Temperature	Relative Usefulness as Coating	Relative Usefulness as Pipe, Ductwork, Vessels	Relative Resistance to				
						Organic Solvents	Salts	Alkalies	Acids	Oxidation
Acetal resin	4	7	7	3	7	9	10	3	3	2
Acrylic resin	6	6	3	6	3	3	10	5	9	4
Acrylonitrile-butadiene-styrene (ABS)	6	6	3	8	6	4	10	8	9	4
Alkyds	7	4	6	10	4	7	10	3	8	5
Allyls (molded)	3	8	8	1	6	8	10	8	10	6
Amine-epoxy resin	5	5	7	10	6	6	10	7	9	2
Asphalt	10	2	1	10	3	1	10	7	10	1
Butyl rubber	7	9	2	6	5	2	10	10	10	7
Cellulose acetate	6	7	3	7	3	3	7	2	2	1
Cellulose acetate butyrate	5	7	3	7	3	3	7	2	2	1
Chlorinated polyether	1	4	8	5	8	9	10	10	10	9
Chlorinated rubber	6	4	3	10	3	2	10	10	10	5
Chlorosulfonated polyethylene	6	9	4	10	6	3	10	10	10	7
Coal tar pitch	10	2	1	10	3	1	10	10	10	1
Cumene resin	10	3	1	10	3	1	10	10	10	2
Diallyl phthalate (reinforced)	4	8	8	3	9	7	10	4	9	4
Epoxy resin (reinforced)	4	8	8	1	10	6	10	7	9	2
Ethyl cellulose	6	9	3	7	3	3	8	9	3	2
Furan resin	7	2	8	3	6	10	10	10	10	2
Hexafluoroethylene copolymer	2	9	8	6	6	10	10	10	10	10
Melamine (resin)	6	2	8	6	3	8	10	8	7	4
Melamine (molded)	5	6	8	1	4	8	10	8	7	4
Methyl cellulose	6	5	3	2	1	10	2	1	1	2
Neoprene	6	9	5	10	6	3	9	10	9	2
Nylon-6/6	4	7	6	3	7	7	10	7	3	2

Material										Cost†
Phenolic (molded)	7	7	9	1	6	9	10	3	10	4
Phenolic (resin)	8	2	8	8	3	9	10	3	10	3
Phenolic (reinforced)	6	8	10	1	9	9	10	3	10	4
Polycarbonate	3	10	8	5	6	6	10	1	7	6
Polyester (chemical-resistant)	7	3	5	8	1	6	10	4	7	6
Polyester (reinforced)	5	8	6	3	10	6	10	4	7	6
Polyethylene	7	8	1	6	7	5	10	10	10	8
Polyfluorocarbons	1	7	9	5	6	10	10	10	10	10
Polymethyl methacrylate	6	6	3	7	3	4	10	7	9	4
Polyolefin sulfide	5	10	4	7	3	1	10	3	5	3
Polypropylene	6	9	3	6	8	5	10	10	10	8
Polystyrene	8	4	8	3	3	2	10	10	10	4
Polytrifluorochloroethylene	2	8	8	6	6	10	10	10	10	10
Polyurethane	4	8	6	7	7	8	10	6	6	4
Polyvinyl alcohol	6	4	3	2	1	10	2	1	1	1
Polyvinyl butyral	5	7	3	7	3	3	8	6	6	2
Polyvinyl chloride (plasticized)	7	9	3	8	5	4	10	9	10	6
Polyvinyl chloride (rigid)										
Type I	5	4	3	3	9	6	10	10	10	9
Type II	5	6	4	3	8	6	10	10	10	6
Polyvinyl dichloride	4	5	7	4	8	6	10	10	10	9
Polyvinylidene chloride	7	4	4	8	7	5	10	7	10	7
Silicones	3	6	9	7	3	3	5	4	3	1
Styrene maleic anhydride	6	4	4	6	1	6	8	1	2	2
Transpolyisoprene	5	8	4	4	5	7	10	10	10	8
Urea (molded)	6	4	7	1	4	8	10	8	7	4
Urea (resin)	8	2	7	6	3	8	10	8	7	4
Vinyl chloride-acetate copolymer	7	6	3	10	6	3	10	9	10	5

*Rated empirically from 1 to 10. Higher ratings indicate greater utility.
†Cost rated from 1 (highest) to 10 (lowest).

near the top. Monel, a copper-nickel alloy, is very resistant to salt water corrosion and finds considerable use for pump impellers. Titanium is very impervious to salt water attack. Its use is increasing as its price drops. Brasses have been used for years in salt water applications.

References

[1]H. H. Uhlig, ed., *Corrosion Handbook* (New York: John Wiley & Sons, Inc., 1948).

[2]H. H. Uhlig, *Corrosion and Corrosion Control* (New York: John Wiley & Sons, Inc., 1962).

[3]U. R. Evans, *The Corrosion and Oxidation of Metals* (New York: St. Martin's Press, Inc., 1960).

[4]H. O. Forest, B. E. Roetheli, R. H. Brown, and G. L. Cox, "Initial Corrosion Rate of Steels," *Ind. Eng. Chem.*, **22** (1930), 1197.

[5]G. L. Cox and B. E. Roetheli, "Effect of Oxygen Concentration on Corrosion Rates of Steel and Composition of Corrosion Products Formed in Oxygenated Water," *Ind. Eng. Chem.*, **23** (1931), 1012.

[6]U. R. Evans and T. P. Hoar, "Velocity of Corrosion," *Proc. Roy. Soc. (London)*, *Ser. A*, **137**A (1932), 343.

[7]Uhlig, *Corrosion Handbook*, p. 127.

[8]G. T. Skaperdas and H. H. Uhlig, "Corrosion of Steel by Dissolved Carbon Dioxide and Oxygen," *Ind. Eng. Chem.*, **34** (1942), 748.

[9]F. N. Speller, *Corrosion Causes and Prevention* (3rd Ed.) (New York: McGraw-Hill Book Company, 1951), p. 188.

[10]F. H. Rhodes and J. M. Clark, "Corrosion of Metals by Water and Carbon Dioxide Under Pressure," *Ind. Eng. Chem.*, **28** (1936), 1078.

[11]J. W. Watkins and G. W. Kincheloe, "Corrosion of Steel in Water by Varied Ratios of Dissolved Gases," *Corrosion*, **14** (1958), 341t.

[12]J. W. Watkins and J. Wright, *Petrol. Engr.*, **25**, No. 12 (1953), B-50.

[13]T. Skei and W. A. Boone, U.S. Patent 2,780,583 (Feb. 5, 1957).

[14]F. H. Myer, O. L. Riggs, R. L. McGlasson, and J. D. Sudbury, "Corrosion Products of Mild Steel in H_2S Environments," *Corrosion*, **14** (1958), 109t.

[15]G. B. Hatch and O. Rice, "Influence of Water Composition on the Corrosion of Steel," *J. Am. Water Works Assoc.*, **51** (1959), 719.

[16]S. C. Britton and U. R. Evans, "Passivity of Metals," *J. Chem. Soc.* (**1930**), 1773.

[17]C. W. Borgman, "Initial Corrosion Rate of Mild Steel, Influence of the Cation," *Ind. Eng. Chem.*, **29** (1937), 815.

[18]G. V. Akimov, "Factors Influencing Corrosion," *Corrosion*, **15** (1959), 455t.

[19]Uhlig, *Corrosion Handbook*, p. 129.

[20]Speller, *Corrosion Causes and Prevention*, p. 42.

[21]R. B. Mears and R. H. Brown, "Determining Effectiveness of Cathodic Protection," *Ind. Eng. Chem.*, **33** (1941), 1007.

[22]R. M. Guest, "Potentials of Zinc and Steel in Tap Water," *Can. J. Technol.*, **34** (1956), 245.

[23]U. R. Evans, *The Corrosion of Metals* (New York: Longmans, Green & Co., Inc., 1926), p. 103.

[24]F. N. Speller and V. V. Kendall, "A New Method of Measuring Corrosion in Water," *Ind. Eng. Chem.*, **15** (1923), 134.

[25]Uhlig, *Corrosion and Corrosion Control*, p. 224.

[26]W. B. Hughes and V. L. Stromberg, "Effect of Inhibitors on Protective Properties of Iron Sulfide Scale," *Corrosion*, **19** (1963), 9t.

[27]O. L. Riggs, Jr. and F. J. Radd, "Physical and Chemical Study of an Organic Inhibitor for Hydrogen Sulfide Attack," *Corrosion*, **19** (1963), 1t.

[28]P. J. Raifsnider and A. Wachter, "Pitting Corrosion by Water Flood Brines," *Corrosion*, **17** (1961), 325t.

[29]L. L. Shreir, ed., *Corrosion*, (New York: John Wiley & Sons, Inc., 1963), I, 2.35.

[30]F. O. Waters, "Cathodic Protection of Water Treatment Plants," *Corrosion*, **16** (1960), 487t.

Water Pollution and Subsurface Brine Disposal

5

Laws Regulating Water Pollution

The production of industrial waste water began with the Industrial Revolution. As industry grew, the amount of waste water produced grew proportionately. Initially, waste waters were disposed of by flowing them into streams, lakes, and oceans. As the waste volumes increased, detrimental effects were noticed, such as killing of fish and plants, and presence of undesirable odors and colors. The Izaak Walton League was one of the first organizations to protest the dumping of wastes into natural waterways. Today, most states have laws regulating the disposal of wastes. These laws can be divided into two general groups: (1) laws which provide for the formation of a state agency for the express purpose of formulating and enforcing regulations pertaining to the disposal of wastes, and (2) laws defining pollution and establishing penalties for dumping wastes. In 1948, Congress passed the Water Pollution Control Act, otherwise known as Public Law 845, which authorized the federal government to study the pollution problem in conjunction with state and local agencies.

In 1956, the Federal Water Pollution Control Act (Public Law 660, 84th Congress) was passed. This law retained the basic enforcement authority of the original act and contained provisions for federal grants of $50 million annually for subsidizing municipal sewage treatment works. On July 20, 1961, President Kennedy signed amendments to this law. These amendments provided for (1) the federal government's own water pollution control measures, (2) field demonstration and research facilities, (3) grants to municipalities, (4) enforcement measures against pollution of navigable waters.

One significant feature of this legislation by the federal government is that water pollution has become a recognized problem and that steps must be taken to eliminate it. This means that field engineers and plant operators will have to be more aware of water pollution in the future and that there will be stricter enforcement of regulations pertaining to pollution. Establishment of research centers to study pollution will ultimately benefit industries having to dispose of potential water pollutants by more clearly establishing water pollution criteria and discovering ways of overcoming pollution.

However, the federal level is generally too broad to control pollution effectively in a given area, while the state level is too limited where the watershed falls between state boundaries. Consequently, the 1948 act provided for the approval of regional or interstate compacts on pollution control. The laws which control pollution and waste disposal are based largely upon the efforts of regional, state, or local agencies, and are not uniform throughout the United States or other countries. Therefore, if a waste disposal problem is anticipated, it would be wise to obtain legal advice concerning pollution and waste disposal laws in that particular area before a waste disposal system is designed.

The pollution regulations in the various states and the activeness of the agencies vary. In recent years, states have become more concerned with water pollution and are enacting legislation against it. Some states passed effective water pollution laws at an early date and are satisfied with their current laws.

Since the late 1930s, Kansas has opposed the use of unlined surface pits as a primary method of brine disposal. This state also carefully polices underground disposal of brines. Kansas produces five million bbl/day of oil-field brines, of which 99 per cent are injected underground through 2,500 disposal systems and 1,800 pressure-maintenance projects. Of 1,889 surface ponds, 869 are sealed-storage or treating ponds used in subsurface injection projects. The remainder are earthen pits placed in impermeable soils. Until 1950, the Walnut river contained 3,000 ppm chloride that resulted from dumping oilfield brines in this river. Pollution abatement practices in Kansas have reduced this to 340 ppm.[1]

California is another state that for many years has been actively engaged in trying to prevent water pollution. The San Joaquin valley is responsible for 60 per cent of California's brine production. In 1962, the valley produced 22 billion gallons of brine, of which 99.5 per cent was discharged in an approved manner.

The East Texas oil field presented a very serious pollution problem in the late 1930s and early 1940s. In 1939, a suit was brought against many operators in the southern part of the field to prevent salt water pollution of the Neches-Angelina watershed. As a result of this suit, the East Texas Salt Water Disposal Company was formed for the purpose of collecting produced brine from operators in the field and disposing of it by injection underground.[2] This has been an effective solution to a serious pollution problem.

Water Pollution Criteria

The criteria of water quality for determining water pollution is somewhat arbitrary. It depends to a certain extent upon the nature of the pollutant and the proposed use of the water. The two variables which primarily influence the concentration of pollutants in water are: (1) the amount of pollutant, and (2) the volume of water available to dilute the pollutant.

Two basic types of criteria have been used for control of water pollution.[3] One type is designated as "stream standards" and pertains to the quality of the receiving body of water. The other type is designated as "effluent standards" and refers to the quality of wastes discharged into the stream. There are proponents as well as advantages and disadvantages of each type. Both types of criteria are used.

Stream standards can be subdivided into dilution requirements and standards of receiving-water quality. Dilution requirements were mostly used in the late 1800s but find little use today. Standards of quality of the receiving water are based on threshold and limiting concentrations of substances in water. These depend on the proposed use of the water and are advocated by those who would zone and classify streams according to specified standards.

Standards of stream quality have the advantage over effluent standards in that they consider dilution and the assimilative capacity of the receiving water. This may result in economy of treatment for pollution abatement. The disadvantage is that stream standards are difficult to formulate and administer.

Effluent standards can be categorized as those that restrict the strength and or amount of substance that can be discharged, and those that specify the amount of treatment or percentage removal of pollutant that must be removed. A regulation limiting the Biochemical Oxygen Demand (*BOD*) of effluents discharged into streams to less than 50 ppm is an example of restriction on strength of wastes. A *BOD* reduction of 85 per cent on wastes entering a stream illustrates effluent standards that specify the percentage removal of pollutant. Effluent standards are simple and well defined, making them easy to administer.

Table 1.5 showed the limiting concentrations of some substances in drinking water. Discharging waste water into a stream that resulted in increasing the concentration of these substances over the mandatory limit would constitute pollution.

Sources of Water Pollutants in Petroleum Processing and Production

Refineries and gasoline plants are sources of waste water that must be disposed of without causing pollution of surface or ground waters. Objectionable substances in these waste waters are oil, salts, and chemicals encountered in processing hydrocarbons. Cooling tower blowdown water, containing toxic corrosion inhibitors, is also a source of water pollutants.

There are two major sources of pollutants in oil production operations. These are oil lost from spills and leaks, and produced brines. There is no suitable treatment for removing salts from the great volume of brine produced daily in oil production. Minor sources of pollutants are spent acidizing waters containing toxic corrosion inhibitors or concentrated salt solutions used as packer or completion fluids.

Disposal of Refinery and Plant Waste Water

Petroleum refineries use large amounts of water in processing crude oil. An approximate figure arrived at from measurements at several refineries is 1,000 gallons of water for each barrel of crude oil processed. The refinery processes are crude distillation, thermal cracking, fluid catalytic cracking, polymerization, alkylation, grease making, light oil treating (consisting of caustic washing, doctor treating, and copper chloride treating), and lubricating oil and wax treating (consisting of propane desalting, phenol extraction, *MEK* dewaxing, clay contacting, and acid treating).

Refinery wastes can be classified into two categories—waste process water from the above refining processes and spent cooling water. Cooling water is used to cool surface condensers and heat exchangers. Normally, the spent cooling water does not contain chemicals, unless corrosion and scale inhibitors are used. Cooling water normally does not contact any oil, but leaks may develop in the system which admit oil to the cooling water. The waste process water contacts both chemicals and oil and may be highly contaminated. Cooling water represents a much larger volume of water than process water. One refinery, processing approximately 90,000 bbl/day of crude oil, uses 97,000 gal/min of cooling water and 4,250 gal/min of process water.[4]

Generally speaking, any oil present in waste water must be removed before the waste water can be discharged into surface waters. From a practical standpoint, it is debatable if minute amounts of oil in surface waters are detrimental to aquatic life or to the future use of the water. This depends to a large extent upon the location of the surface water, its surroundings, interests of future users of the surface water, the use of this water, and the quantity, characteristics, and form of the oil. In some sections of the country, surface waters are used for stock raising and irrigation. Large amounts of oil would, of course, prevent the use of the surface water for these purposes. Generally, water used for human consumption is treated before use, and small amounts of oil would be removed. However, the presence of oil would probably add to the cost of the treatment.

In addition, a major problem in the purification of water for human consumption is the control of tastes and odors. The odor-producing materials are largely organic and may come from several sources, one of which is refinery wastes. An average value of the concentration of organic materials in oil-separator effluents has been given at 50 ppm, and the average threshold odor concentration at 50 ppb.[5] This means that in order to discharge one million gallons of waste water containing 417 pounds of odor-producing organic compounds, one billion gallons of surface water would be necessary to dilute this waste water below the threshold odor level. This assumes that the surface water was initially free of such materials.

Surface waters contain dissolved oxygen that is utilized by fish, plants, and oxidation processes in the self-purification of waters. As the supply of oxygen is used up, it is replenished by oxygen from the air. The presence of oil films interferes with aeration of the water, and can result in the death of fish and termination of the self-purification process. From an aesthetic viewpoint, oil films may mar the appearance of painted boat hulls and prove disagreeable to bathers. Oil-polluted water at shore resorts and beaches can have a strong and undesirable effect on the public attitude toward the petroleum industry.

The colors produced by approximate thicknesses of oil films and the amounts of oil necessary to produce the films are given in Table 5.1. Experimental laboratory work has shown that films up to 0.000003 inches in thickness average 5 hours of life on an agitated water surface.[6] Large-scale tests conducted at sea indicate that an oil film 0.00004 inches thick will disappear from the surface of the sea in less than 24 hours.

Table 5.1

QUANTITY OF OIL REQUIRED TO PRODUCE SURFACE FILMS

(From *Manual on Disposal of Refinery Wastes* (6th ed.) (New York: American Petroleum Institute, 1959), p. 10.)

Approximate Quantity of Oil Required for Film 1 Square Mile in Area (gallons)	Appearance	Approximate Thickness of Film (inches)
25	barely visible	0.0000015
50	silvery sheen on surface	0.0000030
100	first trace of color observed	0.0000060
200	bright bands of color visible	0.0000120
666	colors begin to turn dull	0.0000400
1,332	colors much darker	0.0000800

Chemicals present in refinery waste process waters may also have undesirable effects on the surface waters. The magnitude of this effect depends upon the composition of the waste water and the surface water. If the components of the waste water corresponded to those of the surface water, the discharge of the waste would have no effect on the natural water. However, if the waste water components differed greatly from those of the natural water, the quality of this water might be impaired. The refinery processes influence the following characteristics of the process water: acidity and alkalinity, taste and odor, oxygen demand, toxicity, composition, color, and turbidity.

The effect of the addition of the acid waste water on the pH of natural water is dependent upon the buffer capacity of the natural water and the relative quantities involved. If the natural water is hard, the acid will react with the carbonates, and the water will resist a pH change. Soft waters will not have this buffering capacity, and addition of acid will depress the pH to a greater extent. The effects of pH may be divided into chemical and biological effects. Increasing the acidity of a natural water increases its corrosivity and, generally, increases the cost of treating the water for plant use. Acidity also hinders stream self-purification, because it drives away or destroys the plant and animal forms which are responsible for purification. Fish are sensitive to pH changes and may be killed by the effects of acidity.

Increases in the alkalinity of natural waters due to the addition of alkaline wastes may have adverse effects on aquatic life. Fish are reported to live in the pH range 4.8 to 9.0. Even though alkaline waters are less corrosive than acidic waters, high alkalinities will increase the treating costs for most industrial uses.

The dumping of waste waters which contain readily oxidizable materials into surface waters places an immediate damand upon the dissolved oxygen of the water. This Biochemical Oxygen Demand, or *BOD*, is a measure of the reducing properties of waste and is stated in terms of quality of oxygen required for oxidation and destruction of substances. This demand may deplete the oxygen content at a more rapid rate than it is replenished from the air, resulting in anaerobic conditions. This results in the extermination of all forms of life except anaerobic bacteria. Waters of this nature generally have disagreeable odors. The hardness of waste water generally is of little significance except that it decreases the value of the natural water for other industrial users. It is undesirable to dump waste water containing high concentrations of dissolved salts into fresh waters of low salt concentration. This not only injures or kills the fish, but it increases the treatment difficulties for other users.

The discharge of waste water containing toxic compounds into natural water should be avoided. Some substances are harmless at low concentrations, but become *lethal* at a higher concentration. Other substances may accumulate in the tissues until a lethal amount is reached. Untreated refinery wastes may contain sulfur compounds, phenolic compounds, ammonium compounds, and chloramines, which may be toxic to fish.

Color and suspended matter are also objectionable properties of waste water discharged into surface waters. These qualities may interfere with the penetration of light into the water. The sunlight that penetrates the water is absorbed by algae, and they, in turn, become food for larger animals. Turbidity reduces the amount of light penetration, and thus decreases photosynthesis of organisms living in the water. Some of the suspended matter may eventually settle out, resulting in sludge-covered bottoms and beaches.

In view of these effects that waste water can produce when discharged into surface waters, refinery wastes are generally treated. Since cooling waters are less contaminated than process waters, cooling waters may be treated separately and less expensively. It is cheaper to treat a small quantity of highly polluted water than to apply the same treatment to a large quantity of less polluted water. Heavily polluted wastes can be treated separately and, when the pollution is reduced, added to the general waste water. The volume of waste water can be greatly reduced by the use of cooling towers for recycling cooling water. This adds cooling-tower blowdowns to the waste-disposal problem, but these may be as little as 0.75 per cent of the cooling-tower circulation.[7] Sanitary sewage can be kept separate from other refinery wastes and dumped directly into city sewers or processed separately. Generally, the refinery drainage system will be designed so that uncontaminated storm water is not added to and treated with process or cooling-tower wastes. The treatment of uncontaminated storm water would add to the capacity and cost of the water-treatment plant.

1. OIL SEPARATORS

Oil in refinery waste water is recovered by oil separators. The separator most widely accepted in the industry was designed by the API, and is a gravity-type, oil-water separator. The information necessary for the design of this separator is available in an API publication.[8] This separator depends upon the difference in specific gravity of oil and water for separation. Important factors for effective performance of the separator are design, velocity of flow through the separator, and settling time.

In order to provide continuous operation of refinery separators when separator repair, cleaning, or inspection is necessary, the main separator should be constructed with two or more parallel channels. If certain process waters contain unusually large amounts of oil, auxiliary separators can be used to remove most of the oil before the waste is admitted to the main separator. However, if the waste water contains emulsified oil, not all of this oil will be separated in a gravity separator. If the oil is to be retained in the separator, the emulsion must be broken before the waste reaches the separator.

2. WASTE-WATER EMULSIONS

There are many operations in the refining process which produce emulsions of various properties and locations within the plant. After these emulsions are located, identified, and classified as to type, the method of treatment can be chosen. If treatment in addition to gravity separation is necessary, two approaches to the problem can be considered. The preferable method consists of collecting all the wastes containing emulsions and treating this combined stream before it is added to other waste water. In many cases, this is not practical, and these wastes must be added to the other waste waters and the total volume treated. Again, this is an economic consideration, based upon the cost of an additional sewer or costs of treating larger volumes of water, and is best settled on an individual basis for each plant.

The emulsions may be oil-in-water emulsions, in which extremely small globules of oil are dispersed in water as the continuous phase, or water-in-oil emulsions, in which the reverse is the case. Generally, oil-in-water emulsions are milky in appearance and will pass through gravity separators without breaking. Emulsions lighter than water rise to the surface and are separated with other oils, while emulsions heavier than water are deposited with separator or tank bottoms.

In addition to the oil and water, a third substance, an emulsifier, is present when stable emulsions are formed. Some common emulsifiers for oil-in-water systems are sodium and potassium soaps, and precipitated sulfides plus surface active solids. Some common emulsifiers for water-in-oil systems are multivalent metal soaps, and multivalent metal oxides and sulfides plus sulfide ion.

Since emulsions are formed by the agitation of two immiscible liquids, emulsion formation can be minimized by the selection of proper mechanical methods. The use of oversized pipe in drainage systems will reduce turbulent flow and minimize emulsion formation. Reciprocating pumps give less turbulence than do centrifugal pumps. Steam syphons have a tendency to cause the formation of stable emulsions in water and oil systems. Barometric condensers are also a possible source of emulsions.

Emulsions can be broken by several different methods. Heat is helpful in nearly all emulsion-breaking operations. Heating water-in-oil emulsions lowers the viscosity of the oil and promotes settling of free water. Heating also increases the vapor pressure of the water and tends to break the films around the globule. Separation of the oil and water phases may be facilitated by using caustic to adjust the pH between 9 and 9.5. Distillation is an effective method of breaking emulsions and offers the advantage of separating the water and light oil from the emulsifying agent which remains in the residue.

If there is a large difference between the specific gravity of the oil and water, centrifuging will break relatively stable mixtures. Water-in-oil emulsions stabilized by finely divided solids can be treated effectively by diatomaceous-earth filtration. The emulsion is forced through a layer of diatomaceous earth deposited on a continuously rotating drum. Any suspended solid matter in the emulsion is retained on the filter media, and globules of the dispersed phase are broken on passing through the media, thus breaking the emulsion. The oil and water phases will separate on standing, but if an emulsifier is present, care must be exercised to prevent excessive agitation and the consequent reformation of the emulsion. Some emulsions can be broken by passing them between two electrodes which pass a high-potential, pulsating, unidirectional current through the emulsion. The electrically attracted water globules coalesce, until the mass is sufficiently large to settle by gravity. Crude oil may be desalted and dehydrated using this method.

Emulsions can be broken by chemical methods which vary according to the properties of the emulsions. Perhaps the most widely used chemical method is that of coagulation or flocculation. A coagulating agent such as alum, ferric chloride, or lime is added in doses from $\frac{1}{8}$ to $\frac{1}{2}$ pound per 1,000 gallons, and mixed with the waste by slow stirring. The colloidal oil adheres to the flocculated precipitate and settles to the bottom. However, such a process should be studied in the laboratory before applying it to a particular emulsion. The addition of chemicals for adjusting pH, reacting with sodium soaps, or changing interfacial characteristics of the emulsions can be made directly to the emulsion stream as it is being pumped into the treating tank. The amount of emulsified material to be treated governs the choice of a continuous or batch-treating process.

3. Suspended Oil or Particle Removal by Air Flotation

Oil and other suspended matter can be removed from water by air or gas flotation. The water is saturated with air under pressure and passed into a flotation chamber at atmospheric pressure. Under reduced pressure, the air is released from solution in the form of small bubbles which carry the free oil globules to the surface, where they are removed by mechanical flight scrapers. Air is generally used in treating refinery wastes for disposal. Either air or methane is used to treat produced water for injection in secondary recovery projects. Use of air has the disadvantage of saturating the water with oxygen and thus increasing corrosivity of the water.

In the oil field, gas may be available under pressure, eliminating the need for some mechanical method of compression. If natural gas is used, the flotation tank should be covered and equipped with safety devices to prevent explosions. An explosion-proof electric motor should be used for the scraper or skimmer. The elimination of a compressor helps to defray the added expense of safety devices.

a. Physical Principles of Flotation Process

Minute air (or gas) bubbles are released at reduced pressure and adsorb to the suspended oil globule or particle. This reduces the effective specific gravity of the particle and causes it to move upward. The upward velocity is proportional to the density difference between the particle and water. The primary factor influencing the adsorption of air to the particle is the surface characteristic of the particle. The adsorption characteristics of the particle may be beneficially altered by the addition of surface active agents. Increasing the size of the suspended particle increases the rate of separation. Chemical flocculants can be used to increase the particle size.

b. Flotation System

The flotation system consists of a pressurized aeration chamber, air release chamber, and flight scraper. If flocculation is used, a chemical feeder and flocculation basin are required. In one method of operation, all the water is pressure-aerated. In the second or recycle method, part of the clarified water is pressure-aerated and fed into the flotation tank. This method requires less pump capacity and eliminates the danger of forming a water-oil emulsion from pumping the water-oil mixture. The particles rise to the surface in the flotation tank, where they are removed by the scraper.

In the recycle process, 20 to 33 per cent of the clarified waste or oil-containing injection water is pressure-aerated and returned to the flotation tank. This water is pressurized to from 30 to 50 psig of air or gas. A centrifugal pump can be used for pressuring with air. No pump is needed if natural gas pressure is used. At a pressure of 40 psig, one to 1.3 SCF of air is used per 100 gal of recycle water.[9] The saturation value of methane dissolved in water at 40 psig is approximately 70 per cent higher. This air-pressurized water flows to a tank equipped to increase the air-water surface area, therefore increasing the rate of air dissolution in the water. The residence time in this tank should be one to two minutes.

This water is then released with turbulence in the flotation chamber. The agglomerates formed by this process rise to the surface at rates of 0.5 to 1.0 ft/min. The over-all holding time in the flotation chamber generally ranges from 10 to 20 minutes.

If air is used in this process, ferrous iron in the water will be oxidized to ferric iron and eventually precipitate as ferric hydroxide. In order to remove all of the iron in the flotation chamber, it is advisable to aerate the water before it reaches the flotation chamber. This will give the ferric hydroxide time to form. It will then be removed in the flotation chamber. Water that has passed through the flotation chamber will be saturated with oxygen and, therefore, corrosive.

Natural gas will not oxidize dissolved ferrous iron or saturate the water with air. It will sweep dissolved oxygen out of the water rendering the water less corrosive. Both air and natural gas will remove dissolved carbon dioxide from the water. This will cause the precipitation of calcium carbonate from waters saturated with calcium bicarbonate. This possibility should be considered in designing the system.

It is advisable to conduct preliminary bench-scale tests using the actual field water before installing an air flotation system. These tests should be performed in the field, since the properties of the oil-water suspension may change if shipped to a laboratory. Bench-scale tests will indicate if air or gas flotation is applicable to a particular oil-water suspension.

4. SPENT CAUSTIC SOLUTIONS

Spent caustic solutions may contain sulfides, mercaptides, sulfates, chlorides, phenolates, naphthenates, and other compounds which would contaminate natural waters. When available, direct methods for disposing of spent caustics are used; otherwise, chemical processing is necessary prior to final disposal. Since there are several types of spent caustic solutions, different methods of treatment may be required.[10] The amount or volume of spent caustic solutions influences the disposal procedure. A laboratory study should be made of the spent caustic problem before a decision is reached on the method of treatment.

a. Ponding

Small quantities of waste caustic may sometimes be directly disposed of by ponding. In order to prevent pollution of surface waters by overflow, the pond should be of sufficient size to contain the anticipated volume of spent caustic in addition to the normal rainfall, plus a liberal safety factor. Consideration should be given to locating the pond over geological formations which would not allow seepage to contaminate potable water supplies.

b. Dilution

Spent caustic solutions are often disposed of by flowing directly into large bodies of water or large rivers, where nearly infinite dilution is possible. This is most practical when the receiving waters are brackish streams, lakes, or the ocean.

c. Sale

Spent caustics containing sulfides, phenolates, cresolates, and carbonates are sometimes marketable to sources outside the petroleum industry. Due to transportation cost considerations, these sales are usually limited to concerns in the immediate area.

d. Neutralization by Acid Solutions

Neutralization of highly alkaline spent caustic solutions may be necessary before disposal. Waste acid materials from other refinery processes may be available for this purpose. The salt solution from this neutralization treatment can be discharged into the refinery effluent, or, if necessary, stripped to remove obnoxious odors or oily materials. Waste caustic solutions containing sulfides or cyanides can form hydrogen sulfide and hydrogen cyanide gases on acidization. These highly toxic gases should not be permitted to enter the atmosphere or contact plant personnel. These and any other odorous gases should be incinerated.

If waste sulfuric acid or acid sludges are used for this process, the acid and sludges are generally diluted with water, and the dilute acid transferred to the neutralization equipment. Since the amount of acidity or alkalinity is doubtful, the neutralization equipment is constructed of corrosion-resistant materials. Generally, enough acid is added to give a pH of about 5. After acid treatment, the mixture is discharged into a settling basin or tank where the acid-oils and sludge are separated from the aqueous solution. Heat formed by the neutralization process will keep the temperature in the neutralization chamber to a level that will assist separation of oil and sludge.

e. Neutralization by Acid Gases

Waste caustic solutions can be neutralized by passing acid gases, such as flue gas, through the solution. In water, gases form acids which react with the caustic. This treatment has the added advantage that any oxygen in the gas will tend to oxidize sulfides or mercaptides present in the caustic solution. Sulfides, which are not oxidized by this method, and cyanides will be swept out of the solution and escape as gases. The neutralized solution contains a mixture of bicarbonates, carbonates, sulfates, sulfites, and thiosulfates. Sulfur, resulting from the oxidation of sulfides by oxygen in the flue gas, may also be present.

Spent gases and fumes that pass through the caustic solution are disposed of through the flame burner of a furnace. Any solids formed in the spent caustic solution as a result of oxidation settle out and can be removed; the neutralized solution can be discharged into the refinery waste effluent.

5. Sulfuric Acid Sludges

Refining processes utilize sulfuric acid both as a catalyst and a treating agent. The resulting acid sludges constitute a disposal problem. The characteristics and quantity of the acid sludge influence the choice of disposal method. The use of waste sulfuric acid for the neutralization of waste caustic has been discussed previously. Several disposal methods are used.[11]

a. Dumping

Occasionally, it may be possible to dispose of sulfuric acid sludges by dumping or burying them in a pit. This renders the disposal area useless for any other purpose. This method offers the hazard that seepage may result in contamination of underground water sources, or that surface runoff from rains may contaminate streams or the surrounding soil. Sulfuric acid sludges have been dumped offshore in the oceans.

b. Burning

Sulfuric acid sludges sometimes contain enough combustible material to be disposed of by burning. Pumps and colloid mills are available for blending and homogenizing heavy sludges and fuel oil in order to obtain a mixture which can be handled by burners. The burning of sulfuric acid-sludges results in the formation of sulfur dioxide and some sulfur trioxide which will go out the stack. Sulfur trioxide reacts with moisture in the air to form sulfuric acid, resulting in a sulfuric acid mist that may settle and damage equipment and vegetation.

c. Hydrolysis Process

Sulfuric acid may be recovered from sulfuric acid sludges by heating the sludge with live steam in the presence of water. Sulfonic acids and similar acids are hydrolyzed, and the resulting mixture separates into two layers: a weak sulfuric acid layer containing a small amount of carbonaceous matter, and a tarry acid-oil layer. The amount of water added in the hydrolysis process is regulated so that the water layer has an acid concentration of 40 per cent or more. The recovered acid layer may be used to neutralize alkaline wastes, to dilute strong acid for use in some treating processes; or it may be concentrated by evaporating the water.

d. Complete Combustion or Spray Burning

The waste sulfuric acid sludge is sprayed into a hot combustion chamber. Air is admitted in excess of the amount necessary to oxidize the hydrocarbon. The sulfur present is converted to sulfur dioxide and small amounts of sulfur trioxide. After the hot gases are cooled and the sulfuric acid mist removed, the gases go to a drying tower and then to an absorber to produce new sulfuric acid. Acid sludges low in fuel value may be spray-burned in combination with hydrogen sulfide gas. A sulfuric acid-to-hydrocarbon weight ratio of 7.75 will support its own combustion, but higher ratios will require the use of supplementary fuel.[12]

e. Indirect Combustion

Sulfuric acid may be recovered using the indirect combustion method. The acid sludge is added to granular by-product coke in a decomposition chamber, and heated to form sulfur dioxide, water vapor, carbon dioxide, carbon monoxide, sulfur, and some hydrocarbons. Most hydrocarbons are converted to coke, that is withdrawn as a by-product and may be sold. The sulfur, carbon dioxide, and hydrocarbon gases are oxidized in the combustion chamber. The gases produced in the combustion chamber are cooled and dried. The sulfur dioxide is converted to sulfuric acid.

6. Water Containing Hydrogen Sulfide and Mercaptans

Various methods are available for removing hydrogen sulfide from waste water. Heat and air can be used to oxidize the sulfides. Chlorine or hypo-chlorite ion can be used to oxidize small amounts of sulfide in limited quantities of water. Hydrogen sulfide can be stripped from water, using steam or gas in a packed tower or fractionating column.

7. WASTE-WATER SOLUTIONS OF PHENOL

Waste-water solutions containing 1,000 to 10,000 ppm of phenol can be subjected to solvent extraction processes that will reduce the phenol con-centration to 100 to 500 ppm. By subsequent dilution to bring the phenol concentration in the range of 30 to 50 ppm, and passing the water over trickling filters, biological oxidation can be utilized to reduce the phenol concentration to 1 to 3 ppm.

8. INJECTION OF PLANT WASTE WATER

In some cases, it is not practical to dump or pond waste plant water. The Mobil Oil Company's joint-interest Seeligson Gasoline Plant has no streams available for dumping waste water, and evaporation in pits would leave salt deposits amounting to 3,500,000 pounds per year.[13] Consequently, an underground injection system was designed to dispose of 150 gal/min waste process water. The waste water from cooling tower and boiler blow-down, hydrogen ion exchanger regeneration, and water condensed from cooling compressed gas is treated before injection. Treatment consists of oil skimming, coagulation, sedimentation, and filtration. During the treatment, chlorine is added for sterilization purposes, and carbon dioxide is added before injection to keep calcium and magnesium carbonates in solution. The treated water passes through a concrete-lined flow line to the injection well, and is injected through plastic-lined pipe.

9. WASTE-WATER TREATMENT IN HOLDING PONDS

In some plants or refineries, a series of holding ponds is used to treat waste water before it is discharged into rivers or other bodies of water. A good example of this method of waste treatment is found at Apco Oil Corpo-ration's Arkansas City, Kansas, refinery. An average waste volume of 781,000 gal/day is treated at this refinery in a series of ponds having a 60-day holding time.[14] Characteristics of the raw waste are shown in Table 5.2.

The series of holding ponds is divided into two sections. The first section consists of three oil-settling ponds, connected by submerged pipe. Water

Table 5.2

RAW WASTE CHARACTERISTICS

(From Dorris et al. *Oil Gas J*., **59**, No. 44 (1961), 161, and used with permission.)

	Average*	Range*
Volume, M gal per day	781.0	—
Temperature, °F	90.0	82–98
pH	9.1	8.7–9.3
Alkalinity P, ppm	53.0	14–94
Total, ppm	255.0	174–296
Ammonia nitrogen as N, ppm	25.0	16.4–35.0
PO_4, ppm	1.0	—
Phenols, ppm	2.8	0.3–12.0
Sulfides, ppm	12.7	—
Dissolved oxygen, ppm	0.0	—
Immediate oxygen demand, ppm	9.3	—
Chemical oxygen demand, ppm	284.0	135–547
Biochemical oxygen demand, ppm	70.0	45–85
% COD of BOD	24.0	—
Oil, ppm	50.0	22–86
Total dissolved solids, ppm	2,232.0	2,008–1,817
Toxicity, median tolerance limit (TL_m^{48})	21.0	16.5–24

*After 1.9 days' holding time.

leaves the third pond by a narrow concrete flume and enters a small concrete basin. Water from this basin is sprayed into the first of a series of four oxidation ponds. From the fourth pond, water is discharged into a river. Pond sizes and calculated retention times are shown in Table 5.3.

There was little change in concentration of ammonia nitrogen, pH, chemical oxygen demand (*COD*), phenolphthalein-total alkalinity ratio,

Table 5.3

SIZES AND CALCULATED RETENTION TIMES OF HOLDING PONDS

(From Dorris et al. *Oil Gas J*., **59**, No. 44 (1961), 161, and used with permission.)

Description	Area, ft²	Avg. Depth, ft	Volume	Days' retention time Individual	Cumulative
Arkansas City, Kans.:					
Oil pond 2	10,860	14	1,462,300	1.86	1.86
Bay 3	116,600	5	4,273,600	5.73	31.39
Oxidation pond 1	22,400	5	594,000	0.76	17.14
Oxidation pond 2	10,000	5	594,000	0.76	17.90
Oxidation pond 3					
Bay 1	53,800	5	1,971,900	2.53	20.43
Bay 2	110,000	5	4,031,700	5.23	25.66
Bay 3	116,000	5	4,275,600	5.73	31.39
Bay 4	116,300	5	4,262,600	5.64	37.03
Oxidation pond 4					
Bay 1	119,400	5	4,376,249	10.87	47.90
Bay 2	91,300	5	3,346,300	8.6	56.54
Bay 3	39,150	5	1,434,900	3.8	60.36

toxicity, and oxygen production until after approximately 16 days holding time. Concentration of phenols and *BOD* changed rapidly the first 16 days in the ponds, then more slowly the remainder of time the water was in the ponds. Aeration of the waste water as it passed into the oxidation ponds at the end of 16 days' retention reduced the concentrations of several components. Changes in concentration of components in the waste water expressed as regression are shown in Table 5.4. Regression is the average amount of change expected per day for each component.

Table 5.4
CHANGES OF COMPONENTS OF WASTE WATER IN HOLDING PONDS
(From Dorris et al. *Oil Gas J.*, **59**, No. 44 (1961), 161, and used with permission.)

	Summer		Winter	
	Period of Analysis, Days	Regression	Period of Analysis, Days	Regression
pH	2–18	−0.03	16–26	−0.09
Phenolphthalein/total alkalinity ratio	2–18	−0.006	2–26	−0.0095
Ammonia as N, ppm	2–37	−0.57	—	—
Phenols, ppm	16–60	−0.058	18–60	−0.040
Sulfides, ppm	—	—	—	—
Toxicity, median tolerance limits	2–26	+2.05	2–26	+2.87
Chemical oxygen demand, ppm	2–60	−2.12	2–26	−8.91
Biochemical oxygen demand, ppm	2–26	−1.98	2–60	−1.263
Oxygen production, lb/acre/day	16–37	−2.59	16–60	+0.46

Alkalinity and pH reduction required about 25 days. In five weeks, 80 to 90 per cent ammonia nitrogen was removed, phenol reduced 90 per cent, and *COD* more than 50 per cent. *BOD* was reduced more than 50 per cent after 25 days' retention time. At the end of 40 days' retention time, concentrations of nearly all components were reduced to minimum values.

Disposal of Oilfield Brine

Brine produced with oil represents a tremendous volume of water requiring disposal. Because of the increasing demand for fresh water and the effect of brines on the suitability of fresh water for domestic uses, it is no longer possible to dispose of brines by indiscriminate dumping into rivers, streams, and lakes. An even more serious pollution problem is the pollution of subsurface fresh-water supplies by downward percolation or by direct injection of waste water. Subsurface pollution may require long periods of time to correct because of the slow migration of water in aquifers.

Oilfield brine disposal can be subdivided into surface or subsurface disposal methods. Surface disposal methods include percolation pits, evaporation pits, and controlled dumpage into rivers and streams. Subsurface disposal means injecting brines into underground formations. The choice of disposal methods is influenced by volume of brine, regulations regarding brine disposal, suitability of method, and economic factors.

Surface Disposal of Brines

Surface disposal of brines has been curtailed in recent years and will probably face extinction in the larger oil producing states. Percolation or seepage pits are outlawed in many states. In many areas, annual rainfall is greater than the maximum volume of water that could be evaporated. In future years, antipollution laws will probably require that any brine evaporation pit be lined to prevent seepage into the ground.

1. SHALLOW PITS

Earthen pits, often referred to as evaporation pits, surface pits, retention pits, brine storage pits, and impounding basins, have been used for many years. These pits are a potential pollution hazard, since brine may seep into underground fresh water aquifers or migrate into streams and rivers. Because of this pollution hazard, the Red River Authority of Texas has caused over 15,000 of these pits along the Red river and its tributaries to be leveled and covered.[15]

In some selected cases, pits have been used as seepage basins for the disposal of small quantities of brine. These pits were sometimes permitted where the underlying formation contained no water or only saline water. Even small amounts of brine added up to a considerable quanity over a period of time, so these pits were still a pollution hazard.

2. LINING SURFACE PITS

In many areas, surface pits must be lined to prevent seepage of brine into the soil. Disposal pits, storage basins, or treatment ponds require lining as a precaution against pollution of aquifers and surface streams. Pits used for storage may be lined in an effort to conserve water by eliminating seepage.

There are a variety of materials available for lining pits. Concrete and, more recently, Gunite have been used as lining materials for water reservoirs.

The expense and construction techniques involved in the use of concrete are well-known and will not be discussed further. Asphalt has also found considerable use as a lining material for water reservoirs and brine storage basins. Of more interest here is the use of plastic films as a material for lining water storage pits and treatment basins.

Plastic films made from vinyl, polyethylene, and polyvinyl plastics are used as liners for water storage reservoirs. Generally, these liners are made from plastic sheets, 0.008 inch or thinner, and must be protected from mechanical damage. As a protective measure, the liners are often buried. If the linings are not subject to mechanical damage and the reservoir is kept partially filled, exposed polyethylene will give adequate service. Vinyl films have a tendency to deteriorate when exposed to the weather and oil. If a layer of water is kept on the bottom of the reservoir, only plastic exposed on the sides need be covered for protection.

In constructing a reservoir to be lined with plastic, the slope of the sides should not exceed 3:1. The covering material may slide if the slope is steeper than this. The dirt surface should be free of any sharp stones, stumps, sticks, or clots of dirt. Generally, it is advisable to dress the graded surface with a fine textured cushion material to insure that no sharp objects will puncture the film. An added precaution is to spray the area to be covered with a weed killer to insure that growing weeds do not penetrate the film.

If the plastic liner is to be covered, it is recommended that a 6-inch layer of fine textured material, followed by a 6-inch layer of gravel, be spread over the pit liner. The fine textured material is designed as a cushion layer for the erosion-resistant gravel layer. The cost of a cover layer may exceed the cost of the plastic liner.

A large reservoir was lined with vinyl and the vinyl film covered at a total cost of $1.41 per square yard of surface.[16] The cost of the vinyl film installed was $0.56 per square yard, and the cost of the cover layer was $0.85 per square yard of surface. The vinyl for this reservoir came in four pieces, 61 by 380 feet, and was joined in the reservoir.

Whereas polyethylene is more resistant to weathering than vinyl, vinyl has the advantage that it is easier to join. Polyethylene is not readily joined together by existing cements, but best joined by heat-sealing the sheets together. This is difficult to do on large-scale installations.

Plastic film liners can also be used to repair old reservoirs. Any cracks or sharp edges in the existing reservoir should be filled or smoothed off to prevent rupturing the plastic Because of the low strength of these films, they should be laid so that the hydrostatic pressure will be supported by the surface beneath the film, rather than by the film itself.

The use of these films is not necessarily restricted to water storage. They could be used to line pits used to mix high density salt solutions for use as packer or completion fluids. Plastic liners have been used to line chemical storage pits. One company used a 36,500 square foot piece of polyvinyl plastic to line a reservoir holding 1.4 million gallons of dilute sulfuric acid and copper sulfate.

Plastic film liners may have application in storing fluids in places of difficult access, where the cost of transporting a tank would be extremely high. A large bag can be made from the plastic film and equipped with an inlet and an outlet. This bag can be placed in a pit and filled with water or oil. The bag does not have to fit the contours of the pit but should be large enough so that, when filled, it will not be subject to stresses. If made of opaque material, this bag will also prevent the growth of algae in the stored water.

The low cost of material and installation makes plastic films attractive for lining water reservoirs. As better adhesives are developed for polyethylene, its lower cost and better aging properties will make it more attractive than vinyl as a lining material. Vinyl is easier to join than polyethylene and has more impact resistance. Whereas concrete-lined reservoirs built on swelling or shifting soils may crack, plastic-lined reservoirs will not be affected by the action of these soils.

3. Streams and Rivers

In some areas, the controlled dilution and disposal of brines into streams and surface waters has been permitted during periods of high stream flow or surface runoff. Because of the increased importance of water supplies and antipollution regulations, this practice has largely been eliminated.

Waste Disposal by Injection in Underground Formations

For many years, the petroleum industry has disposed of oilfield brines by injection into underground formations. This type of waste-water disposal is also used by some industrial plants. A formation suitable for the injection of waste water obviously must be available. The formation selected should not allow the waste water to migrate to a fresh water stratum, thereby polluting the water in that stratum. Generally, if the selected formation contains salt water, it is reasonable to expect no future pollution of any fresh water stratum.

Underground formations vary widely in their ability to receive injection water. Cavernous limestones may take several thousand gallons per minute with only the pressure of the hydrostatic head, while dense sandstones may require 2000 psi to inject 100 gal/min. It is evident that the feasibility of disposing of waste water by underground injection depends on the availability of a suitable formation with sufficient capacity to handle the disposal requirements.

The primary purpose of treating injection water, both waste water and water used in secondary recovery, is to prevent plugging of the disposal wells. The wells can be plugged by entrained solids, oil and bottom settlings, sulfur, bacteria, and by precipitation of salts after treatment. While a few parts per million of plugging material do not appear to be a very great amount, the large volume of water injected in some wells can accumulate these few parts per million into a considerable mass of material which can plug a well. When the water is disposed of by injection into a sand formation, the sand face acts as a filter. If 10,000 barrels of water containing 5 ppm of a plugging material are injected daily, 17.4 pounds of solids will collect each day on the surface of the sand, resulting in over 500 pounds per month and probable plugging of the well. However, some injection formations, such as the Arbuckle granite wash in western Kansas, contain fractures and large pores and are therefore not as susceptible as smaller pore sandstones to plugging by suspended solids.

An injection system for waste-water disposal generally consists of a system for gathering the waste water, a collection center, water treatment facilities, and an injection well. Many chemical and bacterial problems face the operator of a water injection system. Plugging is an obvious problem and can be attributed to the suspended materials previously mentioned. Corrosion also requires serious consideration, since, in addition to destroying equipment, it produces corrosion products which may plug the injection well.

An important part of a water disposal system is the water treating plant. In order to achieve the desired results with a minimum of cost, the plant must be well designed by competent personnel. It is essential that thorough laboratory studies be conducted on the proposed injection water, as well as any water which may be present in the receiving formation, in order to determine the minimum amount of water treatment required. The laboratory investigation should provide the following information on the injection water: composition, pH, physical properties, scaling tendencies, compatibility with water in the injection formation, corrosivity, bacteriological properties, and treatment necessary to prepare the water for injection.

Evaluating Suitability of Subsurface Disposal Project

Several factors should be considered in planning and designing a disposal system. These factors influence the performance and operating characteristics of the system. Selection of a disposal formation is based on a study of geologic and hydrologic factors in the area.

1. GEOLOGY

The areal extent, thickness, lithological character, and continuity of the proposed disposal formation are important. Size of the formation is important, since it influences the volume of waste brine that can be injected.

Geology in the immediate area of the disposal project is important. Factors such as stratigraphic position, depth, thickness, lithology, and physical properties of formation rocks in the area should also be considered. Frequently, maps will be available that show well locations and positions with respect to surface topographic features, subsurface structure features, and reservoir boundaries.

2. WATER COMPOSITION

Whenever possible, water samples representing all aquifers penetrated should be collected and analyzed. Samples of the disposal brine should also be analyzed. Compatibility tests should be made with waters that are to be mixed in the disposal operation.

3. WELL AND RESERVOIR DATA

A study of the performance records of existing production and disposal wells is helpful in predicting future requirements for the disposal system. The disposal reservoir and its ability to handle waste water is vital to the success of the project.

a. Porosity

Porosity is used to determine the storage capacity of the reservoir. It is designated as absolute and effective porosity. Absolute porosity is the percentage of pore volume in the rock, without regard for interconnection of pore spaces. Rock of high porosity may have low permeability, because there is no connection between pores. Absolute porosity is expressed in Eq. (5-1).

$$\text{absolute porosity} = \frac{\text{bulk volume} - \text{grain volume}}{\text{bulk volume}} \times 100 \qquad (5\text{-}1)$$

The percentage of interconnected void space with respect to bulk volume is termed effective porosity. It is defined in Eq. (5-2). Porosities are best determined from cores taken during drilling of the well.

$$\text{effective porosity} = \frac{\text{interconnected pore volume}}{\text{bulk volume}} \times 100 \qquad (5\text{-}2)$$

b. Permeability

The ability of reservoir rock to let fluid flow through its interconnected pore volume or its fluid conductivity is termed its *permeability* (K).[17] Permeability is related to effective porosity and also to factors affecting effective porosity, such as grain size and degree of lithification.

Darcy, a French hydrologist, working with filters developed an empirical equation that relates the effluent velocity (v) of the flowing fluid of a specified viscosity (μ) to the pressure difference $(P_1 - P_2)$, causing flow through a filter of length ΔL. The elementary Darcy's law shown in Eq. (5–3) applies to reservoir rock having effective porosity as well as filters.

$$v = \frac{K}{\mu} \frac{(P_1 - P_2)}{\Delta L} \tag{5-3}$$

Permeability is expressed in units of darcys. One darcy is defined as 1 cubic centimeter flowing across a cross-sectional area of 1 square centimeter under 1 atmosphere pressure differential per centimeter of length with a viscosity of 1 centipoise. Porous media encountered in subsurface formations have such low permeabilities that they are frequently expressed in millidarcys.

Permeabilities are best determined in the laboratory from measurements on actual formation cores. Approximate permeability measurements can be made using a caliper log in conjunction with a spinner survey.[18]

c. Calculation of Injection Rate

Darcy's equation can be used to calculate the rate of brine or waste disposal into a subsurface formation containing fluid. Consider disposal into a formation of thickness h, containing a fluid with a static pressure surface P_e that is not changed at distance R_e from the well bore, as shown in Fig. 5.1.

From Darcy's equation, Querio and Powers developed Eq. (5–4) for calculating the injection rate for radial single phase flow of incompressible liquids at equilibrium conditions.[19]

$$Q = \frac{8.95 \times 10^2 \, Kh(P_w - P_e)}{\mu \log R_e/R_w} \tag{5-4}$$

where Q is flow rate in gal/min

h is in ft

K is in Darcys

R_w is radius of well bore in ft

μ is in centipoises

P_w is the dynamic pressure as influenced by injection in lb/sq in.

P_e in lb/sq in.

R_e in ft

The injection rate Q is directly proportional to the product Kh which

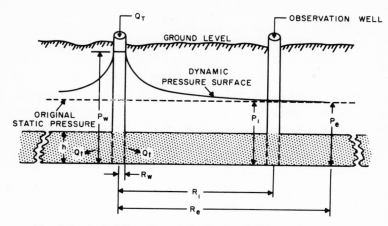

Fig. 5.1. Radial flow from injection well. (From Querio and Powers, *J. Water Pollution Control Federation*, **34**, No. 2 (1962), 136, and reprinted with permission.)

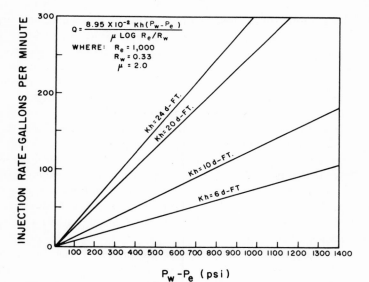

Fig. 5.2. Relationship between injection rate and pressure differential at various formation capacities. (From Querio and Powers, *J. Pollution Control Federation*, **34**, No. 2 (1962), 136, and reprinted with permission.)

represents the formation capacity. The relationship of the injection rate and formation capacity at various pressure differentials is shown in Fig. 5.2. As shown in Eq. (5–5), reservoir pressure will have a direct influence on injection pressure.[20]

$$P_1 = P_w - P_h - P_f \tag{5-5}$$

where P_1 = injection pressure in lb/sq in.

P_w = original bottom hole pressure in lb/sq in.

P_h = pressure of fluid column in well in lb/sq in.

P_f = pressure drop in lb/sq in. caused by friction

Brines of high specific gravities will exert more hydrostatic pressure than waters of low salt content. This will reduce the amount of injection pressure required to force the water into the formation.

Components of a Subsurface Brine Disposal System

1. GATHERING SYSTEMS FOR WASTE-INJECTION WATER

The primary problems involved in gathering systems are those of corrosion and scale formation. Dissolved and entrained gases may also present a problem in gravity flow or low-pressure systems. Since the pressure in the reservoir is much higher than the surface pressure, gases will tend to come out of solution at the lower surface pressures and collect in high spots in the flow lines. These gas pockets can result in decreased water flow due to gas locks, unless vents for releasing this gas are located at high points.

Gathering systems are subject to the accumulation of various scales deposited from the water. Since the various scales and conditions for their deposition have been previously discussed, it suffices to say here that these scales can greatly restrict the flow through the lines. Scale inhibitors can be used to prevent the deposition of scale, or provision can be made for the use of scrapers to remove the deposits. Acid can be used to remove accumulated carbonate scale, but sulfate scales generally require removal by mechanical methods. The use of either scrapers or acid may damage protective linings on the inner surface of the pipe.

From the laboratory investigation of the proposed waste or injection water and the discussion covered in Chapter 4 on water and corrosion, the corrosion character of the water can be estimated. This should influence the selection of materials used for flow lines in the gathering systems. The use of corrosion inhibitors should also be considered, but the cost of adding corrosion inhibitors to large volumes of corrosive water may be greater than would the use of corrosion-resistant gathering lines. Closed systems are sometimes used to prevent the contact of air and water and alleviate the corrosion problem. Several types of corrosion-resistant pipes or lined pipes are commonly used for oilfield gathering or distribution lines.

a. Cement-Asbestos Pipe*

This type of pipe has the advantage of resisting interior corrosion from the water transported and exterior soil corrosion. Couplings are available that permit rapid installation and can allow a maximum deflection of 6 degrees. The light weight of the pipe and its salvage value are additional advantages. However, asbestos-cement pipe has the disadvantage of being somewhat fragile, thus requiring careful handling and coverage protection. It also is limited by strength to low-pressure applications.

b. Plastic Pipe

Plastic pipe has the advantage of corrosion resistance, light weight, and ease of coupling. Its use is limited by its strength and relatively high cost. Two-inch diameter fiberglass-reinforced plastic pipe that will stand 1,200 psi pressure at 80°F is available.

c. Plastic-Lined Pipe

Steel pipe can be plastic-coated and used as gathering lines. A variety of plastics are used for coating pipe, and if properly applied, most of them will give satisfactory service. Generally, coatings applied in a mill are superior to coatings applied in place. Plastic-coated pipe is expensive, and the coating is subject to mechanical damage. Any break in the coating exposing bare metal results in increased corrosion at that point.

d. Cement-Lined Pipe

This pipe is particularly well suited to water lines, since the cement coating provides adequate corrosion protection, is more resistant to mechanical damage, and is cheaper than plastic coatings. Care should be exercised in joining the pipe, in order to prevent chipping off any cement and exposing the bare pipe to corrosion. When cement-lined pipe is joined by threaded couplings, measures should be taken to prevent the exposure of the uncoated steel coupling to the water. In general, pipe with cement lining applied at the mill has been much more satisfactory than pipe with lining applied in place. In place cement-lining has the advantage of coating all joints, but it is difficult to distribute the cement evenly and flow restriction has resulted from some in place lining applications.

2. COLLECTION CENTER

Essentially, a collection center is a tank or lined pond used to collect waste water from the various heater treaters and separators in the field. From here, the water is pumped or gravity-flowed to the treating plant.

*Trade names Century and Transite.

Injection water containing oil will generally plug the injection formation. Since waste water from heater treaters contains a small amount of oil which was not removed, or oil accumulated from leaks, it is necessary to remove this oil before the water is injected. The collection center may also serve as an oil-brine separator. The incoming water passes through a baffle system which separates the oil by gravity; then a skimmer removes it.

3. WATER TREATMENT PLANT

A water treatment plant generally consists of facilities for aeration, chemical coagulation, sedimentation, filtration, and storage for treated water. If a bacterial problem is anticipated, apparatus for the addition of chlorine or some other bactericide should be provided. A chemical feeder is also necessary if a corrosion inhibitor is added to the water. A diagrammatic sketch of a Mobil Oil Company brine-disposal system is shown in Fig. 5.3.

The aerator serves to remove dissolved gases and to oxidize dissolved iron, manganese, hydrogen sulfide, and any other easily oxidized materials. The water from the aerator is in a turbulent state, and may contain finely divided and colloidal matter as well as some calcium and magnesium compounds. In order to coagulate this finely divided matter, a flocculating or coagulating agent is added. This may be hydrated lime, which will partially react with the calcium and magnesium; it may also be aluminum sulfate or ferrous sulfate in combination with lime. If microorganisms present a problem, chlorine can be added. The addition of chlorine serves the twofold purpose of a bactericide and an oxidizer for any remaining iron which was not oxidized by aeration. The majority of the solids are then removed by sedimentation, and the remainder removed by filtration. If post treatment precipitation of calcium compounds is anticipated, a scale inhibitor can be added as the treated water passes to the storage tank. A corrosion inhibitor may also be added at this time. Each of these steps in water treatment will be discussed more fully in the following chapters.

There are two general types of disposal systems: the open and the closed type. The water in an open system is exposed to the atmosphere, contacting air and light. Since surface temperature and pressure are different from those in the reservoir, the chemical equilibrium of the water may be changed. Dissolved carbon dioxide, hydrogen sulfide, methane, and other gases will probably escape from the water. These gases certainly will be removed on aeration, and oxygen will be dissolved in the water. Slightly soluble carbonates will precipitate due to the loss of carbon dioxide. These solids are removed by coagulation, sedimentation, and filtration. The dissolved oxygen may cause the water to be very corrosive. However, oxygen corrosion can be minimized by using a de-aerator to remove the oxygen or using corrosion-resistant flow lines and injection tubing.

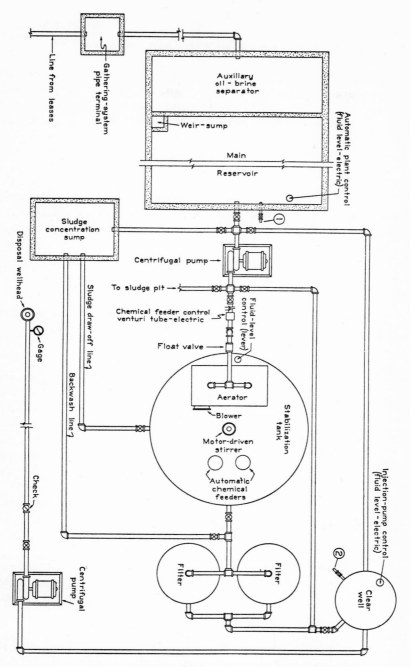

Note: Numerals indicate sampling-point and corrosion-specimen locations

Fig. 5.3. Diagrammatic sketch of the Mobil brine-disposal system, Fitts Pool, Pontonoc Country, Oklahoma. (From Taylor and Owens, *Subsurface Disposal of Oil-Field Brines in Oklahoma*, R. I. 3603, (Washington, D. C.: U.S. Bureau of Mines, 1942).)

As the name implies, a closed system is one in which the disposal water never comes in contact with the atmosphere. In theory, water produced and injected using a closed system remains in equilibrium throughout the process and requires a minimum of treatment. However, the pressure and temperature may be different from those in the reservoir, resulting in the deposition of some solids and requiring sedimentation or filtration. In order to keep a closed system free of oxygen, a slight pressure of natural gas is maintained in the vapor space of brine-conditioning equipment. It is not uncommon for waters from different strata to be mixed before injection. It is important that these waters be compatible, or mixing will result in the formation of a precipitate. In some cases, scale inhibitors might be useful in preventing the formation of these precipitates from incompatible waters.

4. Injection Well

Disposal of brines into subsurface formations can be made through completed wells, using several different methods.

a. Special Wells

Wells can be drilled especially for use as injection wells. Precautions should be taken during the completion of these wells to insure that they do not cause pollution by salt water leakage into any fresh water aquifers penetrated by the wells. Casing and cement programs should be adequate to prevent brine contamination of other reservoirs. In corrosive areas, casing leak tests should be conducted on a regular basis. Waste brine is sometimes injected directly through the casing. Usually, tubing is run and the tubing-casing annulus closed off with a packer. The annulus can be filled with corrosion-inhibited water to guard against internal casing corrosion. A schematic drawing of a waste disposal well is shown in Fig. 5.4.

b. Reworked Wells

In many fields, dry holes or abandoned producing wells exist that can be reworked to serve as injection wells. This is a particular economic advantage if the wells were originally completed in the proposed disposal formation.

c. Annular Space Wells

Small volumes of brine can sometimes be disposed of by injecting them into annular space wells. In these wells, an uncased interval is left between casing strings or perforations made opposite a suitable formation. Brine is then injected into the annular space and subsequently into the disposal formation. Such a well serves as both a production and disposal well. These wells are at best, only a temporary solution to the disposal problem.

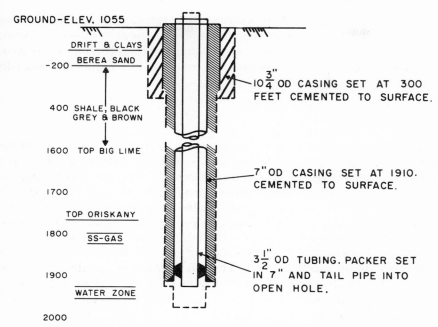

GROUND-ELEV. 1055

DRIFT & CLAYS

-200   BEREA SAND

400 SHALE, BLACK
GREY & BROWN

1600 TOP BIG LIME

1700

TOP ORISKANY

1800   SS-GAS

1900

WATER ZONE

2000

$10\frac{3}{4}''$ OD CASING SET AT 300
FEET CEMENTED TO SURFACE.

7" OD CASING SET AT 1910.
CEMENTED TO SURFACE.

$3\frac{1}{2}''$ OD TUBING. PACKER SET
IN 7" AND TAIL PIPE INTO
OPEN HOLE.

Fig. 5.4. Cross section of waste disposal well. (From Querio
and Powers, *J. Pollution Control Federation*, **34**, No. 2 (1962),
136, and used with permission.)

The water treating plant is designed to treat the water so that it will
not carry suspended solids, or precipitate solids after treatment and plug
the formation. In some systems, algae and bacteria may grow in the injection
well and plug the formation. Chlorination, either by batch or continuous
treatment, generally will prevent the growth of these organisms in the
injection well. Other bactericides may also give satisfactory results. If
sulfate-reducing bacteria are present, a strong bactericide will probably be
necessary to control their growth. Reduced sulfur, such as that produced by
these bacteria, has been removed by shutting the well in, pouring 2 or 3
barrels of carbon disulfide into the tubing, and resuming injection.

Corrosion of the injection well tubing or casing also requires consideration.
Corrosion products from the tubing can plug the formation. Corrosion can
be prevented by the use of plastic-lined or cement-lined tubing or casing.
Properly applied linings in good condition can provide effective protection.
However, these linings have the disadvantage of being damaged by tools or
drill pipe that may be run in and out of the hole during a workover. Cement-
lining has the additional disadvantage that it will be damaged by acid
treatment.

Any insoluble carbonates which may form in the injection well after treatment can be removed by acidizing. More troublesome deposits are those formed by sulfates. Some formation waters may contain dissolved barium or strontium. If the injected water contains sulfate, barium or strontium sulfate may form in the injection well, resulting in plugging and generally a workover.

5. PUMPS

In selecting pumps for use in salt-water disposal and injection systems, the corrosion-resistant properties are as important a criteria as the performance characteristics of the pump. Since salt water is a good electrolyte, bimetallic couples can cause serious corrosion in brine disposal systems. In salt-water disposal systems, the usual oilfield fittings, such as pistons, rods, liners, valves, seals, and packings, give poor service, because the salt water does not provide lubrication like that provided by oil; also, the salt water is very corrosive. In one successful salt-water disposal system, rubber-covered pistons and Monel metal liners have given long trouble-free service. High-alloy steels may have a tendency to pit in salt water service. In the future, titanium will probably find considerable use in pistons and liners because of excellent corrosion resistance.

Diaphragm pumps can handle corrosive chemical solutions used in treating injection water. The working parts of these pumps can be sealed, and only the corrosion-resistant diaphragm contacts the solution.

Advantages of Subsurface Brine Disposal into Production Reservoirs

Returning produced brine to its parent formation reduces the pollution hazard to surface waters and fresh water aquifers. An economic saving may be realized if dry holes or abandoned production wells can be used as injection wells. Lower injection pressures will be realized, since injected brine will be balanced by produced brine. In addition, the return of brine to the reservoir results in conservation of reservoir energy; it may also prolong the life of flowing wells and result in greater economic recovery of oil through increased recovery efficiency.

References

[1] R. J. Enright, "Oil-Field Pollution," *Oil Gas J.*, **61**, No. 21 (1963), 76.

[2] *Salt Water Disposal East Texas Oil Field* (2nd Ed.) (Austin, Tex.: Petroleum Extention Service, 1958).

[3]J. E. McKee and H. W. Wolf, eds., *Water Quality Criteria* (Sacramento, Calif.: State Water Quality Control Board, 1963), p. 29.

[4]N. J. Gothard and J. A. Fowler, "Petroleum Refineries—Pollution Abatement at Sinclair Refining Company," *Ind. Eng. Chem.*, **44** (1952), 503.

[5]C. C. Ruchhoft, F. M. Middleton, H. Barnes, and A. A. Rosen, "Waste Disposal in the Petroleum Industry," *Ind. Eng. Chem.*, **46** (1954), 284.

[6]*Manual on Disposal of Refinery Wastes*, (6th ed.) (New York: American Petroleum Institute, 1959), **1**, 10.

[7]Gothard and Fowler, *op. cit.*

[8]*Manual on Disposal of Refinery Wastes*, **1**, 17.

[9]W. J. Katz, "Dissolved Air Flotation as Applied to the Treatment of Oil-Production Water or Refinery Wastes," *American Petroleum Institute, Drilling and Production Practice* (1960), 140.

[10]*Manual on Disposal of Refinery Wastes*, (4th ed.) (New York: American Petroleum Institute, 1960), **III**, 65.

[11]*Ibid.*, **III**, 67.

[12]T. R. Harris, "Disposal of Refinery Waste Sulfuric Acid," *Ind. Eng. Chem.*, **50**, (December, 1958), 81A.

[13]L. K. Cecil, "Underground Disposal of Process Waste Water," *Ind. Eng. Chem.*, **42** (1950), 594.

[14]T. C. Dorris, B. J. Copeland, and D. Patterson, "The Case for Holding Ponds," *Oil Gas J.*, **59**, No. 44 (1961), 161.

[15]R. J. Enright, "Oil-Field Pollution," *op, cit.*

[16]C. W. Lauritzen, "Plastic Films for Water Storage," *J. Am. Water Works Assoc.*, **53** (1961), 135.

[17]S. J. Pirson, *Elements of Oil Reservoir Engineering* (2nd ed.) (New York: McGraw-Hill Book Company, 1958), p. 56.

[18]C. W. Querio and T. J. Powers, "Deep Well Disposal of Industrial Wastewater," *J. Water Pollution Control Federation*, **34**, No. 2 (1962), 136.

[19]*Ibid.*

[20]*Ibid.*

[21]*Salt Water Disposal East Texas Oil Field*, p. 40.

Water Treatment Microbiology

6

Bacteria present in injection water or other oilfield water may cause corrosion or plugging of lines and reservoir formation rock. It should be pointed out that the mere presence of bacteria or other microorganisms in water does not necessarily mean that they present a problem. Elimination or reduction of bacteria is justified only if it represents an economical solution to a corrosion or plugging problem. The engineer must determine if bacteria are a problem before measures to counteract their presence are taken.

Bacteria are found virtually everywhere on the surface of our earth. A wide variety of inorganic and organic materials serve as food for bacterial growth. Some additives such as citric acid or polyphosphates which have reverted to orthophosphates can provide nourishment for bacteria. In water systems, bacteria flourish best in the pH range between 5 and 9 and in the temperature range 0° to 180°F. Bacteria grow best in fresh waters, but some are capable of growth in brines of concentrations as high as 100,000 ppm.

For purposes of oilfield water treatment, where open and closed systems are used, bacteria may best be classified according to their oxygen requirement. *Obligate aerobes* grow only in the presence of molecular oxygen, while *obligate anaerobes* grow best in the absence of oxygen in environments of low oxidation-reduction potentials. *Facultative anaerobes* grow either in the presence or absence of oxygen.

There are many species of bacteria. All do not exhibit their best growth under the same set of conditions, but some species grow well in an environment where other species do not. In general, bacteria grow better in the warm summer than in cooler weather. Those that do not grow in a particular environment may lie dormant until conditions change, and then they grow. This in part explains why bacteria are a problem in some systems and not in others. Troublesome bacteria may be present, but conditions are not optimal for their growth, so that a bacterial population is too small to present a problem.

Microbiological Corrosion

Microorganisms can contribute to corrosion in several different ways. Some microorganisms act as cathodic depolarizers, while others form slimes or growths that shield a portion of the metal and produce an oxygen concentration cell. Sulfate reducer bacteria can produce hydrogen sulfide, which is itself corrosive. Although there are many different kinds of bacteria that can contribute to corrosion,[1] only a few are of major importance in oilfield corrosion.

1. SULFATE-REDUCING BACTERIA

Desulfovibrio desulfuricans, commonly referred to as sulfate-reducing bacteria, are the most important and damaging bacteria, from the corrosion standpoint, encountered in oilfield water-handling systems. These organisms grow in anaerobic or oxygen-free environments, but they will survive in systems containing dissolved oxygen. They may grow under scale, debris, or other bacterial masses where oxygen cannot penetrate.[2]

Sulfate-reducing bacteria grow if a reaction such as that shown by Eq. (6-1) occurs, in which they utilize nascent hydrogen to reduce sulfate ion.

$$SO_4^= + 8H° = S^= + 4H_2O \qquad (6\text{-}1)$$

In the corrosion of steel, the cathode often becomes polarized by atomic hydrogen. These bacteria can then obtain their hydrogen from the cathode, causing it to be depolarized and increasing the rate of corrosion. In addition, sulfide ion formed in this process can combine with ferrous ions at the anode, giving black ferrous sulfide.[3]

2. IRON BACTERIA

Iron bacteria such as *Gallionalla* and *Crenothrix* can also cause corrosion in water-handling systems. One mechanism postulates that ferrous salts oxidize to hydrated ferric hydroxide, removing oxygen from the water and causing anaerobic conditions at the bottom of a mass of the bacteria.[4] Sulfate-reducing bacteria can then grow under this mass of iron bacteria. In effect, corrosion is caused by the sulfate-reducing bacteria, and deposits on the metal surface are caused by iron bacteria.

In a second mechanism, corrosion is attributed to the formation of an oxygen concentration cell by the iron bacteria.[5] In areas of low oxygen concentration, iron bacteria convert ferrous to ferric iron, which then precipitates as ferric hydroxide on the metal surface and effectively shields the surface from oxygen. This produces an oxygen concentration cell, causing corrosion under the deposit.

3. SLIME FORMERS

Slime-forming bacteria belong to the genera *Pseudomonas*, *Flavobacterium*, *Escherichia*, *Aerobacter*, and *Bacillus*.[6] These organisms proliferate on surfaces, producing dense masses which prevent the penetration of oxygen to the surface. Slime formers are not actually corrosive themselves, but by shielding the metal surface from oxygen can cause oxygen concentration cells or provide an environment for the growth of sulfate reducing bacteria.

4. CLOSTRIDIUM

Clostridium are obligate anaerobic, spore-forming bacteria that have reportedly formed hydrogen sulfide in oilfield water.[7] The ability of *Clostridium* species to cause corrosion has not been well established and requires additional investigation.[8]

Microbiological Plugging of Water-Handling Systems

Microorganisms can contribute to plugging injection wells and fouling flow lines and equipment in several different ways. By actual growth, these organisms can produce masses that will plug wells and reduce flow in lines. Iron bacteria can cause the precipitation of iron as ferric oxide, resulting in an accumulation of this material in injection wells. Corrosion products resulting from increased corrosion caused by sulfate-reducing bacteria can also accumulate in wells or on filters, reducing flow or causing plugging.

The microorganisms mentioned as causing microbiological corrosion can grow sufficiently large masses to cause plugging. This is particularly true of the slime formers and iron bacteria. In addition, minute plants called algae may grow in fresh-water systems. Algae require sunlight for growth, so that problems with algae are confined to open systems. Fresh-water algae grow on the surface of the water and may serve as a source of food for bacteria. If they form a blanket over a pond or tank, the reduction in oxygen intake into the water can make conditions ideal for growth of sulfate reducers in the areas of deep water. Algae growths often slough off and plug pipes and filters.

Detecting Microbial Problems

As stated previously, the mere presence of bacterial organisms in water does not necessarily mean that bacteria are a problem. Conversely, low bacterial counts do not necessarily mean that bacteria are not a problem, since they may be thriving hidden from the stream by a corrosion deposit or slime deposit. There is a lack of correlation between bacteriological examinations and damage actually done to a system. Some observations are useful in detecting microbial corrosion problems that also are applicable to plugging problems.

1. PRESENCE AND TYPE OF BACTERIA

A trained microbiologist using a microscope can identify iron and slime bacteria, algae, and fungi. One technique consists of passing a quantity of the water in question through a membrane filter. The filter is then dried and cut into squares. These squares are placed on microscope slides and rendered transparent with drop a of immersion oil. Microscopic examination of bacteria can then be made.[9] Both *Standard Methods for the Examination of Water and Wastewater*[10] and *Manual on Industrial Water and Industrial Waste Water*[11] give information on the microscopic identification and culture growth of bacteria.

Culture techniques are the most widely used method of identifying bacteria and estimating their numbers. When dealing with oilfield waters, microbiologists do not necessarily attempt to identify each type of bacteria present, but only those such as sulfate-reducing ones which contribute to corrosion or plugging. The American Petroleum Institute has recommended methods and materials for the biological analysis of water flood injection waters.[12] Their recommended procedures are found in the Appendix.

A procedure known as the extinction dilution technique can be used to determine the range of microbial contamination.[13] This technique utilizes procedures and media described in API RP 38, found in the Appendix. A series of serum bottles each containing 9 ml of sterile medium is lined up. One milliliter of microbe-contaminated water is injected into the first serum bottle. After mixing, 1 ml of the contents of this bottle is drawn into a sterile syringe and transferred to the second bottle. This bottle now contains one-tenth of the organisms originally present in the 1 ml water sample. The bottle is designated as the 1:10 dilution.

After mixing, 1 ml is transferred from the 1:10 dilution to the third bottle, which then contains one-hundredth of the organisms present in the 1 ml water sample. The procedure is repeated with each succeeding bottle. Figure 6.1 represents the necessary dilutions required to obtain a 1:10,000,-000 dilution and the growth interpretations.

Using this technique with a 1 ml sample of flood water, the first three bottles showed a blacking color indicating the presence of sulfate-reducing bacteria. The fourth bottle, representing a dilution of 1:1,000, showed no evidence of the bacteria. Based on the fact that the lowest dilution to show the presence of sulfate-reducing bacteria was the 1:100, the water must then contain approximately 100 sulfate-reducing bacteria per milliliter.

The rating chart shown in Table 13.2 gives values for both sulfate-reducing and total bacteria counts. The API procedure does not consider general bacterial counts of less than 10,000 organisms per milliliter as being significant.[14] The significance of bacterial contamination greater than 10,000 per milliliter is determined from injectivity pressure and volume data. Smaller numbers of harmful organisms such as sulfate-reducing bacteria may certainly constitute a problem.

Bacteria which grow on the surfaces of pipe are not necessarily detected by culture-growth methods. A submerged slide technique has been developed for the identification of these bacteria. With this technique a microscopic slide is exposed in a diverted side stream. Organisms growing only on

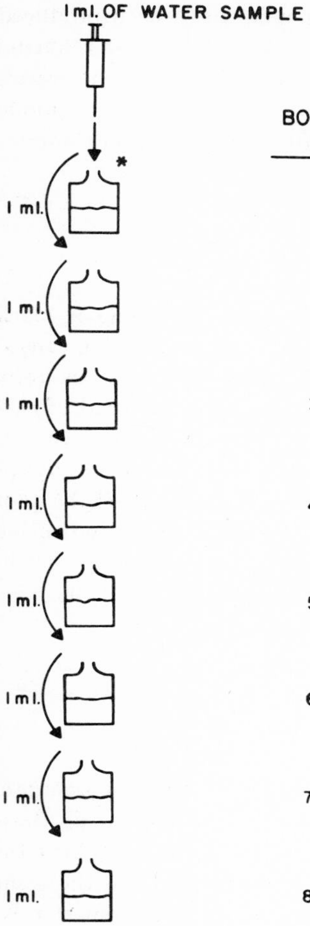

I ml. OF WATER SAMPLE

	BOTTLE NO.	DILUTION FACTOR	GROWTH INTERPRETATION
I ml.	I	O	I
I ml.	2	I:IO	IO PER ml.
I ml.	3	I:IOO	IOO PER ml.
I ml.	4	I:IOOO	IOOO PER ml.
I ml.	5	I:IO,OOO	IO,OOO PER ml.
I ml.	6	I:IOO,QOO	IOO,OOO PER ml
I ml.	7	I:I,OOO,OOO	I,OOO,OOO PER ml.
I ml.	8	I:IO,OOO,OOO	IO,OOO,OOO PER ml.

*EACH BOTTLE CONTAINS 9ml. OF DILUTION FLUID

Fig. 6.1. Extinction dilution technique. (From Whitesell, AIME Rocky Mountain Section 7th Meeting, 1961, Paper No. SPE-64.)

surfaces will attach themselves to the glass surface, sometimes yielding slime masses within 48 hours.[15] These can then be identified with a microscope.

2. PRODUCTION OF HYDROGEN SULFIDE

The presence of sulfate-reducing bacteria sometimes can be detected from the presence of hydrogen sulfide. If water entering a system is sweet (contains no dissolved hydrogen sulfide), but at some point removed from its entry the water contains hydrogen sulfide, it must have been produced within the system. This is certainly a clue to the presence of sulfate-reducing bacteria. In some systems, black particles of iron sulfide color the water, indicating sulfide has been produced within the system. Black iron sulfide obtained from back-flowing injection wells can indicate the growth of sulfate-reducing bacteria in the well.

3. EXAMINATION OF CORROSION PRODUCT

Pitting-type corrosion occurring under a tubercle, producing a black corrosion product instead of a rust-colored one, can indicate corrosion caused by sulfate-reducing bacteria. The presence of sulfate-reducing bacteria cannot be assumed, because black magnetite can be formed instead of rust if the oxygen supply is deficient. Iron sulfide is nonmagnetic and can be differentiated from magnetite by the use of a magnet. An even better identification technique consists of dropping acid on the black deposit. If the odor of sulfide is detected, the deposit is iron sulfide. This is a strong indication that sulfate reducers are causing corrosion if no sulfide was present in water entering the corroded equipment.

Chemicals for Controlling Microorganisms

A wide variety of chemicals is used to control the growth of microorganisms in water-handling systems. These chemicals can be classed as those that kill bacteria, called bactericides, and those that inhibit or retard the growth of bacteria, called bacteriostats. If these chemicals have the same affect on other forms of life, they are called biocides and biostats, respectively.

Some inorganic chemicals such as chlorine, chromates, and compounds of mercury or silver find use as bactericides, but the largest number of chemicals used to control microorganisms are classified as organic chemicals. Most of these are amines, peroxygens, polychlorophenols, and quaternary ammonium derivatives, but many other types of compounds are used. Some typical chemical compounds used as bactericides are shown in Table 6.1.

Proprietary preparations sold as bactericides contain one or more chemical compounds. The amount of chemical present which actually has the bactericidal properties is expressed as per cent active ingredient. This influences the price of the preparation and the concentration necessary for control of microorganisms.

Reliable service companies provide data sheets that are useful to the

Table 6.1

SOME CHEMICALS WITH BACTERICIDAL PROPERTIES

Type of Chemical Compound	Example Name	Compound Formula	Physical Form	Concentration Range (ppm)	Approximate Price per Pound
Chromium	sodium chromate	Na_2CrO_4	solid	500	$0.16
Mercury	mercuric chloride	$HgCl_2$	solid	50–300	3.78
Silver	silver nitrate[16]	$AgNO_3$	solid	0.05	11.57
Amine	coco primary amine acetate[17]	$(R — NH_3)^+(CH_3CO — O)^-$	solid	10–40	0.533
Diamine	coco trimethylene diamine	$C_{12}H_{25} — NH(CH_2)_3NH$	liquid	5–25	0.643
Quaternary Ammonium[18, 19]	alkyl trimethyl quaternary ammonium chloride	$RN(CH_3)_3Cl$	liquid	25–>100	0.463
Imidazolines	1-phenyl-4, 4-dimethyl,-imidazoline[20]	$C_6H_5NCHNC((CH_3)_2CH_2$	solid	75–>100	
Chlorinated Phenols[21]	sodium tetrachlorphenate[22, 23]	$NaOC_6HCl_4$	solid	12–50	0.35
Aldehydes	gluteraldehyde	$C_5H_8O_2$	liquid	20–75	0.42
Mercurials[24]	methyl mercuric acetate	$CH_3HgCOOCH_3$	solid	250	
Peroxygens[25]	peracetic acid	CH_3COO_2H	liquid	>10	

field engineer in selecting a bactericide that has the right solubility characteristics for use in his particular water.

Chemicals used for bactericides also show varying amounts of toxicity to humans. Safety precautions should be taken and extreme care used whenever these chemicals are handled. They should never be added to water that is used for human comsumption or for cattle.

Evaluation of Bactericides

Chemical bactericides are not universal in their killing power. Each bactericide should be tested against the bacterial flora present in the subject system. If possible, water in which the bacteria are growing should be used in the test. Bacteria are very adaptible and may develop resistant strains to a particular bactericide after a long period of treatment, so more than one material should be selected during the test. The second material can then be used if future tests indicate bacteria have developed strains resistant to the first bactericide.

Bactericides should be evaluated in the laboratory before being used in the field. Recommended procedures, including time-kill tests, for evaluating the effect of bactericides on sulfate-reducing bacteria are given in API RP 38, found in the Appendix. These tests could be used to evaluate bactericides for other than sulfate-reducing bacteria, if the growth media were changed to one more suitable for the particular bacteria.

The bactericide should also be evaluated when it is used in the field.

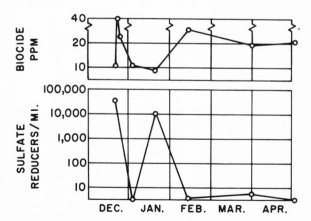

Fig. 6.2. Variation in bacterial count with concentration of an alkyl polyamine salt. (From Conger *et al.*, SPE-AIME Meeting, New Orleans, 1963, Paper No. SPE-700.)

Bacterial counts before and after use of the bactericide are helpful in determining its effectiveness. Bacterial counts are shown graphically in Fig. 6.2, where an alkyl polyamine salt is being added to a flood water. This particular bactericide was most effective in this application at a continuous feed of 20 ppm.[26] At lower concentrations, the bacterial population increased.

Some indirect methods may also be useful in evaluating the ability of the bactericide to decrease bacterial activity.[27] If sulfate-reducing bacteria have been responsible for the presence of hydrogen sulfide in the water, any decrease in sulfide content will indicate a decrease in bacterial activity. Positive changes in oxidation-reduction potential, or *Eh*, of the water after treatment with a bactericide (if the bactericide itself does not affect this potential) indicate a gross decrease in bacterial activity and, therefore, effectiveness of the bactericide.[28] Microscopic count or culture techniques are the most reliable methods used to estimate the number of bacteria present.

Treatment with Bactericide or Bacteriostat

The sole purpose of treatment with a bactericide or bacteriostat is to control the growth of microorganisms in the water-handling system. Use of a bactericide has the advantage of a more positive solution to the problem, as well as reducing the possibility of the development of a strain of bacteria resistant to the bactericide. Bactericides can also be used on a continuous or slug treatment basis. Bacteriostats are best utilized where it is desirable to control the growth of bacteria that are not necessarily harmful except in large numbers. An example would be the control of slime formers.

1. SELECTION OF BACTERICIDE

The initial step in treatment with a chemical bactericide is to select one that will kill the microorganisms as cheaply as possible. A bactericide effective in one flood will not necessarily prove effective in another water flood project. Chemicals selected for trial should be evaluated in the laboratory for effectiveness of kill at various concentrations. The upper limitations on concentration of bactericide are usually governed by cost rather than kill requirements.

In addition to being an effective bactericide, the chemical selected must be compatible with the water in the system and with other chemicals used to treat the water. Some materials like the chlorphenols are only slightly soluble in high brines and "salt out" or precipitate. The effectiveness of the bactericide is then lost.

2. CLEANING THE SYSTEM

Bactericides cannot kill bacteria unless they contact them. This means that colonies of bacteria growing under debris, sludge, or scale will not be contacted, unless the covering deposits are removed. Therefore, the first important field operation in applying a bactericide is to clean the system. This includes cleaning lines, back-flowing wells, purging filters, and removing tank bottom sludge.

One of two cleaning procedures is used. The easiest consists of using a bactericide that has detergent properties. Chemical feed levels are started low, and increased as the system is cleaned. The water should be filtered at the wellhead to prevent accumulation of the removed material in the injection well. A more reliable method is to clean the system by acidizing and/or scraping. This treatment can then be followed by solvent and detergent flushes. Water used in acidizing or flushing the system should not be injected without filtration. It is apparent that it is easier to apply bactericide to a new system than to an old one.

3. FEEDING BACTERICIDE

Investigation of the microbial problem and the system should indicate the proper location for feeding the chemical into the water. A water injection project is graphically shown in Fig. 6.3. In this system, the bactericide is added just after the water passes from the pump into flow lines. This represents the nearest convenient location to the water supply for chemical addition. Addition of 7.5 ppm bactericide here protects the remainder of the system, which includes storage tanks and filters.[29]

Bactericides are fed from chemical feeders, discussed in Chapter 10. The bactericide should be fed in a part of the system that is moving sufficiently to mix the bactericide and water. Addition of chemical in stagnant areas does not permit mixing, resulting in ineffectual use of bactericide. Bactericides used in continuous treatment should be fed on a uniform rate basis, rather than an average of so much a week.

In another illustration, two sources of water are used to provide a sufficient volume of flood water. One was a fresh water containing only 1,300 mg/liter dissolved solids, while the other water contained 120,000 mg/liter dissolved solids.[30] The mixed waters were treated unsuccessfully with daily batches of bactericide and corrosion inhibitors. Sulfate-reducing bacteria continued to grow. The waters were separated and the chemical treatment concentrated on the brine. This permitted low chemical costs by treating only that portion of the water which really required the bactericide, and resulted in effective treatment.

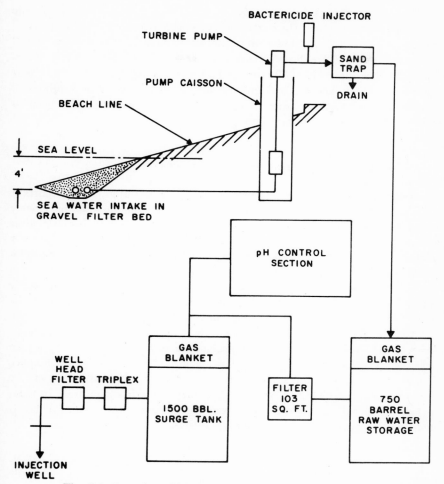

Fig. 6.3. Location of bactericide feed, (From Sudbury *et al.*, *J. Petrol. Technol.* 8, (September 1956), 85.).

4. Type of Treatment

Bactericides or biocides do not kill instanteously, so sufficient time must be allotted for the chemical to kill the microorganisms. In continuous treatment, bactericide is constantly added to the system, so that sufficient time is available for killing the microorganisms. Chemicals can also be added on an intermittent basis, this is referred to as slug treatment. When using it, the treating period must be of sufficient duration to give the chemical time to kill the bacteria. This can be estimated from time-kill tests.

The choice of continuous or slug treatment is influenced by economic factors and the success of the particular type of treatment. As an illustration, 20 ppm of bactericide are added continuously to 5,000 bbl of water per day.[31] This amounts to 4.25 gallons of chemical per day. Changing to a slug treatment at a concentration of 30 ppm for 12 hours per day would give a greater assurance of complete kill and only require a little more than 3 gallons of chemical per day. Some slug treatments with bactericides have been as infrequent as 4 to 6 months.[32]

5. Determining Effectiveness of Treatment

After treatment with a bactericide has been initiated, it is important to evaluate its effect on the microbial problem. One method previously mentioned was to count the bacteria present. A decrease in bacteria after treatment indicates the bactericide is having some success. Samples for bacterial count should be taken from various parts of the system. Samples should be obtained particularly from the injection wellheads farthest from the point of bactericide addition. Samples are preferably taken in sterile containers by methods described in Chapter 2. Bacterial samples must be delivered promptly to the laboratory for counting.

Additional evidence of effectiveness can be obtained from water analyses. Decreases in total iron and hydrogen sulfide can represent a decrease in activity by sulfate reducers. Back-flowing injection wells are also helpful. The absence of black iron sulfide in this water usually indicates that sulfate reducers are not growing on the formation face in the injection well. In some instances, decreased corrosion rates may also indicate the success of treatment with a bactericide to kill microorganisms.

Chlorination

The application of chlorine to water is an effective method of controlling microorganisms. Chlorination is widely used to sterilize drinking water. The treatment of oilfield waters differs only in the degree of bacterial kill required.

When chlorine is added to water, it hydrolyzes, as shown in Eq. (6–2), to form hypochlorous and hydrochoric acids. As shown by Eq. (6–3), hypochlorous acid ionizes to hydrogen ions and hypochlorite ions.

$$Cl_2 + H_2O \rightleftharpoons H^+ + Cl^- + HOCl \qquad (6\text{–}2)$$

$$HOCl \rightleftharpoons H^+ + OCl^- \qquad (6\text{–}3)$$

The above reactions are reversible and are influenced by pH and temperature. In water of pH 5 or less, molecular chlorine is present, but in the pH range 5 to 6, hypochlorous acid predominates. Hypochlorite ion is present above pH 6 and predominates above pH 7.5.[33]

Chlorine is a very reactive chemical and a strong oxidizing agent. As mentioned in Chapter 7, 1 ppm chlorine will oxidize 1.6 ppm of ferrous iron, usually resulting in the precipitation of ferric hydroxide. This is beneficial if a coagulant is needed. Chlorine oxidation of hydrogen sulfide will be discussed in Chapter 11. Some organic compounds react with chlorine. Sulfite ion used to scavenge oxygen is also oxidized by chlorine. Chlorine reacts with ammonia to form chloramine, which also has bactericidal properties.

It is evident that chlorination is economically limited to oilfield waters that do not contain large amounts of oxidizable substances. Also, the addition of large concentrations of chlorine can cause corrosion. This is especially true when aluminum pipe is used. In systems where the customary chlorine residual of 0.2 ppm is sufficient, chlorine addition does not necessarily increase corrosion.

Both catalyzed sodium sulfite and chlorine can be used in the same system, if the sodium sulfite is added first and only in the minimum amount necessary to scavenge oxygen. After the sulfite-oxygen reaction is complete, chlorine can be added to control microbial growth.

Usually a residual chlorine of 0.2 ppm is sufficient to control microorganisms in water. Free chlorine or residual chlorine is the chlorine present as elemental chlorine (Cl_2), hypochlorous acid (HOCl), or hypochlorite ions (OCl^-). In order to obtain a chlorine residual, enough chlorine will have to be added not only to provide the residual amount but also to react with all oxidizable substances present. The amount of chlorine reacting with substances in water is called chlorine demand. This limits the economic applicability of chlorination to waters containing appreciable amounts of iron and hydrogen sulfide, unless a preceding treatment reduces the concentration of these substances.

1. CHOICE OF CHLORINATING AGENTS

Several chlorinating agents are available. These include liquid chlorine, sodium hypochlorite solution, calcium hypochlorite and chlorine gas produced by electrolysis of brine *in situ*. For oilfield use, liquid chlorine and chlorine gas generation are probably the most economical, although calcium hypochorite finds application when limited chlorination is required.

a. Liquid Chlorine

Liquid chlorine is obtained in cylinders and fed directly to the water by procedures which will be discussed under "Gas Feeders" in Chapter 10. Chlorine is a very hazardous chemical and should be handled with extreme care. Because of the possibility of forming chlorine ice at water temperatures below 49.2°F, it is advisable in cold climates to warm that portion of the water which contacts chlorine in the chlorinator.[34] The price of liquid chlorine at Dallas in 1964 is $0.11 per lb, compared with $0.35 per lb for calcium hypochlorite. Where applicable, chlorine is the cheapest bactericide available.

b. Chlorine Gas by Electrolysis

Chlorination of brines containing appreciable amounts of sodium chloride can be accomplished by electrolysis *in situ*. Electrodes are placed directly in the water to be chlorinated, resulting in a constant volume of chlorine generated and absorbed by the water. Depending on electrode efficiency, between 1.2 and 2.2 kw hours of electricity are required to produce 1 lb chlorine.

In one salt water disposal project, 440-volt ac current was rectified to 500-ampere, 6-volt direct current, which was used by carbon-plate electrodes to produce chlorine.[35] In 1958, the cost of chlorine produced by electrolysis in this project was $0.06/lb compared with $0.135/lb for liquid chlorine fed into the salt water.

2. Required Concentration of Chlorine

The amount of chlorine required for control of bacteria depends on the chlorine demand of the water, contact time, temperature, and water pH. The chlorine demand is determined by actual measurement. Ten 200 ml portions of the water to be chlorinated are measured out in beakers or jars.[36] A standardized solution, containing approximately 1 mg of chlorine per ml, is added to the first jar in an amount such that there will be no chlorine left at the end of a specified contact time. Increasing amounts of chlorine water are added to the other portions. The contact time should represent the time required for water to pass from the point of chlorination to some selected point in the water-handling system that requires the desired chlorine residual.

The rate of killing action of chlorine increases with increasing temperature. When chlorinating a flood water, the concentration should be adjusted in cold weather so that it will give a successful kill. The rate of kill increases with increases in chlorine concentration.

The pH of the water also influences the rate of kill.[37] When the pH of the water is in the range of 6 to 8, a chlorine residual of 0.2 ppm is required for the complete destruction of bacteria at the end of 10 minutes' contact time. Water in the pH range 8 to 9 requires a residual of 0.4 ppm, and at pH 9 to 10 a minimum chlorine residual of 0.8 ppm for complete kill at the end of 10 minutes' contact time. At longer contact times, lower residuals are required for complete kills.

3. CHLORINATION TREATMENTS

Chlorine, like the bactericides, can be used on a continuous or intermittent basis. The choice of treatment for flood waters depends on the cost of the respective treatments and success of the treatment. Some source waters may contain such a high bacteria count that continuous treatment is required. Others may only require periodic treatment to control the bacteria. The engineer should be aware, if comparatively large colonies of bacteria grow between treatments, that when the system is slugged with chlorine, these colonies will slough off, becoming plugging agents. Bacteria do not develop strains resistant to continuous chlorination.

a. *Flow lines*

Continuous chlorination to a chlorine residual of 0.2 ppm is usually satisfactory to keep flow lines free of bacteria. When an intermittent treatment is used, sufficient chlorine should be added to provide a residual where the water leaves the line.

b. *Filters*

Filters can be blocked by bacteria or slime growth, when water entering the filter is not chlorinated. Filters blocked by microorganisms can be cleared by flooding with water containing 100 ppm chlorine and allowing it to stand overnight. The filter is then back-washed to waste. Continuous chlorination will keep the filter free of microbial growth.

c. *Cooling Towers*

It is sometimes necessary to kill algae growths and other microorganisms in cooling towers. Intermittent treatment with 1 ppm free residual chlorine is generally sufficient to kill these organisms. Because of the danger of chemical attack of cooling tower wood, no more than 1 ppm chlorine should be used. Cooling tower treatment will be more fully discussed in Chapter 14.

d. *Ion Exchange Units*

Chlorine can be used to kill bacteria in ion exchange units utilizing natural glauconites, synthetic siliceous gels, or sulfonated polystyrene resins. Chlorine should not be used in units containing organic ion-exchange materials.

e. Condensers

Slime formation in condensers can be controlled by periodically treating with sufficient chlorine to give a free chlorine residual of 0.5 to 1.0 ppm in the water leaving the condenser.[38] Usually a total treatment time of one hour per day is sufficient. If the cooling water is contaminated with materials having a chlorine demand, such as hydrogen sulfide, it may be advisable to sterilize the makeup water and thus prevent the entrance of slime organisms.

f. Water Storage Basins

Algae growths in water storage basins can be controlled by intermittent chlorination to give 0.5 to 1.0 ppm free residual chlorine.

Mechanical Factors in Microbial Problems

Some mechanical factors can aid in controlling microorganisms. Bacteria and slime do not grow on surfaces exposed to high-velocity water streams.[39] The elimination of stagnant or quiescent areas in a water-handling system will aid in minimizing the bacterial problem.

Removal of accumulated sludge and deposits in tank bottoms eliminates some areas ideal for growth of sulfate-reducing bacteria. Keeping flow lines free of scale and other deposits will be helpful in controlling microorganisms.

Sources of Help in Solving Microbial Problems

Some laboratory work is nearly always necessary in the successful solution of microbial problems. Most oilfield service companies which sell bactericides have access to laboratories. Representatives of reliable companies will send samples of the water to their laboratories and obtain recommendations as to which of their products, and at what concentration, is required to control the microorganisms.

There are also many independent laboratories, not connected with the sale of chemicals, that provide technical help in solving these problems. For example, one such laboratory in Dallas estimates the sulfate-reducing bacteria population for as little as $5.00 per sample. It also evaluates bactericides and determines the proper concentration for use in a system.

References

[1] J. M. Sharpley, "Microbiological Corrosion in Waterfloods," *Corrosion*, **17** (1961), 386t.

[2] A. V. Baumgartner, "Microbiological Corrosion," Fifth Biennial Secondary Recovery Symposium, SPE, May 7–8, 1962.

[3] U. R. Evans, *The Corrosion and Oxidation of Metals* (London: Edward Arnold, Ltd., 1960), p. 276.

[4] C. H. Oppenheimer, "How To Detect and Control Corrosion-Causing Bacteria," *World Oil*, **147**, No. 7 (1958), 144.

[5] J. F. Bogtstra, "Corrosion of Unprotected Steel and Cast Iron Pipes in a Variety of Soils," *Corrosie-Inst, T.N.O.; Meded.*, **27** (1954), 108.

[6] L. L. Wolfson, "Microbiology in Secondary Recovery Systems," *Corrosion*, **16** (1960), 298t.

[7] *Ibid.*

[8] P. H. Krumperman, "A Study of Tant's Medium as a Method of Isolating *Clostridium* Species from Water Injection Systems of Four California Oilfield Waterfloods," First Biennial Symposium on Microbiology, API, Dec. 4 & 5, 1962.

[9] *Recommended Practice for Biological Analysis of Flood Injection Waters*, RP 38 (Dallas, Tex.: American Petroleum Institute, 1959).

[10] *Standard Methods for the Examination of Water and Wastewater* (11 th ed.) (New York: American Public Health Association, Inc., 1960).

[11] *Manual on Industrial Water and Industrial Waste Water* (2nd ed.) (Philadelphia: American Society for Testing Materials, 1960).

[12] *Recommended Practice for Biological Analysis of Flood Injection Waters.*

[13] L. B. Whitesell, "Field Evaluation of Microbial Problems and Their Control," AIME, Rocky Mountain Section Seventh Meeting, Paper No. SPE-64 (1961).

[14] *Recommended Practice for Biological Analysis of Flood Injection Waters.*

[15] Sharpley, *op. cit.*

[16] C. W. Chambers, C. M. Procter, and P. W. Kabler, "Bactericidal Effect of Low Concentrations of Silver," *J. Am. Water Works Assoc.*, **54** (1962), 208.

[17] H. C. Conger, W. R. Bass, and P. J. Butler, Jr., "Biocides—A Case History Study at the Rangely Weber Sand Unit," SPE-AIME Meeting, New Orleans, October, 1963, Paper No. SPE-700.

[18] *Ibid.*

[19] J. D. Sudbury, C. F. Knutson, M. Felsenthal, and J. D. Lung, "Conditioning of Pacific Ocean Water for Waterflood Injection," *J. Petrol. Technol.* **8**, (September, 1956), 85.

[20] E. O. Bennett, G. J. Guynes, and D. L. Isenberg, "The Sensitivity of Sulfate-Reducing Bacteria to Antibacterial Agents—III," *Producer's Monthly*, **24**, No. 5 (1960), 26.

[21] E. O. Bennett, G. J. Guynes, and D. L. Isenberg, "The Sensitivity of Sulfate-Reducing Bacteria to Antibacterial Agents (Phenolic Compounds)," *Producers Monthly*, **23**, No. 1 (1958), 18.

[22]R. C. Allred, J. D. Sudbury, and D. C. Olson, "Corrosion is Controlled by Bactericide Treatment," *World Oil*, **149**, No. 6 (1959), 111.

[23]D. O. Hitzman and L. B. Whitesell, Jr., "The Effect of Seasonal Variations and Various Treatments on Counts of Sulfate-Reducing Bacteria in a Waterflood," *API Drilling and Production Practices* (1957), p. 203.

[24]G. J. Guynes and E. O. Bennett, "The Sensitivity of Sulfate-Reducing Bacteria to Antibacterial Agents," *Producers Monthly*, **23**, No. 1 (1958), 15.

[25]W. H. Kibbel, Jr. and D. F. Kreuz, "An Evaluation of Peroxygens as Waterflood Bactericides," API First Biennial Symposium on Microbiology, Long Beach, Calif., 1962.

[26]Conger, Bass, and Butler, *op. cit.*

[27]C. C. Wright, "The Evaluation of Bactericides in the Field," *Producers Monthly*, **27**, No. 5 (1963), 2.

[28]R. W. Amstutz and L. C. Reynolds, "Engineering Aspects of Waterflood Bacteriology," *J. Petrol. Technol.*, **15** (1963), 1073.

[29]Sudbury *et al.*, *op. cit.*

[30]Amstutz and Reynolds, *op. cit.*

[31]Baumgartner, *op. cit.*

[32]Amstutz and Reynolds, *op. cit.*

[33]*Water Quality and Treatment* (2nd ed.) (New York: American Water Works Association, 1951), p. 205.

[34]*Ibid.* p. 191.

[35]*Salt Water Disposal East Texas Oil Field*, (2nd ed.) (Austin, Tex.: Petroleum Extension Service, 1958), p. 82.

[36]*Standard Methods for the Examination of Water and Wastewater*, p. 103.

[37]*Water Quality and Treatment*, p. 219.

[38]P. Hamer, J. Jackson, and E. F. Thurston, *Industrial Water Treatment Practice* (London: Butterworth & Co., Ltd., 1961), p. 345.

[39]C. C. Wright, "Effectiveness of Biocides in Field Applications," API First Biennial Symposium on Microbiology, Long Beach, Calif., 1962.

Processes of Water-Softening and Removal of Silica, Iron, and Manganese

7

Although water-softening is only infrequently used as a method of preventing scale deposition from injection waters, it is often used to treat plant and boiler feed waters. When iron is a problem in injection waters, iron removal methods can be used. Generally, the processes of silica and iron and manganese removal also find their greatest application with plant and boiler feed waters.

Precipitation processes of water-softening also remove iron and manganese, and sometimes silica. In some of these softening processes, the presence of iron in the water is advantageous, since the flocculant ferric hydroxide precipitate acts as a coagulant, aiding clarification of the water.

177

Water-Softening

The process of softening hard water consists of removing the dissolved mineral matter, which has soap-destroying power and which deposits scale in pipelines, boilers, engine jackets, and on cooling coils. The bicarbonates and sulfates of calcium and magnesium are the principal salts responsible for hardness in water.

The bicarbonates of calcium and magnesium are referred to as "temporary" hardness or carbonate hardness. These can be destroyed by heating the water and causing the slightly soluble carbonates to form. The sulfates and other salts which may cause scale are referred to as "permanent" or noncarbonate hardness, since they cannot be effectively removed by the simple process of heating the water.

Raw water may be softened by precipitation softening, ion exchange softening, or distillation. Each of the three methods can be used independently to soften water or in combination. The factors that influence the choice of a water-softening method are required quality of softened water, volume of water needed, cost of softening, and personnel available to operate the equipment.

Distillation and demineralization by ion exchange are expensive and are used only when high-quality water is required. Demineralization by ion exchange is cheaper with a water of low dissolved solids content, but distillation is a more economical method of removing dissolved solids from brackish waters. Ion exchange demineralization has the advantage that treated water can be obtained immediately on starting the plant.

Approximate order-of-magnitude costs for a 250 gpm installation of some various water-softening and demineralizing methods are presented in Table 7.1, which also shows the effect of treatment on water quality. It is evident from this table that cost of treatment increases with increases in water quality. These costs will be influenced by the quality of raw water softened.

Lime and Soda Ash Process

The oldest method of softening water is the lime and soda ash process. This process utilizes hydrated lime (calcium hydroxide), or burnt lime (calcium oxide) and soda ash (sodium carbonate), to remove calcium bicarbonate, magnesium, ferrous iron, and bicarbonate ions. The total salt content of the water is reduced when carbonate hardness is removed by the

Table 7.1

RELATIVE COSTS OF WATER SOFTENING PROCEDURES

(From Gilwood, *Chem. Eng.*, June 10, 1963, p. 183.)

Treatment	Effect on Water Quality	Operating Cost $/1,000 gal*	Installed Cost, $/gpm
Clarification (alum coagulation)	Reduce turbidity to 5, color to 5, Fe and Mn to 0.1 ppm.; increase SO_4 by 15 ppm.	0.015	120
Cold lime	Reduce total hardness to 85 ppm., M alkalinity to 35 ppm., Fe and Mn to 0.1 ppm.	0.02†	120
Hot lime soda (sludge contact)	Reduce total hardness to 26 ppm., turbidity to 5, combined CO_2 to 12 ppm., silica to 1 ppm.	0.03†	120
Hot lime zeolite	Reduce total hardness to 3 ppm., turbidity to 5, combined CO_2 to 12 ppm., silica to 1 ppm.	0.04†	140
Sodium cation exchange	Reduce total hardness to 5 ppm., Fe and Mn to 0.05 ppm.	0.025‡	50
Sodium hydrogen exchange (split treatment)	As above, but reduce M alkalinity to 0–15 ppm., CO_2 to 3 ppm.	0.03§	85
Two-stage weak-base demineralizing	Remove almost all electrolytes except SiO_2 and CO_2, reduce conductivity to 5–20 micromhos.	0.03 to 0.10§	100
Two-stage strong-base demineralizing	Remove almost all electrolyte, reduce conductivity to 5 to 10 micromhos, silica to 0.02 ppm.	0.05 to 0.15§	120
Mixed-bed demineralizing	As above, except reduce electrolyte conductivity to 0.1–1.0 micromhos.	0.05 to 0.25§	140
Electrodialysis	Reduce electrolyte to 500 ppm.	0.20 to 0.50§	250
Evaporation	Reduce total solids to 1 ppm.	2.00	330

*Operating costs are approximate, and include costs of chemicals, electricity and fuel.
†Operating costs vary with bicarbonate hardness.
‡Operating costs vary with total hardness.
§Operating costs vary with electrolyte content.

addition of lime. When soda ash is added, sodium ions are substituted by means of chemical reactions for the scale-forming cations. The chemical reactions involved in this process are:

$$CaO + H_2O \rightarrow Ca(OH)_2 \tag{7–1}$$

$$CO_2 + Ca(OH)_2 \rightarrow CaCO_3\downarrow + H_2O \tag{7–2}$$

$$Ca(HCO_3)_2 + Ca(OH)_2 \rightarrow 2CaCO_3\downarrow + 2H_2O \tag{7–3}$$

$$Mg(HCO_3)_2 + 2Ca(OH)_2 \rightarrow 2CaCO_3\downarrow + Mg(OH)_2\downarrow + 2H_2O \tag{7–4}$$

$$Fe(HCO_3)_2 + 2Ca(OH)_2 \rightarrow 2CaCO_3\downarrow + Fe(OH)_2 + 2H_2O \tag{7–5}$$

$$2NaHCO_3 + Ca(OH)_2 \rightarrow CaCO_3\downarrow + Na_2CO_3 + 2H_2O \tag{7–6}$$

$$MgSO_4 + Ca(OH)_2 \rightarrow Mg(OH)_2\downarrow + CaSO_4 \tag{7–7}$$

$$CaSO_4 + Na_2CO_3 \rightarrow CaCO_3\downarrow + Na_2SO_4 \tag{7–8}$$

As indicated in Eq. (7–1), the burnt lime dissolves in water to form calcium hydroxide. The calcium hydroxide removes carbon dioxide from the water by forming the slightly soluble calcium carbonate, as illustrated by Eq. (7–2). Additional lime reacts with calcium bicarbonate, according to Eq. (7–3), to form calcium carbonate and water. In this reaction, the salt content of the water is actually decreased. It requires the addition of a two-to-one mole ratio of lime to magnesium bicarbonate in order to remove the magnesium bicarbonate. This is caused by the solubility of magnesium carbonate, which necessitates the removal of magnesium by the formation of magnesium hydroxide. This is more easily understood by considering Eq. (7–4) as two reactions:

$$Ca(OH)_2 + Mg(HCO_3)_2 \longrightarrow CaCO_3\downarrow + MgCO_3 + 2H_2O \qquad (7\text{–}9)$$

$$MgCO_3 + Ca(OH)_2 \longrightarrow Mg(OH)_2\downarrow + CaCO_3\downarrow \qquad (7\text{–}10)$$

Initially, soluble magnesium carbonate is formed by the addition of lime. The addition of another mole of lime forms the slightly soluble magnesium hydroxide.

Eq. (7–8) shows the reaction of soda ash in the softening process. The soda ash reacts with the noncarbonate hardness to give the slightly soluble calcium carbonate and the soluble sodium salt. It is also evident from this equation that the salt content of the water is not reduced because of the formation of the soluble sodium salt. Eqs. (7–7) and (7–8) show that both lime and soda ash are required to soften water containing magnesium sulfate.

Waters containing more carbonate hardness than noncarbonate hardness require more lime than soda ash for their treatment—waters with more noncarbonate hardness require more soda ash than lime. Because soda ash is more expensive than lime, it costs more to soften sulfate waters than carbonate waters. It is more expensive to remove magnesium bicarbonate than calcium carbonate, because twice as much lime is required.

Because of the slight solubility of calcium carbonate and magnesium hydroxide, complete elimination of calcium and magnesium ions is not possible by this process. Theoretically, the water can be softened to a hardness of 25 ppm as calcium carbonate by this process, but in practice the hardness is reduced to 50 or 60 ppm. Generally, space is not available to retain the water until the reactions have gone to completion so that the water is still encrustant when it leaves the retention basin. This can be eliminated by retention in storage, addition of an acid salt such as aluminum sulfate to act as a coagulant and to convert residual alkalinity into sulfate, recarbonation with carbon dioxide to form the more soluble bicarbonates, or the addition of a complexing agent such as sodium hexametaphosphate to prevent the calcium from precipitating.

1. CHEMICALS USED IN LIME AND SODA ASH PROCESS

a. Chemical Lime

Chemical lime or calcium oxide is also called quicklime. It is cheaper on an equivalent basis than hydrated lime; however, it must be slaked, according to Eq. (7–1), in a limited amount of water before it can be used. Precautions must also be taken to keep it dry while stored. A large amount of heat is generated when it hydrates.

b. Hydrated Lime

Hydrated lime, calcium hydroxide, is also called slaked lime, and averages 93 per cent calcium hydroxide in its commercial form. It is more easily stored than chemical lime.

c. Dolomitic Lime

Dolomitic lime should contain 58 per cent calcium oxide and 40 per cent magnesium oxide. Hydrated dolomitic lime should contain 62 per cent calcium hydrated lime and 32 per cent magnesium oxide.

d. Soda Ash

The usual commercial grade of soda ash used in water-softening contains 58 per cent sodium oxide, which is equivalent to 99.2 per cent sodium carbonate. The chemical should be in the dry powdered form, containing no lumps or large crystals.

e. Coagulants

Aluminum sulfate is the most widely used coagulant, but ferric sulfate, ferrous sulfate, and sodium aluminate are also used, generally in dosages of 10 to 20 ppm.

2. EQUATIONS FOR CALCULATING CHEMICAL DOSAGES

The dosage of lime for removing carbonate hardness and the dosage of soda ash for removing noncarbonate hardness can be calculated using the following equation:

$$\text{lb } 100\% \text{ CaO per } 100 \text{ bbl} = 0.0445 \, (\text{ppm } CO_2 + \text{ppm half-bound } CO_2) + 0.08 \text{ ppm } Mg^{++}$$

$$(7\text{–}11)$$

lb 100% Na_2CO_3 per 100 bbl = 0.038 (ppm noncarbonate hardness as $CaCO_3$
— noncarbonate hardness to be left
in the water) (7–12)

These equations are based on pure chemical composition so that the results should be corrected for the purity of the particular commercial chemical used.

3. TYPES OF LIME AND SODA ASH PROCESS SOFTENERS

There are four basic types of lime and soda ash softeners. All are continuous, except the batch-process type.

a. Sludge-Blanket Type

In this type of softener, the raw water passes upward through a suspended-sludge blanket of previously formed precipitates. This has the advantage that any hydrated lime suspended in the sludge has an opportunity to come into contact with raw water. Also, the intimate contact of the solid phases in the sludge blanket and water prevents supersaturation. The detention time of one hour is less than in other methods, and the effluent is clearer.

b. Gravity Type

This type of lime and soda ash softener does not employ a sludge blanket, but lets the sludge settle to the bottom of the softener. The detention time averages four hours. The reactions do not go to completion, so recarbonation is used to prevent postprecipitation of calcium carbonate. The softened water usually requires filtration.

c. Catalyst Type

In this type of softener, a conical tank is two-thirds filled with a finely divided granular catalyst, such as graded calcite. Raw water and chemicals are added at the bottom of the tank. The calcium carbonate formed adheres to the catalyst grains. The detention period is only 8 to 12 minutes. Approximately 0.18 lb of new catalyst must be added per 100 bbl per 100 ppm of calcium hardness removed. Since magnesium hydroxide will not adhere to the catalyst, this method is limited to calcium removal.

d. Batch-Process Type

This type of softener is constructed in three units. One unit is used to mix water and chemicals, one unit serves as a settling basin, and the clear effluent is taken from the third unit. This type of softener is used mainly for the cold lime-soda process. It has the disadvantage of high space requirements.

4. VARIATIONS IN THE LIME AND SODA ASH PROCESS

a. Cold Lime Process

The addition of hydrated lime and a small amount of coagulant will reduce calcium alkalinity and, to some extent, magnesium alkalinity. This process will reduce calcium alkalinity to 35 ppm and remove approximately 10 per cent of the magnesium by co-precipitation.

b. Excess Lime Treatment

An excess of 35 to 70 ppm of lime necessary to precipitate magnesium is added to the water. Enough soda ash is then added to combine with the noncarbonate hardness and excess lime. A small amount of coagulant is also used.

c. Split Lime Treatment

This process consists of treating a large portion of the hard water with an excess of lime, then neutralizing this excess with raw water. The proper proportions are determined from the analysis data. This treatment reduces the hardness of a volume of water by a greater amount than the same quantity of chemical would accomplish by the usual method, but it is not as effective as the excess lime treatment.

d. Cold Lime-Barium Process

The use of barium carbonate instead of sodium carbonate in the softening process results in removal of sulfates by precipitation as barium sulfate. When lime and barium carbonate are added to the water, the following reactions occur:

$$CaSO_4 + BaCO_3 \longrightarrow BaSO_4\downarrow + CaCO_3\downarrow \qquad (7\text{--}13)$$

$$MgSO_4 + Ca(OH)_2 + BaCO_3 \longrightarrow BaSO_4\downarrow + CaCO_3\downarrow + Mg(OH)_2 \quad (7\text{--}14)$$

Approximately 0.0760 lb of barium carbonate are added per ppm of sulfate hardness per 100 bbl of water.

Since barium carbonate is approximately three times as expensive as sodium carbonate, the cold lime-barium process finds limited application. The process has been considered for treatment of a sulfate-containing water for injection in a reservoir containing barium water. Treatment cost was estimated at two cents a barrel.

Hot Lime and Soda Ash Process

The hot lime and soda ash process is carried out at temperatures near the boiling point. Since the velocities of chemical reactions increase with increases in temperature, the process occurs at a more rapid rate than the lime and soda ash process. The precipitates which form in this process are larger and heavier, and settle at a more rapid rate. No coagulant is needed. The water softener consists of chemical feeders, a heater, settling tank, and filters. Hydrated lime and soda ash are the principal chemicals used in the process.

This process finds its greatest use in treating boiler waters. The hot lime and soda ash process is occasionally used for treating water to be used at elevated temperatures.

Ion-Exchange Water Softening

Raw water can be softened or demineralized by means of ion exchange. Ion exchange is a reaction between a solid and a liquid, resulting in replacement of an ion of the solid with one from the liquid. The process of ion exchange for softening waters is preferable to the precipitation process when one or more of the following conditions exist:

(1) Less than 100 ppm of hardness expressed as calcium carbonate is present in the water.

(2) An extremely low dissolved solids content is required.

(3) Disposal facilities are not available for the sludge produced in the precipitation process.

(4) Only a limited volume of treated water is required.

The use of sodium zeolites for softening water was the first industrial application of ion exchange. In addition to natural zeolites, certain synthetic resins now find use as ion-exchange material in water-softening operations. Ion exchange can be used alone to soften water or in conjunction with some of the other methods. There are three methods of softening water by ion exchange: the sodium cycle, split-stream, and deionization. The ion-exchange material and method used will depend to a large extent upon the quality of water required for a particular use.

1. MECHANISM OF ION EXCHANGE

The constituents of an ionic solid may be considered to be present as ions rather than molecules, and the ion at the surface of a crystal is held by less attractive forces than a similar ion in the body of the crystal. Water, being a highly polar medium, will reduce the net attractive forces holding the surface ion to such an extent that an exchange reaction between this surface ion and an ion in solution is possible. The ease of this exchange reaction depends upon: (1) the forces binding the ion to the crystal, (2) concentration of the exchanging ion, (3) charge of the exchanging ion, (4) sizes of the two ions, (5) accessibility of lattice ions, and (6) solubility effects.

Because of the inaccessibility of the cations of mica and feldspar, these silicates do not normally exchange cations unless finely ground. However, some zeolites, such as chabazite, heulandite, analcite, and sodalite, are highly porous chainlike silicate structures, and the sodium and calcium ions are easily accessible. The sodium and calcium ions in the crystal may exchange with ions that are small enough to penetrate the porous crystal structure. Some clays, such as montmorillonite, also will exchange lattice ions under certain conditions.

Lattice anions as well as cations may participate in exchange reactions. Some substances, called amphoteric exchangers, exchange both anions and cations. The hydroxyl ion of kaolinite or montmorillonite can exchange with chloride, sulfate, and phosphate ions. The pH of the solution in contact with montmorillonite influences the exchange of the anions or cations. The exchange of anions occurs best at low pH and decreases with increasing pH, while cations exchange best at higher pH and the exchange decreases with decrease in pH.

Although ion-exchange resins lack crystallinity, the exchange mechanism is similar to that of the zeolites and clays. The anion and cation-exchange resins are insoluble, high molecular weight, polymeric electrolytes. The functional groups of cation-exchange resins may be sulfonic, carboxylic, or phenolic groups. The exchange capacity of these resins can be determined from their sulfur, carboxylic, or phenolic content, indicating that the exchange takes place throughout the resin rather than only on the surface. Anion-exchange resins are polyamines.

The relative replacing power for alkali and alkaline-earth cations increases in the order of: Li, Na, K, Rb, Cs, Mg, Ca, Sr, and Ba.[1] At low concentrations and ordinary temperatures, the extent of exchange increases with increasing valence or, for constant valence ions, with increasing atomic number. At high concentrations of ions, this exchange trend is diminished. The relative replacing power of anions for a weak-base anion exchanger is in the order of: hydroxide, sulfate, chromate, citrate, tartrate, nitrate, arsenate, phosphate, molybdate, acetate = iodide = bromide, chloride, and fluoride.

The exchange capacity varies with the ion exchange resin or zeolite. For example, a standard greensand sodium cation exchanger may have a capacity of 3 kg/cu ft (where the cations are expressed as grains of calcium carbonate), and an Amberlite cation-exchange resin such as IR-120 may have a capacity of 41.5 kg/cu ft as calcium carbonate.

As water is softened by the ion-exchange process, the ion-exchange medium becomes saturated, with the cations or anions being removed. It is then necessary to regenerate the media. In the case of zeolites, this means replacing the removed cations with sodium ions or, in the case of hydrogen cation exchangers, with hydrogen ions. Sodium chloride solution is generally used to regenerate zeolites, but sodium nitrate or potassium chloride can also be used. Very dilute sulfuric acid (1 to 8 per cent) or hydrochloric acid can be used to regenerate synthetic hydrogen cation-exchange resins. Sodium hydroxide, ammonia, and sodium carbonate solutions are used to regenerate weakly basic anion exchangers. A 2 to 4 per cent sodium hydroxide solution is the best regenerant for a strong-base anion exchanger.

2. QUALITY OF WATER

The quality of the effluent or water passed through the ion exchanger is influenced by the "leakage." Leakage is the passage through the ion exchanger of the ion which it is desirable to remove. Leakage is a function of influent water composition, regenerant dosage level, and the condition of the lower levels of the exchanger bed. The metallic cation leakage from a mixed-bed demineralizer is less than that from a two-bed system under identical operating conditions. Water quality similar to that obtained by distillation can be obtained by use of ion-exchange equipment and, generally, at less cost. In distillation, the entire volume of water is removed from the solids, while, in ion exchange, only the dissolved solids are removed from the water. However, for waters of high dissolved solids' content, distillation is more economical than ion exchange.

3. RATE OF EXCHANGE

The rate of exchange is influenced by the particle size of the resin, the exchange type, flow rate, and temperature. These factors also influence the breakthrough capacity and the leakage. For a given resin, a decrease in particle size results in an increased rate of exchange and increased breakthrough capacity. However, the rate of exchange may vary between different resins of the same particle size. Increasing the water temperature tends to increase the diffusion and, consequently, increases the rate of exchange.

4. FLOW RATE

Flow rates may be expressed as volume of water per square foot of cross-sectional area per minute, or as volume of water per volume of resin per minute. A zeolite softener may have a normal flow rate of 1.2 bbl/min per 10 sq ft, while the flow rate for an Amberlite exchange resin might be 0.48 bbl/10 cu ft per min. The flow rate is influenced by the characteristics of the water and the rate of exchange.

The normal water demand and any peak demand should be considered in determining a flow rate. If peak demands occur frequently, it may be necessary to design the ion-exchange softener to meet these demands. Otherwise, storage facilities must be of sufficient volume to provide additional soft water for these periods and during regeneration periods. A multiple-unit system may be necessary in order to provide the necessary flow of soft water when one unit is out for regeneration.

Flow rates are more critical during regeneration than during exhaustion of the exchanger. For an Amberlite ion-exchange resin, the regeneration flow rate may be as low as 0.12 bbl/10 cu ft per minute. When excess regenerants are being rinsed out of the bed, the flow should be maintained at about the regeneration rate, until a volume of rinse water equal to half the volume of resin has passed through the exchanger; then the rate can be increased.

5. Ion-Exchange Resins

Ion-exchange resins may be divided into four major groups: strongly acidic resins containing sulfonic acid groups; weakly acidic resins containing carboxylic acid groups; strongly basic resins containing quaternary ammonium groups; and weakly basic resins containing a mixture of primary, secondary, and tertiary amine groups. Weakly acidic and weakly basic exchange resins can absorb acids and bases or exchange ions, but they cannot "split" salts. ("Salt splitting" is the term referring to the replacement of the metal ion in solution by a hydrogen ion from the resin.) In addition to undergoing the same reactions, the strongly acidic and strongly basic resins can split salts.

The capacity of the ion exchanger is the amount of ions it can remove from water. Exchanger capacities are used in characterizing ion-exchange materials and in numerical calculations pertaining to ion-exchange operations. Capacity of an exchanger is usually expressed as weight capacity or volume capacity. The weight capacity of an ion exchanger is defined as the number of ionogenic or exchange groups per specified weight of material.[2] This is usually expressed as milliequivalents per gram of exchanger.

Where the number of exchangeable ions and the size of the column are important variables, it is more practical to use volume capacity. Volume capacity is the number of ionogenic groups per unit volume of packed bed. It can be expressed as meq/ml, or equivalents per liter of fully swollen bed. Other units used to express exchanger capacity are shown in Table 7.2.

Some of the most common commercial ion exchangers are shown in Table 7.3. This table is divided into two groups; cation exchangers and anion exchangers. Both weight and volume capacities are given in this table.

Table 7.2

ION EXCHANGER CAPACITY DEFINITIONS

(From F. Helfferich *Ion Exchange* (New York: McGraw-Hill Book Company, 1962.) Used by permission.)

	Definition	Remarks
Capacity (maximum capacity, ion-exchange capacity)	Number of ionogenic groups per specified amount of ion exchanger.	Constant used for characterizing ion exchangers.
Scientific weight capacity	Units: meq/g dry H^+ or Cl^- form.	
Technical volume capacity	Units: eq/liter packed bed in H^+ or Cl^- form and fully water-swollen. Other units: eq/ft³ bed, lb CaO/ft³ bed, etc.	
Apparent capacity (effective capacity)	Number of *exchangeable* counter ions per specified amount of ion exchanger. Common units: meq/g dry H^+ or Cl^- form (apparent weight capacity).	Is lower than maximum capacity when ionogenic groups are incompletely ionized; depends on experimental conditions (pH, solution concentration, etc.).
Sorption capacity	Amount of solute, taken up by sorption rather than by ion exchange, per specified amount of ion exchanger.	Depends on experimental conditions.
Useful capacity	Capacity utilized when equilibrium is not attained.	Depends on experimental conditions (ion-exchange rate, etc.).
Breakthrough capacity (dynamic capacity)	Capacity utilized in column operations.	Depends on operating conditions.
Concentration of fixed ionic groups	Number of fixed ionic groups in meq/cm³ swollen resin (molarity) or per gram solvent in resin (molality).	Depends on experimental conditions (swelling, etc.). Used in theoretical treatment of ion-exchange phenomena.

6. EXCHANGER TYPES

Ion exchangers may be classified as cation exchangers, anion exchangers, and mixed-bed exchangers or deionizers.

a. Cation Exchangers

Cation exchangers may be of the sodium-cycle type or the hydrogen-cycle type. In the sodium-cycle type, the magnesium and calcium ions in the water replace sodium ions on the zeolite or resin. The reactions may be expressed by the following equations:

$$Mg^{++} + Na_2Z \longrightarrow MgZ + 2Na^+ \tag{7-15}$$

$$Ca^{++} + Na_2Z \longrightarrow CaZ + 2Na^+ \tag{7-16}$$

When the capacity of the exchanger to remove hardness has been utilized, the unit is taken out of service and backwashed before regeneration. The backwash serves to remove any silt or turbidity accumulated during the softening process and also expands the bed to promote efficiency of the regenerant. The regeneration consists of passing sodium chloride brine through the unit, replacing the calcium and magnesium ions with sodium ions. The regenerating solution, along with water used to rinse the softener after regeneration, is discharged to waste.

The hydrogen-cycle type of cation exchanger produces a different quality of treated water than the sodium-cycle type. The water is passed over the hydrogen-cation exchange resin and calcium, magnesium, and sodium ions are exchanged for hydrogen ions. The hydrogen ions form acid with the ions in the water. Carbonic acid, formed by combination of the hydrogen ions with the carbonate or bicarbonate ions, breaks up into carbon dioxide gas and water. The carbon dioxide can be removed by degasification. The other acids can be neutralized by the addition of an alkali or by blending with some of the raw water, containing alkali. When the exchange capacity of the resin has been reached, the unit is taken out of service, backwashed, and regenerated with dilute sulfuric or hydrochloric acid. The regenerating solution and rinse are discharged to waste.

Leakage through the hydrogen-cation exchanger is dependent upon the degree of regeneration. The leakage generally occurs at the beginning of and at the end of the exhaustion cycles. If the ion-exchange column is not completely regenerated, the bottom portion of the bed will contain some cations. As raw water is added to the top of the exchanger, the cations are exchanged for hydrogen ions. These hydrogen ions percolate down the column and exchange with the cations on the resin in the bottom of the exchanger. This leakage exists until all the cations on the resin are exchanged for hydrogen ions. The leakage will then be minimal, until the exchanger is exhausted.

When appreciable amounts of calcium are exchanged on a resin, regeneration with hydrochloric acid has an advantage over sulfuric acid. When sulfuric acid is used, the calcium removed from the resin may combine with the sulfate from the acid and precipitate as calcium sulfate. As the regenerant is rinsed out of the bed, the calcium sulfate dissolves and the calcium ion is exchanged. This partially consumes the exchange capacity of the resin, reducing the efficiency of the regeneration process. Since calcium chloride

Table 7.3
MOST COMMON COMMERCIAL ION EXCHANGERS

(From Helfferich, *Ion Exchange* (New York: McGraw-Hill Book Company, 1962. Used by permission.)

Matrix	Ionic Group	Trade Name	Manufacturer	Capacity meq/g Dry Resin	Capacity meq/ml Resin Bed	Moisture Content, % wt	Maximum Temperature, °C	pH Range	Physical Form	Remarks
		CATION EXCHANGERS								
Polystyrene resins	$-SO_3^-$	Amberlite IR-120	Rohm & Haas Co.†	4.3–5	1.9	44–48	120	0–14	spherical beads	standard resin, ca. 8% DVB
		Amberlite IR-122	Rohm & Haas Co.†	4.3–5	2.1	40–44	120	0–14	spherical beads	ca. 10% DVB, higher resistance to oxidizing agents
		Amberlite IR-124	Rohm & Haas Co.†	4.3–5	2.1	37–41	120	0–14	spherical beads	ca. 12% DVB, higher resistance to oxidizing agents
		Amberlite 200	Rohm & Haas Co.†	4.3	1.75	47–52	120	0–14	spherical beads	higher mech. and chem. stability, lower capacity
		Amberlite XE-100	Rohm & Haas Co.†	4.5	1.2	58–65	120	0–14	spherical beads	ca, 4% DVB
		Amberlyst 15	Rohm & Haas Co.†	4.9	1.2	60–66	120	0–14	spherical beads	"macroreticular" resin
		Dowex 50	Dow Chemical Co.‡	4.9–5.2	Depends on crosslinking		150	0–14	spherical beads	available with different degrees of crosslinking
		Dowex 50W	Dow Chemical Co.‡	4.9–5.2			150	0–14	spherical beads	(Dowex 50-X2 has 2% DVB, etc.); Dowex 50W is improved resin replacing older Dowex 50
		Duolite C-20	Chemical Process Co.	5.1	2.2	45–51	150	0–14	spherical beads	standard resin, ca. 8% DVB; other degrees of crosslinking on request

Duolite C-25	Chemical Process Co.	5.1	1.7	55–62	120	0–14	spherical beads	porous resin
Duolite C-27	Chemical Process Co.	5.0	2.1	45–50	150	0–14	spherical beads	resin of lighter color
Imac C-12	"Activit," Holland	4.5	2		120	0–14	spherical beads	standard resin, ca. 8% DVB
Imac C-19	"Activit," Holland	4.5	1.4		120	0–14	spherical beads	porous resin
Ionac C-240	(Permutit Q, marketed by Ionac Co.)							
Lewatit S-100	Farbenfabriken Bayer, Germany (West)	4.75	2.5	40–45	110	0–12	spherical beads	standard resin, ca. 8% DVB
Lewatit S-115	Farbenfabriken Bayer, Germany (West)	4.6	2.4	40–45	110	0–12	spherical beads	higher resistance to oxidizing agents
Nalcite HCR	(Dowex 50-X8, marketed by Nalco Chemical Co.)							
Nalcite HGR	(Dowex 50-X10, marketed by Nalco Chemical Co.)							
Nalcite HDR	(Dowex 50-X12, marketed by Nalco Chemical Co.)							
Permutit Q	Permutit Co., U.S.A.	4.8	2.0	45–50	120	0–14	spherical beads	standard resin; other degrees of crosslinking available
Permutit RS	Permutit A.G., Berlin, Germany (West)	5.5			150		spherical beads	
Resex P	Jos. Crosfield, England						spherical beads	
Wofatit KPS	VEB Farbenfabrik Wolfen, Germany (East)	4.5			115		spherical beads	standard resin with 10% DVB; resins with 2, 4, 6, and 16% DVB also available
Zeo-Karb 225	Permutit Co. Ltd., England§	4.8	2.1	45–50	120		spherical beads	standard resin with 8% DVB; resins with 1, 2, 4.5, 12, and 20% DVB also available

Matrix	Ionic Group	Trade Name	Manufacturer	Capacity meq/g Dry Resin	Capacity meq/ml Resin Bed	Moisture Content, % wt	Maximum Temperature, °C	pH Range	Physical Form	Remarks
	$-PO_3^{2-}$		(Duolite C-63, analytical grade, marketed by Bio-Rad Laboratories)							
		Bio-Rex 63 Duolite ES-61	Chemical Process Co.					4–14	spherical beads	experimental resin
		Duolite C63	Chemical Process Co.	6.6	3.1–3.3			4–14	spherical beads	experimental resin, ca. 6% DVB, more porous than ES-61
		Nalcite X-219	Nalco Chemical Co.					4–14	spherical beads	experimental resin
	$-HPO_2^-$		(Duolite C-62, analytical grade, marketed by Bio-Rad Laboratories)							
		Bio-Rex 62 Duolite ES-60	Chemical Process Co.					4–14	spherical beads	experimental resin
		Duolite C-62	Chemical Process Co.	6.0	2.6			4–14	spherical beads	experimental resin, more porous than ES-60
	$-N(CH_2COOH)_2$		(Dowex A-1, analytical grade, marketed by Bio-Rad Laboratories)							
		Chelex 100 Dowex A-1	Dow Chemical Co.	1–1.2	0.33	71–76		4–14	spherical beads	chelating resin
Vinyl addition polymers	$-OSO_3^-$	CFB-P	Chem. Fabrik Budenheim, Germany (West)				100			
	$-COOH$	Amberlite IRC-50	Rohm & Haas Co.†	9.5	3.5	43–53	120	5–14	spherical beads	
		Amberlite XE-89	Rohm & Haas Co.†		4.2	52–60	120	5–14	spherical beads	special resin for pharmaceutical applications
		Bio-Rex 70 Duolite CS-101	(Duolite CS-101, analyt. grade, marketed by Bio-Rad Laboratories) Chemical Process Co.	10	3.5		100	6–14	spherical beads	
		Ionac C-270 Permutit C	(Permutit H-70, marketed by Ionac Co.) Permutit A. G., Berlin, Germany (West)	10	4		100	6–14	spherical beads	

Phenolic resins —SO_3^-

Resin	Source					Mesh	Form	Remarks
Permutit H-70	Permutit Co., New York	7.9	3.6		95	6–14	spherical beads	
Wofatit CP	VEB Farbenfabrik Wolfen Germany (East)	10			30		spherical beads	
Zeo-Karb 226	Permutit Co. Ltd., England§	10	3.5		100		spherical beads	available with 2.5 and 4.5% crosslinking
Bio-Rex 40	(Duolite C-3, analytical grade, marketed by Bio-Rad Laboratories)							
Duolite C-3	Chemical Process Co.	2.9	1.2		60	0–9	granules	resins with —$CH_2SO_3^-$ groups; C-10 more porous than C-3
Duolite C-10	Chemical Process Co.	2.9	0.6		40	0–9	granules	
Lewatit KSN	Farbenfabriken Bayer, Germany (West)	4.0	1.6	45–50	30	0–8	granules	
Wofatit F	VEB Farbenfabrik Wolfen, Germany (East)	2.9			50		granules	
Wofatit P		1.9			35		granules	
Zeo-Karb 215	Permutit Co. Ltd., England§	2.6	0.9		40		granules	—SO_3^- groups
Duolite ES-65	Chemical Process Co.	3.3	1.4				granules	experimental resin
Duolite CS-100	Chemical Process Co.	1.9	0.8				granules	
Ionac C-265	(Permutit H, marketed by Ionac Co.)							
Lewatit CNO	Farbenfabriken Bayer, Germany (West)	4.0	2.5	30–35	40	0–8	granules	
Permutit H	Permutit Co., New York	5.0	1.9		65		granules	
Permutit HC	Permutit A. G., Berlin, Germany (West)	4.0			40		granules	
Resex W	Jos. Crosfield, England	2.5–3					granules	
Wofatit CN	VEB Farbenfabrik Wolfen, Germany (East)	2.0			30		granules	

—PO_3^{2-}
—COOH

193

Matrix	Ionic Group	Trade Name	Manufacturer	Capacity meq/g Dry Resin	Capacity meq/ml Resin Bed	Moisture Content, % wt	Maximum Temperature, °C	pH Range	Physical Form	Remarks
		Zeo-Karb 216	Permutit Co. Ltd., England§	2.5	1.1		30		granules	
	$-SO_3^-$ and $-COOH$	Lewatit CNS	Farbenfabriken Bayer, Germany (West)	5.0	2.8	36–43	40	0–8	granules	
Coals	$-SO_3^-$	Dusarit S	"Activit," Holland	1.8	0.6		100		granules	
		Soucol	Jos. Crosfield, England				30		granules	
Alumosilicates		Decalso	Permutit Co., New York	1.4	0.5		40		granules	
		Doucil	Jos. Crosfield, England	1.2					granules	
		Molecular Sieve 4A	Linde Co.				400		pellets	synthetic zeolites, microcrystals pelletized in clay binder; pore widths: ca. 4, 5, and 12A; for use as specific sorbents
		Molecular Sieve 5A	Linde Co.				400		pellets	
		Molecular Sieve 13X	Linde Co.				400		pellets	
Zirconium-base ion-exchangers	$-OPO_3^{2-}$	Bio-Rad ZP-1	Bio-Rad Laboratories				300	1–6	crystals	
	$-OWO_3^-$	Bio-Rad ZT-1	Bio-Rad Laboratories	1.0	0.7		300	1–6	crystals	
	$-OMoO_3^-$	Bio-Rad ZM-1	Bio-Rad Laboratories				300	1–6	crystals	
Ammonium molybdophosphate		Bio-Rad AMP-1	Bio-Rad Laboratories						microcrystals	
Cellulose	$-OC_2H_4SO_3^-$	Cellex SE	Bio-Rad Laboratories	0.2					small rods	

	Trade name	Manufacturer						Form	Remarks
$-OPO_3^{2-}$	Cellex P	Bio-Rad Laboratories	0.8					small rods	
$-OCH_2COOH$	Cell Cex M	Bio-Rad Laboratories	0.7					small rods	

ANION EXCHANGERS

	Trade name	Manufacturer						Form	Remarks
Polystyrene resins $-N(alkyl)_3^+$									
	Amberlite IRA-400	Rohm & Haas Co.†	2.6	1.2	42–48	60	0–12	spherical beads	standard resin, ca. 8% DVB
	Amberlite IRA-401	Rohm & Haas Co.†	3	1.0	54–59	60	0–12	spherical beads	porous resin
	Amberlite IRA-401S	Rohm & Haas Co.†		0.8	59–65	60	0–12	spherical beads	special resin for sugar treatment
	Amberlite IRA-402	Rohm & Haas Co.†		1.3	53–60	60	0–12	spherical beads	
	Amberlite IRA-405	Rohm & Haas Co.†		1.6	45–49	60	0–12	spherical beads	special resins for uranium recovery
	Amberlite IRA-425	Rohm & Haas Co.†		1.3	50–53	60	0–12	spherical beads	
	De-Acidite FF	Permutit Co. Ltd., England§	4.0	1.6		60		spherical beads	standard resin 7–9% DVB; lower degrees of crosslinking available
	Dowex 1	Dow Chemical Co.‡	3.5	Depends on crosslinking		50		spherical beads	standard resin Dowex 1-X8; other crosslinking available
	Dowex 11	Dow Chemical Co.‡				50		spherical beads	special resin for uranium recovery
	Dowex 21K	Dow Chemical Co.‡	4.5	1.2	57	50		spherical beads	
	Duolite A-42	Chemical Process Co.	2.3	0.7		60	0–14	spherical beads	improved mech. stability, easier regeneration
	Duolite A-101	Chemical Process Co.	4.0	1.3		60	0–14	spherical beads	
	Duolite A-101D	Chemical Process Co.	4.2	1.4		60	0–14	spherical beads	improved resins, more porous than A-42

| Matrix | Ionic Group | Trade Name | Manufacturer | Capacity | | Moisture Content, % wt | Maximum Temperature, °C | pH Range | Physical Form | Remarks |
				meq/g Dry Resin	meq/ml Resin Bed					
		Ionac A-540	(Permutit S-1, marketed by Ionac Co.)							
		Lewatit M-500	Farbenfabriken Bayer, Germany (West)	4.0	1.6	35-45	70	1-14	spherical beads	
		Lewatit MP-500	Farbenfabriken Bayer, Germany (West)	4.0	1.2	55-60	70	1-14	spherical beads	exact nature of fixed ionic groups not disclosed; MP resins are porous varieties
		Lewatit M-600	Farbenfabriken Bayer, Germany (West)	3.7	1.6	40-50	40	1-14	spherical beads	
		Lewatit MP-600	Farbenfabriken Bayer, Germany (West)	3.7	1.1	60-65	40	1-14	spherical beads	
		Nalcite SBR	(Dowex 1, marketed by Nalco Chemical Co.)							standard resin with 8% DVB
		Nalcite SBR-P								more porous resin
		Permutit ESB	Permutit A. G., Berlin, Germany (West)	3.2	1.2		70		spherical beads	
		Permutit ESB-26	Permutit A. G., Berlin, Germany (West)	3.3	1.3		70		spherical beads	
		Permutit S-1	Permutit Co., New York	3.1	0.9		50		spherical beads	
		Resanex HBL	Jos. Crosfield, England	3.5	1.5		60		spherical beads	
		Resanex HBT	Jos. Crosfield, England	3.5			60		spherical beads	more porous than HBL
		Wofatit SBW	VEB Farbenfabrik Wolfen, Germany (East)	3.5			60		spherical beads	

Group	Trade name	Manufacturer						Shape	Remarks
$-N(\text{alkylol})(\text{alkyl})_2^+$	Amberlite IRA-410	Rohm & Haas Co.†	3.0	1.2	40–45	40	0–12	spherical beads	standard resin, ca. 6% DVB
	Amberlite IRA-411	Rohm & Haas Co.†	3.0	0.7		40	0–12	spherical beads	more porous resin
	Dowex 2	Dow Chemical Co.‡	3.0	Depends on crosslinking		30		spherical beads	standard resin Dowex 2-X8, other degrees of crosslinking available
	Duolite A-40	Chemical Process Co.	3.7	1.1		40	0–14	spherical beads	
	Duolite A-102	Chemical Process Co.	4.0	1.3		40	0–14	spherical beads	
	Duolite A-102D	Chemical Process Co.	4.2	1.4		40	0–14	spherical beads	improved resins, more porous than A-40
	Ionac A-550 Nalcite SAR	(Permutit S-2, marketed by Ionac Co.) (Dowex 2, marketed by Nalco Chemical Co.)							
	Permutit ES	Permutit A. G., Berlin, Germany (West)	3.2	1.2		40		spherical beads	
	Permutit ES-26	Permutit A. G., Berlin, Germany (West)	3.3	1.3		40		spherical beads	
	Permutit S-2	Permutit Co., New York	3.3	1.2		40		spherical beads	
weak-base amino groups	Amberlite IR-45	Rohm & Haas Co†	5	2	37–45	100	0–9	spherical beads	
	De-Acidite G	Permutit Co. Ltd., England§	4.0	1.6		100		spherical beads	$-N(C_2H_3)_2$ groups only
	De-Acidite M	Permutit Co. Ltd., England§	5.5	2.2		100		spherical beads	polyamine groups
	Dowex 3	Dow Chemical Co.	6	3		65		spherical beads	
	Duolite A-14	Chemical Process Co.	8	2.5				spherical beads	
	Ionac A-315	(Permutit W, marketed by Ionac Inc.)							
	Lewatit MP-60	Farbenfabriken Bayer, Germany (West)	6.3	2.2	40–50	100		spherical beads	tertiary amino groups

Matrix	Ionic Group	Trade Name	Manufacturer	Capacity meq/g Dry Resin	Capacity meq/ml Resin Bed	Moisture Content, % wt	Maximum Temperature, °C	pH Range	Physical Form	Remarks
		Nalcite WBR	(Dowex 3, marketed by Nalco Chemical Co.)	5.7	2.0		95		spherical beads	
		Permutit W	Permutit Co., New York							
	strong-and weak-base groups $-SR_2^+$	De-Acidite H	Permutit Co. Ltd., England	3.8	1.5		100		spherical beads	
		Duolite ES-105	Chemical Process Co.		1.2				spherical beads	experimental resin
Condensation polymers	$-N(alkyl)_3^+$	Imac S-3	"Activit," Holland		0.6		40		granules	highly porous resin
		Lewatit MN	Farbenfabriken Bayer, Germany (West)	2.3	0.9	46–54	30	1–14	granules	
	Weak-base amino groups	Duolite A-2	Chemical Process Co.	8.4	2.3		40		granules	
		Duolite A-2M	Chemical Process Co.	6.5	1.8		50		granules	tertiary amino groups only
		Duolite A-4	Chemical Process Co.	7.7	2.0		50	0–5	granules	tertiary amino groups only
		Duolite A-5	Chemical Process Co.	9.0	2.5		60		granules	
		Duolite A-6	Chemical Process Co.	7.0	2.2		60	0–5	granules	tertiary amino groups only
		Duolite A-7	Chemical Process Co.	9.1	2.5		40	0–4	granules	
		Duolite A-30T	Chemical Process Co.	8.9	2.8		80	0–5	spherical beads	epoxy-polyamine resin with tertiary amino groups
		Imac A-17	"Activit," Holland						granules	
		Imac A-19	"Activit," Holland	1.3			120		granules	
		Lewatit MIH-59	Farbenfabriken Bayer, Germany (West)	6.0	2.5	40–50	30		granules	

	Name	Manufacturer					Form	Remarks
	Permutit E-3	Permutit A. G., Berlin, Germany (West)	6		40		granules	tertiary amino groups only
	Permutit E-7P	Jos. Crosfield, England	6		40		granules	highly porous resin
	Resanex		9	3	60		granules	
	Wofatit N	VEB Farbenfabrik Wolfen, Germany (East)	4.3		30		granules	
Strong- and weak-base groups	Duolite A-30B	Chemical Process Co.	8.7	2.6	80	0–9	spherical beads	epoxy-polyamine resin
	Ionac A-300	(Permutit A, marketed by Ionac Co., New York)						
	Permutit A	Permutit Co., New York	8	2	40		granules	
	Wofatit L-150	VEB Farbenfabrik Wolfen, Germany (East)	10		50		granules	polyalkyleneimine resin
Zirconium oxyhydrate	Bio-Rad H20-1	Bio-Ral Laboratories			300			
Cellulose								
$-OC_2H_5N(C_2H_5)_3^+$	Cellex T	Bio-Rad Laboratories					small rods	
$-OC_2H_5N(C_2H_5)_2$	Cellex D	Bio-Rad Laboratories					small rods	
Amino groups	Cellex E	Bio-Rad Laboratories					small rods	
$-OCH_2-$⟨ring⟩$-NH_2$	Cellex PAB	Bio-Rad Laboratories					small rods	

*Properties given are manufacturers' data and are not strictly comparable since testing procedures differ.

†Amberlite resins (A.R. and C.P. grades) are also marketed by Mallinckrodt.

‡Dowex resins (analytical grade) are also marketed by Bio-Rad Laboratories.

§Zeo-Karb and De-Acidite resins are also marketed under the name Zerolit (with otherwise same designation) by United Water Softeners, London.

is extremely soluble, this does not happen when hydrochloric acid is used as a regenerant. However, passing a sodium chloride solution through the exchanger replaces the calcium ions with sodium ions. This can then be followed with sulfuric acid regenerant.

b. Anion Exchangers

In the deionization of water, anion exchange units can be used to treat the effluent from the cation exchanger. The choice of the anion exchanger is influenced by the desired degree of anion removal. The effluent from a hydrogen-cation exchanger may contain the strong acids, hydrochloric, sulfuric, nitric, and phosphoric; and the weak acids, hydrogen sulfide, carbonic, boric, and silicic. The strong acids will adsorb on a weakly basic anion exchanger, but a strongly basic anion exchanger is required to adsorb the weak acids. In the interest of economy, it is desirable to adsorb as much acidity as possible on a weakly basic anion exchanger because of lower regeneration costs. Treatment with sodium hydroxide (a relatively expensive process) is required for regeneration of strongly basic exchangers. If a weakly basic exchanger is used to treat the cation-exchange effluent first, vacuum de-aeration can be used to remove some of the carbon dioxide and hydrogen sulfide, decreasing the load on a strongly basic anion exchanger. The water can then be passed through a strongly basic anion exchanger to remove boric acid and silicic acid, as well as the residual hydrogen sulfide and carbon dioxide.

The regenerant used with anion exchangers influences the economy and quality of the unit's operation. Regenerants for weakly basic exchangers, listed in order of decreasing efficiency, are: sodium hydroxide, sodium carbonate, and ammonia. However, because of its low equivalent weight and low cost, ammonia is attractive as a regenerant. Weakly basic anion exchange resins can be completely regenerated, with a slight excess of the theoretical amount of base necessary for regeneration. As was previously stated, a strong base, such as sodium hydroxide, is required to regenerate strongly basic anion exchangers.

A cutaway view of an ion-exchange unit is shown in Fig. 7.1. This unit can serve as either an anion or cation exchanger, depending upon the resin used.

c. Mixed-Bed Exchangers

Mixed-bed exchangers, sometimes called monobed exchangers, contain cation and anion exchange resins, intimately mixed. The cations and anions are thus removed by passage through a single unit. The regeneration of a mixed-bed unit is more complicated than that of either the cation or anion exchangers. The initial step in regeneration consists of vigorously backwashing the unit. The resins are synthesized, so that their densities and

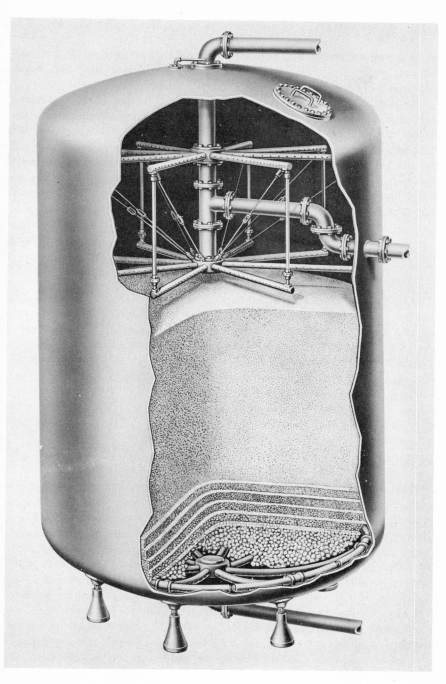

Fig. 7.1. Cutaway view of ion exchange unit. (Courtesy of Graver Water Conditioning Company.)

particle size are sufficiently different to enable them to separate into two distinct layers. The cation exchange resin is made denser than the anion-exchange resin and settles in the bottom of the tank.

By using a central distributor located at the boundary of the two resins, the anion exchanger can be regenerated by flowing the base through the top of the unit and out the central distributor. The cation exchange resin can then be regenerated by passing the acid through the central distributor and out the bottom, or vice versa. Both resins should be rinsed using the same flow pattern used in regeneration. After rinsing, the regenerated resins are mixed by injecting compressed air in the bottom of the tank—allowing it to escape out of the top.

7. Methods of Ion-Exchange Softening

a. Sodium Cycle

This method consists of passing the water to be softened through a sodium cation exchanger of the zeolite or resin type. This replaces the calcium and magnesium ions in the water with sodium ions. The quality of the effluent depends to some extent upon the concentration of calcium, magnesium, and sodium salts in the raw water. A raw water containing 499 ppm (as $CaCO_3$) of calcium, magnesium, and sodium salts on passing through a zeolite softener will have this hardness reduced to 2 to 5 ppm. However, if the concentration of these salts is 1,999 ppm (as $CaCO_3$), the zeolite softener will reduce this hardness to 40 to 50 ppm.[3] This process does not reduce the bicarbonate, sulfate, or chloride content of the water.

b. Split Stream

This method of softening consists of passing part of the stream of raw water through a sodium cation exchanger and the other part of the stream through a hydrogen cation exchanger. The two effluents are then combined. The water passing through the hydrogen cation exchanger has the calcium, magnesium, and sodium ions replaced with hydrogen ions, resulting in the formation of the respective anion acids. The portion of the stream which passes through the sodium cation exchanger has the calcium and magnesium ions replaced with sodium ions. Any sulfate or chloride present in the water will bring about a neutral solution with the sodium ions. However, if the bicarbonate ion is present in the water, alkalinity will result from the exchange of sodium for calcium. The volumes of the two effluents are mixed in a ratio so that this alkalinity serves to neutralize the acidity from the hydrogen cation exchanger. The water is then passed through a degasifier to remove carbon dioxide.

If the complete removal of hardness is not required and the reduction of alkalinity to a specified amount is satisfactory, the effluent from a hydrogen cation exchanger can be mixed with a suitable volume of raw water so that the bicarbonate content neutralizes the acidity of the effluent and gives the desired alkalinity.[4] The mixed volume is then passed through a degasifier.

c. Deionization or Demineralization

In deionization, all the ionic electrolytes are removed by ion exchange. Any soluble, nonionized, organic, or inorganic material will not be removed by ion exchange. The water can be deionized by passage through a multiple-bed ion-exchange system or through a mixed-bed exchanger.

In using a multiple-bed system, the water is first passed through a hydrogen cation exchanger to remove calcium, magnesium, sodium, and any other cations present. The effluent from this exchanger is passed through an anion exchanger, where the acid ions are removed. Since silica is weakly ionized, it will not be removed if the anion exchanger is the weakly basic type. The desirability of removing silica depends upon the proposed use of the water and the amount of silica present in the raw water. If it is desirable to remove the silica, the deionized water is passed through a strongly basic anion exchanger. The silica can also be removed by adding sodium fluoride to the water before it passes through the anion exchanger.

The water can also be deionized by passing through a mixed-bed exchanger. If the required quantities of deionized water are small, a mixed-bed system would offer savings in equipment and space over the multiple-bed system. With either system, the quality of the water can be monitored by measuring the electrical conductivity of the water with an instrument such as a "Solu-bridge."

A schematic drawing of some typical ion exchange systems is shown in Fig. 7.2. The first two types are multiple-bed systems, in which cations are removed in one exchanger and anions in a second. Carbon dioxide produced by action of the hydrogen ion from the cation exchanger on the bicarbonate in the water is removed by vacuum de-aeration or degasification. In the second type, a strongly basic anion exchanger is used in place of a weakly basic one in order to remove silica. The third type is a mixed-bed exchanger.

8. Operating Difficulties

There are some common difficulties which may occur in the operation of an ion-exchange system. One of these, resin capacity failure, includes

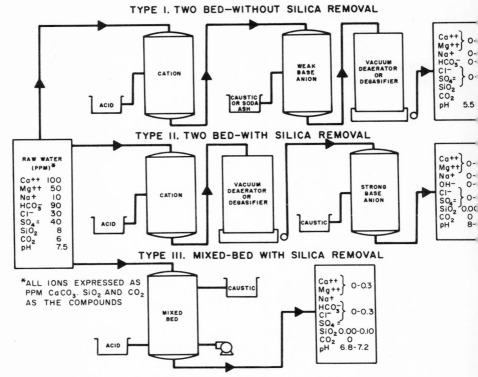

Fig. 7.2. Some typical ion-exchange systems. (Courtesy of Graver Water Conditioning Company.)

organic fouling, coating of the resin particles with iron deposits, loss of basicity of strongly basic anion exchange resins, and loss of total capacity.[5, 6] Resin capacity failures may result in excessive rinse times, below normal capacity, or failure of a mixed-bed system to regenerate.

Generally, regeneration failures are due to difficulties in delivering regenerants at specified concentrations, temperatures, and amounts. These may be caused by malfunctions of pumps and valves, or variations in water pressure. In order to avoid difficulties with the regenerating solution, the chemical and water should be mixed by batch process rather than in the flow lines.

As might be expected, the use of acids and caustics require special precautions in order to prevent damage to the ion-exchange equipment. Generally, the tanks holding the resins are coated or lined with a corrosion-resistant material. Flow lines and batch-mixing tanks also require the use of corrosion-resistant material.

Distillation

In the process of distillation, the volatile liquid is separated from the nonvolatile impurities. Silica, as well as the strongly ionized salts, is removed by this method, giving demineralized or nearly pure water. Theoretically, all nonvolatile constituents are removed in this process, but in actual practice there is a slight carry-over of dissolved solids resulting in up to 25 ppm of dissolved solids in the distilled water. This is influenced by the design of equipment and method of operation. Distillation or evaporation produces high-quality water for select use, such as feed water for high-pressure boilers.

Several different types of evaporators are available for producing distilled water. Tube-type evaporators circulate steam through tube bundles to boil water. Flash evaporators heat the water to 180–185°F and then, at reduced pressure, pass it into a chamber where water vapor is removed. This method encounters less scaling problems than the higher-temperature methods. Steam economy can be realized by using the vapor evolved from one evaporator to heat steam for a second one. When available, old low-pressure boilers can be used as evaporators. Condensed steam from the boiler is used as feed water for a high-pressure boiler.

The cost of softening or demineralizing water by distillation is higher than that of the other methods discussed above. Distillation cost will be highest for single-effect evaporators and less for multiple evaporators. The formation of hard scale in evaporators is a major problem in distillation.

Silica, Iron, and Manganese Removal

Silica, iron, and manganese are not generally troublesome in oilfield production waters. When iron does present a problem, it is usually caused by air oxidation of ferrous iron. This is usually prevented by handling the water in a closed system, rather than by removing the iron. In some instances it is desirable to remove iron in a closed system. The biggest problems with silica or iron and manganese are when they are present in sufficient amounts to require removal from water selected for use in a boiler or as cooling water.

Silica Removal

The amount of silica in natural waters is rarely more than 100 ppm and usually not more than a few ppm. Silica is most objectionable in boiler-feed water used for high-pressure boilers. Here, the presence of silica will result in silicate scale formation in the boiler or on turbine blades. There are six general methods in use for silica removal.

1. HOT LIME-SODA ASH-MAGNESIA PROCESS

Silica can be removed by using dolomitic lime or magnesia in the sludge-blanket-type of hot lime and soda ash softener. The magnesium compounds have the property of absorbing silica. At the high temperature present in the hot process, water-softening proceeds rapidly.

In this process, incoming water is mixed with magnesia and flows downward through a downtake. At the bottom of the downtake, flow is reversed upward through a sludge blanket. In rising through the sludge blanket, the water comes in intimate contact with magnesium hydroxide in the sludge blanket, resulting in efficient silica removal. The water rises to the top of the softener, where it is withdrawn and passed to filters.

In removing silica, magnesium hydroxide is more active than magnesium oxide. Magnesium oxide hydrates more rapidly in hot than in cold water, and removal of silica is more efficient in hot water. In the regular hot-lime and soda ash process, magnesium in raw water is precipitated as magnesium hydroxide, reducing the silica content of the water. If the magnesium content of raw water is high and the silica content low, this softening process may remove or reduce the silica content to the desired level without addition of magnesium.

If additional magnesia is required, dolomitic lime, hydrated dolomitic lime, or activated magnesia may be used. In calculating the amount of dolomitic lime used, the amount of calcium oxide or hydroxide present should be considered. Hydrated dolomitic lime is 32 per cent magnesium oxide, and unslaked dolomitic lime is 40 per cent magnesium oxide. The lime should be slaked before feeding. Activated magnesia is essentially all magnesium oxide. The amount of magnesium (expressed as magnesium oxide and calcium carbonate) necessary to remove a given silica content in the hot lime-soda ash-magnesia process is shown in Fig. 7.3. The amount of magnesium present in the water converted to ppm magnesium oxide or calcium carbonate can be subtracted from the amount obtained from the graph.

2. COLD LIME-SODA ASH-MAGNESIA PROCESS

In the cold lime-soda ash-magnesia process, magnesium hydroxide precipitated from water is more effective than magnesium oxide. Since the

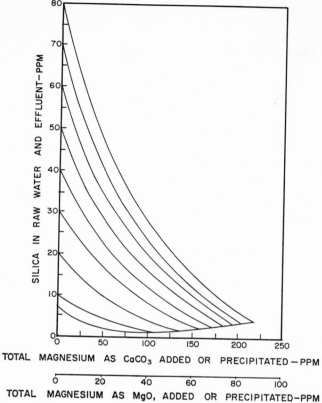

Fig. 7.3. Amount of magnesium necessary for silica removal by the hot lime-soda ash-magnesia process. (From Nordell, *Water Treatment for Industrial and Other Uses* (2nd. ed.) (New York: Reinhold Publishing Corp., 1961). Used with permission.)

magnesium content of the raw water may be insufficient to remove silica, magnesia must be added to reduce silica to the desired limit. Dolomitic lime or magnesia is added to the water and the sludge recirculated through a magnesia dissolver containing raw water, where some magnesia is dissolved as the carbonate or bicarbonate. If an insufficient amount of magnesium from the sludge dissolves in the raw water, carbon dioxide from flue gas or another source can be added to the raw water to increase magnesium solubility. The magnesium introduced by this process, in addition to that already present in the water, is precipitated by the addition of lime in the softening process.

As has previously been stated, the efficiency of silica removal by the magnesia process increases with increasing temperature. Warming the water may also reduce the amount of magnesia required to remove a given amount of silica. The effect of temperature on the removal of silica by the magnesia process is shown in Fig. 7.4.

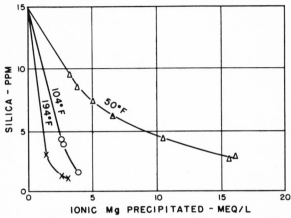

Fig. 7.4. Effect of temperature on silica removal by the magnesia process. (From Nordell, *Water Treatment for Industrial and Other Uses*, (2nd ed.) (New York: Reinhold Publishing Corp., 1961). Used with permission.)

3. Ferric Hydroxide Process

In this process, ferric sulfate is added in conjunction with lime to precipitate ferric hydroxide, according to this equation:

$$Fe_2(SO_4)_3 + 3Ca(OH)_2 \longrightarrow 2Fe(OH)_3\downarrow + 3CaSO_4 \qquad (7\text{–}17)$$

The silica is removed by coagulation produced by the ferric hydroxide. This process requires 15 to 20 ppm of ferric sulfate to remove 1 ppm silica when applied to waters containing less than 10 ppm silica.[7] The added sulfate ion ultimately forms soluble sodium sulfate, increasing the dissolved solids content of the softened water.

4. Highly Basic Anion Exchanger Process

Silica can be removed from water being demineralized by use of a strongly basic anion exchanger. The water is first passed through a hydrogen ion exchanger to remove cations and a weakly basic anion exchanger. Carbon dioxide is removed by aeration or degasification. The water is then passed through the strongly basic anion exchanger to remove the silica.[8] The residual silica in the effluent from this exchanger is usually less than 1 ppm. The strongly basic anion exchanger is regenerated with warm sodium hydroxide (caustic soda), which removes the silica.

5. DISTILLATION

In the distillation process, silica is removed with the other dissolved mineral matter.

Iron and Manganese Removal

Iron is frequently found in well and connate waters. The presence of manganese is rarer and usually in lower concentrations than iron. Where manganese is present in concentrations high enough to cause a problem, iron is usually present also. Essentially the same procedures used for iron removal are used for manganese removal.

In addition to iron and manganese occurring naturally in some waters, iron may be present because of the corrosion of flow lines. Iron and manganese may react with hydrogen sulfide present in the water or produced by sulfate-reducing bacteria to form the insoluble sulfides. Ferrous salts may be oxidized by oxygen in the system to form insoluble ferric compounds. The disposition of iron or manganese on the surface of an injection well can be a particularly serious problem. If well water containing iron is used as cooling or boiler water, iron scales will usually deposit from the water. Several methods are available for iron and manganese removal.

1. AERATION

Aeration is especially effective in removing iron present as ferrous bicarbonate. In order to remove iron present as ferrous bicarbonate or ferrous hydroxide, the iron is oxidized to ferric iron. This can be accomplished by aeration. Theoretically 1 ppm of oxygen will oxidize 7 ppm of dissolved iron. The oxidation is more rapid at high pH values than at low ones.

As an illustration of the effect of pH, consider the aeration of a water containing 100 ppm dissolved iron. At pH 5 and after a 15-minute detention period followed by filtration, the water contained 9 ppm iron; whereas, a water of the same iron content, but at pH 7 and after a 15-minute detention period followed by filtration, contained 0.1 ppm dissolved iron.[9] Generally, prolonging the detention period before filtration increases the amount of iron removed by this process.

In aerating waters to remove both iron and manganese, it is possible to oxidize all the iron but not the manganese. In order to insure oxidation of the manganous iron by aeration, the pH of the water should be 9.5 or 10. Prolonged detention periods for the aerated water result in increased manganese removal. Following aeration and detention, the water is filtered. Manganese oxides and hydroxides deposited on the filter exert a catalytic effect on the oxidation of manganous manganese by dissolved air. This catalytic effect will assist the oxidation of any manganous ions reaching the filter.

2. OXIDATION WITH CHLORINE

Chlorine may be used to oxidize iron and manganese. While 1 ppm of oxygen will oxidize 7 ppm of ferrous iron, 1 ppm of chlorine will oxidize only 1.6 ppm of ferrous iron. However, chlorine will completely oxidize ferrous iron at pH 5 in less than 15 minutes, while pH 7 was required for the oxidation by dissolved oxygen.[10] For the effective oxidation of manganous ion by chlorine, the water should be at pH 10.

3. ION-EXCHANGE PROCESS

Iron and manganese ions can be removed from water by using a zeolite or hydrogen-cation exchanger. Since the water is also softened when passed through these exchangers, the process is limited by economic reasons to waters of low dissolved solids content or to situations where only small volumes of water are required.

Raw water to be treated by ion exchange for iron and manganese removal should not contact air or other oxidizing agents before it passes through the exchanger. If oxidized, iron will precipitate and clog the ion-exchanger bed. Unclear water should be filtered before being passed through the exchanger. Synthetic resins have an advantage over greensand zeolite, in that synthetic resin beds clogged with ferric hydroxide can be cleaned with inhibited hydrochloric acid. However, the beds can become so clogged that even successive acid cleanings will not restore their original capacity.[11]

4. LIME AND SODA-ASH SOFTENING PROCESS

Both iron and manganese can be removed when water is subjected to the lime and soda-ash softening process. Because of the high pH of the water during the softening process, oxidation of ferrous to ferric iron occurs rapidly. The ferric iron then forms ferric hydroxide precipitate, as shown in Eq. (7–18) for the over-all reaction:

$$4Fe(HCO_3)_2 + O_2 + 2HOH \longrightarrow 4Fe(OH)_3 + 8CO_2 \qquad (7\text{--}18)$$

If the water contains more than 5 ppm dissolved iron, the gelatinous ferric hydroxide precipitate formed acts as a coagulant for the softening process, eliminating or reducing the need for addition of chemicals especially for coagulation.

When removing iron in the cold-lime soda-ash process, aeration is usually provided prior to softening. This serves a twofold purpose of supplying needed oxygen for the ferrous ion oxidation and also removing dissolved carbon dioxide, thus reducing the lime requirements. It is frequently convenient to locate the aerator directly over the softener. After iron removal, the water is filtered before use.

5. MANGANESE-ZEOLITE PROCESS

The manganese-zeolite process for removing iron and manganese from water is closely related to ion exchange but is not an ion-exchange process. Iron and manganese are removed, but the water is not softened. In this process, the water is filtered through manganese zeolite (greensand), which oxidizes iron and manganese so that they react with water and form insoluble compounds and then filters them out of the water. Accumulated insoluble iron and manganese compounds are removed by backwashing the filter. The manganese-zeolite bed is regenerated with potassium permanganate before the oxidizing power of the bed is completely lost.

Manganese-zeolite is produced by alternately treating greensand zeolite with manganese sulfate and potassium permanganate. By this process, the higher oxides of manganese are precipitated on and in the granules of greensand. The manganese zeolite has a combined iron and manganese removal capacity of 0.09 lb/cu ft.[12]

Rate of water flow through a manganese-zeolite unit should not exceed 3 gal/min per sq ft, and the minimum back flow rate is 8 gal/min per sq ft. The frequency of regeneration depends upon the iron and manganese content in the water. Regeneration requires 0.18 lb of potassium permanganate per cu ft of manganese zeolite.

The principal economic disadvantage of this method is that, because of the excess potassium permanganate required in regeneration, there is a waste of the chemical. This method has been modified by adding potassium permanganate solution directly to the water at a point from 6 to 20 feet ahead of the manganese zeolite filter.[13] This takes full advantage of the oxidizing power of permanganate to oxidize iron and manganese before they reach the filter. The chemical reactions for the oxidations are shown in Eqs. (7–19) and (7–20):

$$3Fe(HCO_3)_2 + KMnO_4 + 7H_2O \rightarrow MnO_2 + 3Fe(OH)_3 + KHCO_3 + 5H_2CO_3 \tag{7–19}$$

$$3Mn(HCO_3)_2 + 2KMnO_4 + 2H_2O \rightarrow 5MnO_2 + 2KHCO_3 + 4H_2CO_3 \tag{7–20}$$

The amount of permanganate required to oxidize iron is shown in Fig. 7.5 and the amount to oxidize manganese in Fig. 7.6.

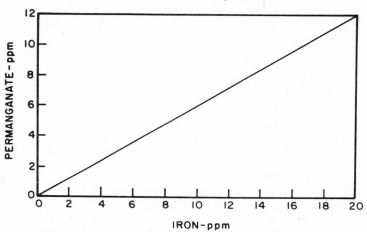

Fig. 7.5. Permanganate demand curve for oxidation of ferrous iron. (From Willey & Jennings, *J. Am. Water Works Assoc.*, **55** (1963), 729.)

The amount of potassium permanganate required can be decreased by aerating the water before the addition of chemical. This will generally serve to oxidize the easily oxidizable iron. Some waters contain organic matter that may complex the iron, making it more difficult to oxidize. With these waters, it may be necessary to increase the distance between the point of permanganate addition and the manganese-zeolite filter, so that there will be more time for the oxidation reaction to take place.

Permanganate is added to the water as a solution of potassium permanganate. This chemical is a strong oxidizing agent and will attack rubber, but is not particularly corrosive to metal. Potassium permanganate weighs about 100 pounds per cubic feet and gives a pink solution. In one application of this modified manganese-zeolite method, 13 ppm iron and 1.5 ppm manganese were removed from water at a cost of 3.5 cents per 1,000 gallons.[14]

Adding potassium permanganate directly to the water has the advantage of oxidizing most of the iron and manganese before the water reaches the

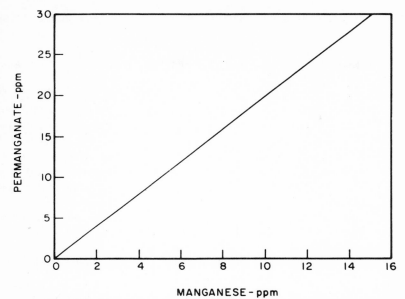

Fig. 7.6. Permanganate demand curve for oxidation of manganous manganese. (From Willey & Jennings, *J. Am. Water Works Assoc.*, **55** (1963), 729.)

manganese-zeolite filter. The manganese-zeolite acts primarily as a filter for removing the insoluble iron and manganese compounds and seldom requires regeneration. Another advantage is that limited amounts of over- or undertreatment will not be noticed in the effluent because of the reaction of either unoxidized iron and manganese or excess permanganate with the manganese-zeolite. Excessive overtreatment of the water may produce a pink color in the filter effluent. The addition of anthracite filter medium on top of the manganese-zeolite increases filter runs, because it removes most of the precipitates without binding the filter media.[15]

6. POTASSIUM PERMANGANATE OXIDATION

Potassium permanganate can be used without the manganese-zeolite filter to remove iron and manganese. The permanganate oxidizes ferrous and manganous ions, as shown in Eqs. (7–19) and (7–20), to ferric and tetravalent manganese. Ferric ions form the insoluble hydroxide, and tetravalent manganese the insoluble manganese dioxide. These compounds are then removed by a sand filter.

Theoretically, 1 ppm potassium permanganate ($KMnO_4$) is required to oxidize 1.06 ppm ferrous iron to ferric iron, and 0.52 ppm manganous manganese to tetravalent manganese. In actual practice, the required amount of potassium permanganate is less because of the secondary oxidation reactions shown in Eqs. (7–21) and (7–22):

$$Mn^{++} + MnO_2 \cdot 2H_2O \longrightarrow Mn_2O_3 \cdot x(H_2O) \tag{7–21}$$

$$2Mn^{++} + MnO_2 \cdot 2H_2O \longrightarrow Mn_3O_4 \cdot x(H_2O), \quad MnO \cdot Mn_2O_3 \cdot x(H_2O) \tag{7–22}$$

The required amount of potassium permanganate can be determined empirically by analysis of the treated water for iron, manganese, and permanganate. Readily oxidizable substances present in the water will be oxidized also, influencing the amount of permanganate required.

Sufficient time must be allowed for the permanganate to oxidize all the ferrous and manganous ions. The allotted time is influenced by water flow rate through the pipe and the distance between the point of permanganate addition and the filter. If unusually long reaction times are required, a tank or retention pit can be installed between the point of chemical addition and the filter.

Potassium permanganate also functions as a bactericide and algicide. It is less toxic to fish than are many other algicides.

7. Iron Removal in a Closed System

The chief disadvantage in the methods of iron removal utilizing aeration is the increased corrosivity of the water caused by the dissolved oxygen. Iron can be removed in a closed system by the precipitation of ferrous carbonate.[16] In this process, a lime slurry is fed into water as it is pumped from the well. The lime and water pass through a mixing pipe to a filter. The precipitated iron is collected on the filter. The system can also be altered to admit, by suction, enough air to oxidize the iron. This air is removed from the water by the oxidation process.

The amount of lime required is calculated on the basis of water analysis data. It must be enough to neutralize the free carbon dioxide. Generally, about 0.35 lb of hydrated lime (65 per cent calcium oxide) per 1,000 bbl is required to neutralize 1 ppm carbon dioxide.

Ion exchange, manganese-zeolite, and potassium permanganate methods for iron removal are adaptable for use in closed systems. In water floods, where large volumes of water require treatment, ion exchange systems would prove too expensive. If it were necessary to remove iron from water in a closed system, the potassium permanganate oxidation method would be the simplest to use.

8. Colloidal or Organic Iron and Manganese

Iron or manganese may occasionally be present in organic or colloidal form, not removed by aeration, settling, and filtration. Iron and manganese in this form can be removed with a coagulant, such as alum, followed by sedimentation and filtration.

References

[1] R. Kunin and R. J. Myers, *Ion Exchange Resins* (New York: John Wiley & Sons, Inc., 1950), p. 31.

[2] F. Helfferich, *Ion Exchange* (New York: McGraw-Hill Book Company, 1962), p. 73.

[3] E. Nordell, *Water Treatment for Industrial and Other Uses* (2nd ed.) (New York: Reinhold Publishing Corporation, 1961), p. 417.

[4] *Ibid.*, p. 457.

[5] H. E. Bacon, "Mixed-Bed and Multiple-Bed Demineralizing Systems," *J. Am. Water Works Assoc.*, **48** (1956), 19.

[6] N. W. Frisch and R. Kunin, "Organic Fouling of Anion-Exchange Resins," *J. Am. Water Works Assoc.*, **52** (1960), 875.

[7] M. D. Schwartz, "Removal of Silica from Water for Boiler Feed Purposes: The Ferric Sulfate and Hydrous Ferric Oxide Process," *J. Am. Water Works Assoc.*, **30** (1938), 551.

[8] P. Hamer, J. Jackson, and E. F. Thurston, *Industrial Water Treatment Practice* (London: Butterworth & Co., Ltd., 1961), p. 111.

[9] E. Nordell, *op, cit.*, p. 393.

[10] *Ibid.*, p. 396.

[11] H. A. Alsentzer, "Ion Exchange in Water Treatment," *J. Am. Water Works Assoc.*, **55** (1963), 742.

[12] *Ibid.*

[13] B. F. Willey and H. Jennings, "Iron and Manganese Removal with Potassium Permanganate," *J. Am. Water Works Assoc.*, **55** (1963), 729.

[14] S. F. Alling, "Continuously Regenerated Greensand for Iron and Manganese Removal," *J. Am. Water Works Assoc.*, **55** (1963), 749.

[15] A. W. Welch, "Potassium Permanganate in Water Treatment," *J. Am. Water Works Assoc.*, **55** (1963), 735.

[16] F. E. Hale, "Iron Removal Without Aeration—The Precipitation of Ferrous Carbonate in a Closed System," *J. Am. Water Works Assoc.*, **28** (1936), 1577.

Coagulation and Sedimentation 8

In water flood operations it is important to inject water that is free from suspended solids and oil. Plant, cooling, and boiler waters also should be free of turbidity. Filtration is one method of clarifying water, but because of the large volume required in some water flood projects, it is not entirely satisfactory. Fine filter media are required to remove small particles from water, and the filtration rate is usually slow. By enlarging the small particles before filtration, a higher quality of water is obtained, and filters capable of rapid flow can be used. The process of enlarging the small particles and removing most of them is called coagulation and sedimentation Small amounts of oil can also be removed in this way.

Water may contain suspended solids and turbidity which may be either organic or inorganic matter of a colloidal nature. The addition of a chemical, called a coagulant, to the water causes the aggregation of some fine particles and the absorption of others to produce a larger particle called floc. This process, called coagulation, is one of decreasing agitation. Initially, the coagulant is added with violent mixing or agitation in order to insure rapid solution and mixing of chemicals in the water. This is followed by floc formation at a lower speed of intermediate mixing, while a final slow movement promotes further floc buildup.

The process by which suspended or coagulated material separates from water by gravity is called sedimentation. Sedimentation alone, is an effective means of water treatment but is made more effective by coagulation. Sedimentation was used in water treatment by the ancient Egyptians and Romans, and until 1915 was used chiefly without coagulation. Presedimentation basins or sand traps are sometimes used when waters to be treated contain large amounts of heavy suspended solids. This decreases the amount of sediment which accumulates in the sedimentation basin as a result of the coagulation and sedimentation process. If water is to be filtered in the course of treatment, coagulation and sedimentation will reduce the load on filters.

Sedimentation

Sedimentation occurs naturally in lakes, ponds, and slow-moving streams. It can be observed in ponds that become muddy and turbid after rains, but,

Table 8.1

SETTLING VELOCITIES OF SOME PARTICLES OF SAND AND SILT IN STILL WATER*

(From *J. Am. Water Works Assoc.*, 47 (1955), 768.)

Diameter of Particle, mm	Order of Magnitude	Hydraulic Subsiding Value, mm/sec	Time Required to Settle 1 ft
10	gravel	1,000	0.3 sec
1		100	3.0 sec
0.4	coarse sand	42	
0.15		15	38.0 sec
0.08		6	
0.04	fine sand	2.1	
0.015		0.62	33 min
0.008		0.098	
0.004	silt	0.0247	
0.0015		0.0035	35 hours
0.001	bacteria	0.00154	230 days
0.0001	clay particles	0.0000154	63 years
0.00001	colloidal particles	0.000000154	

*Temperature at 50°F; specific gravity of particles assumed to be 2.65.

after a period of quiet water, the large particles settle out. The velocities at which particles of sand and silt subside in still water are shown in Table 8.1.

Sedimentation basins are used to remove natural and flocculated turbidity. When used prior to filtration, sedimentation normally delivers water low in turbidity and suitable for rapid sand filtration. If sedimentation is used without filtration, the basins are normally large enough to provide 'one or more days' settling time.

1. THEORY OF SEDIMENTATION

A particle having a density greater than one will settle in water at increasing velocity until the resistance of the liquid equals the weight of the particle. Essentially, the settling velocity will be constant and will depend upon the density, the size, and the shape of the particle, as well as the viscosity and density of the water. The shape of particles is assumed to be spherical, for most theoretical and practical computations of settling velocities in sedimentation basins.

Stokes's law of sedimentation conforms to the experimental data for discrete spheres settling through still water.[1] The situation, in practical sedimentation basins, is modified because of the specific gravity and shape of particles, coagulation of particles, concentration of particles, and movement of water through the settling tank. The specific gravity of suspended matter may vary from 2.65 for sand to 1.03 for flocculated particles or organic matter and mud containing 95 per cent water.[2] Floc particles resulting from coagulation with aluminum compounds have a specific gravity of about 1.18, and those obtained using ferrous sulfate as a coagulant have a specific gravity of 1.34. These values can be increased by clay or silt or decreased by organic matter. However, most of the particles in a settling basin settle at velocities within Stokes's law.

Because of the difference in shape, size, and specific gravity of particles, there is a wide range of settling velocities. This results in some subsiding particles' overtaking others, thus increasing the natural tendency of suspended matter to flocculate. Settling velocities change as the subsiding material varies in size and density.

A diagram of a sedimentation basin is shown in Fig. 8.1. The water enters the basin and spreads out uniformly over the vertical plane A-A, so that the concentration of suspended particles of all sizes and densities is constant throughout a volume of the tank with length ΔL. This incremental volume of water moves through the settling zone at a uniform velocity v and arrives at the entrance to the outlet zone A'-A' without change in shape. Assuming that all the particles settle discretely and that the particles which settle to the bottom stay there, the path V represents the maximum elevation

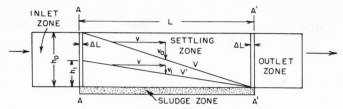

Fig. 8.1. Settling basin. (From *J. Am. Water Works Assoc.*, **47** (1955), 768.)

where particles of the smallest diameter D_0 will be removed. A particle of diameter D_0 entering the basin at height h_0 above the bottom of the basin, will travel along path V and be removed at the entrance to the outlet zone. Particles of equal size and density which enter at heights lower than h_0 will follow paths parallel to V and be removed nearer the entrance zone.

Particles D_1 of the same density but of smaller diameter than D_0 will follow a path parallel to V'. Therefore, particles of this size which enter above h_1 will not be removed in the settling basin, and those which enter at h_1 or below will be removed.

The settling time and settling velocity may be expressed by the following relationships:[3]

$$T = \frac{h}{v} = \frac{Ah}{Q} \tag{8-1}$$

$$v = \frac{h}{T} = \frac{h}{Ah/Q} = \frac{Q}{A} \tag{8-2}$$

Where T = time in hrs necessary for a particle to settle through a depth, L
  h = inlet height, ft
  v = velocity of settling, ft/hr
  A = surface area of the settling basin, sq ft
  Q = inflow rate, cu ft/hr

Theoretically, then, the smallest diameter particle which will be completely removed in a sedimentation basin is a function of the surface loading rate rather than of the depth of the basin. Surface loading is the most important criterion of sedimentation efficiency, when the horizontal velocity of the water through the basin is uniform.

Aluminum floc has a settling velocity of 2 to 3 ft/hr. Effective sedimentation is achieved at a loading rate of 8.6 to 12.8 bbl/day per sq ft of surface area. Lime softening floc settles at 3 to 6 ft/hr and may be effectively removed at a loading rate of 12.8 to 25.7 bbl/day per sq ft.[4]

Particles that strike the bottom in a sedimentation basin are not always removed. They may be transported by rolling along the bottom; the minimum velocity at which this occurs is referred to as the critical velocity. In a properly designed sedimentation basin, the ratio of the mean horizontal velocity in the tank to the settling velocity of the smallest particle to be removed should not exceed 20:1 to 40:1.[5]

2. FACTORS INFLUENCING THE DESIGN OF SEDIMENTATION BASINS

Sedimentation basins are often designed on the basis of existing installations which are handling the same type of water. Experience and judgment of the engineer are also instrumental in the design. However, there are some important points, other than structure, which should be considered in the design of a basin.

The basin should be large enough to insure an adequate supply of treated water during periods of peak load. The characteristics and type of water treatment also affect the design of the basin. Such things as the nature of the suspended material and the amount and type of coagulant needed, if any, must also be considered. The influence of temperature is also important, since the viscosity of the water is less on a warm summer day than in cold weather.

The number of basins depends upon the amount of water and the effect of shutting a basin down. It is desirable to have more than one basin to provide for alternate shutdown of individual basins for cleaning or repairs. Basins vary in shape—square, rectangular, and round. However, regardless of shape, most basins have sloping bottoms to facilitate the removal of deposited sludge.

Sedimentation basins are equipped with inlets in order to distribute the water uniformly among the basins and uniformly over the cross section of each basin. Inlets and outlets should be designed to avoid short-circuiting through the basin. If inlet pipelines or flumes are used, the inlet pipes or orifices should have a high head loss compared with the head available at the inlet. The velocity should be great enough to prevent settling before the water enters the basin, but not great enough to break up the floc. The velocity range for a water and floc can be determined by test, but generally will fall in the range 0.5 to 2.0 ft/sec.[6]

Circular basins with the inlet at one side and the outlet on the opposite side are not very efficient because of dead areas in the tank and short-circuiting of water flow across the tank. The efficiency of circular tanks is much greater if the water is fed to the tank from an inverted siphon located in the center of the tank, and the effluent taken from a weir passing around the entire periphery. The length of the effluent weir—equal to the circumference of the tank—permits a very thin film of water to pass from the settling basin. Square basins may be operated in the same manner or may be fed from one side with effluent removed from the opposite side.

In many sedimentation basins, baffles are used to reduce short-circuiting and improve settling efficiency.[7] If the same basin is used for mixing, coagulation, and sedimentation, a baffle can be installed between the coagulation and sedimentation sections. The baffle generally extends from the top of the water halfway to the bottom of the basin. This reduces short-circuiting but may produce dead spaces and disturb sediment on the floor of the basin. Longitudinal round-the-end baffles also reduce short-circuiting and have the added advantage of bringing the water in one end of the basin and discharging it at the same end.

In order to prevent high velocity and the subsequent lifting of sludge from the bottom, effluent should be collected uniformly across the basin. The circumferential outlet arrangement described previously for circular tanks is an efficient outlet. Weirs may be constructed across rectangular basins; also, slots or effluent ports may be provided. The important consideration is to provide sufficient discharge capacity so that there is no increase in water velocity near the outlet.

The required area of the sedimentation basin can be calculated using Eq. (8–3):

$$A = \frac{Q}{v} \qquad (8\text{–}3)$$

The velocity of settling, v, can be measured, or calculated from Eq. (8–4):

$$v = \frac{64.4(\sigma - \rho)D^2}{\mu} \qquad (8\text{–}4)$$

Where σ = density of particle in g/cm³
ρ = density of fluid in g/cm³
μ = viscosity of liquid in poises
D = diameter of particle in mm
v = velocity in ft/hr

Eq. (8–4) is applicable when the particles are spherical, from 0.001 to 0.1 mm in diameter, falling under gravity, and independent of each other.[8] Settling velocities for particles outside this size range or for nonspherical particles should be measured.

The depth of the horizontal flow basin should not be less than one-twentieth of the length. When determining the depth of the basin, provision should be made for accumulation of sludge during operations, usually by allowing 25 per cent of the tank volume.

A tank designed using the above equations would treat approximately 15 gal/ft² per hour of unflocculated water and 25 gal/ft² per hour of flocculated water.

In vertical flow tanks, suspended particles are eliminated if free-falling velocity of the particles, as calculated from Eq. (8–2), is equal to or more than the upward speed of the water.

3. Detention Time

The detention time is the time required for a unit volume of water to flow through a sedimentation basin. This can be calculated by dividing the basin volume by the flow rate, or by measuring the time required to fill the basin at a given flow rate. As shown in Table 8.1, the time necessary for particles to settle out is influenced by their size. Other important factors are the amount of coagulation which the settling particles undergo, the depth and shape of the basin, the viscosity of the water as influenced by temperature, presence of convection currents or wave action, and the method of operation of the basin. The detention time must be of sufficient length to allow the particles of desired size to fall to the bottom.

The detention time depends on the purpose of the basin. If the basin is primarily designed to remove coarse sand or silt, the detention time will be less than if it is designed to remove extremely small particles or turbidity. Generally, large particles of sand or silt will be removed with a detention time of 1 to 3 hours, while smaller particles may require several days. If effective coagulation is used, a detention time of 2 to 4 hours will usually prepare the water for filtration.

The removal of suspended solids in a sedimentation basin is largely a function of the detention time. Usually, most of the suspended material is removed in the first few hours—additional detention time results in diminishing returns. As with other aspects of water treatment, the detention time is governed by economics and the quality of the water required.

The velocity of flow through the basin is related to the detention time. A flow velocity of 1 ft/min is considered good practice.[9] Even though the inlets and outlets are designed for uniform distribution, the velocity of flow through a sedimentation basin is not uniform over the cross section. Because of drag, the velocity at the walls and floor is zero. At other points, eddy currents, varying temperature of the water, and volume of sludge may alter the velocity.

The minimum time required for a particle of water to pass through the basin is called the flowing-through time. The ratio of the flowing-through time to the detention time multiplied by 100 is called the efficiency of displacement. The flowing-through period can be determined experimentally by adding a salt at the inlet and titrating outlet water samples for the salt. The addition of a dye at the inlet will give a qualitative estimate of flow patterns.

4. Sludge Storage and Disposal

In the design of sedimentation basins, provisions must be made for sludge storage or for continuous sludge removal. Basins without provision for continuous sludge removal must be *shut down* in order to remove the accumulated sludge. Sedimentation basins are generally designed with sloping bottoms, provided with a sludge removal outlet. The outlet may be opened and the sludge washed out with a water hose. Sludge may also be removed by a dragline or by manual methods. If the water to be treated is very turbid, most of the sludge will deposit near the inlet to the basin. The slope of the bottom should be *greatest* in this area.

Several devices are available for continuous sludge removal. Round and square basins can be equipped with rakes or blades which travel slowly, in a circular path around the floor, and push the accumulated sediment to the center of the floor, where it is continuously washed out with a small stream of water. The movement of the sludge is facilitated by sloping the floor of the basin toward the center. Rectangular basins may use the same principle, with the sludge being pushed into sludge hoppers at the inlet end of the basin.

Sludge removed from sedimentation basins becomes a disposal problem. Some sludges may be made into a slurry and disposed of by pumping into streams or lakes, provided there are no laws against it. Impounding basins may be used to hold the sludges until rivers are at high water, then the sludge is discharged into the river. Sludge can be removed and used for fill. In some instances, sludge from coagulation basins is returned to the raw water to improve sedimentation.

Mixing Basins

Mixing basins are used to provide rapid or flash mixing of coagulant with water. They serve the additional purpose of promoting flocculation of the coagulated material. It is advantageous to add the coagulant at an upstream point to permit flocculation before the water reaches the basin.

1. Conduit Mixing Basins

A conduit mixing basin is a long pipe from the point where the coagulant is added to the sedimentation basin. Flocculation occurs in straight-line flow, but the velocity must be sufficiently high to provide turbulence for mixing, and the conduit must be long enough to provide suitable coagulation time. Other types of mixing basins are more economical, if the sole purpose of the long line is to coagulate the water.

2. HORIZONTALLY BAFFLED MIXING BASINS

In a horizontally baffled mixing basin, the baffles are so arranged that the water flows in one end of the basin, around a baffle at the other end, and returns to the inlet end of the basin. Additional baffles can be added to increase the distance the water flows. The velocity of flow through the basin influences the violence of agitation and the efficiency of coagulation. It is not possible to control the agitation closely when it depends on the velocity; consequently, this is the most serious objection to baffled basins.

The necessary velocity of flow through a mixing basin is difficult to determine because of related factors, such as the amount of agitation, the quality and type of chemical used, the temperature and characteristics of the water, and the period of coagulation. For example, a velocity of 2 ft/sec might be suitable for coagulating a highly turbid water; while sedimentation might occur in the mixing basin at a velocity of 1 ft/sec. A velocity of 0.8 ft/sec has been suggested for waters of low turbidity, 1 ft/sec for slightly turbid waters, and 1.3 ft/sec for highly turbid waters.[10] These velocities refer to flocculation and the avoidance of sedimentation, rather than to velocities necessary for mixing the coagulant with the water.

3. VERTICALLY BAFFLED MIXING BASINS

These basins are similar to the horizontally baffled basins, except that the water travels vertically over and under baffles. This alternate rise and fall of the water as it flows through the vertical baffles is believed to produce a more homogeneous mixture of the floc and to prevent the deposition of sludge which sometimes occurs in a horizontal mixing basin. It is difficult to calculate the loss of head that will take place in either of the baffled mixing basins because of differences of basin construction.

4. MECHANICAL MIXING BASINS

Some basins are equipped with mechanical devices for agitating the water to the desired degree. Rapid or flash mixers generally range from 3 to 10 ft in diameter. The flash mix disperses the coagulant in the water so that immediate and intimate contact is made. The mixing period ranges from 10 to 13 seconds. Mixers used for floc formation provide a gentler mixing action than those used to mix the coagulant with the water.

Suspended-Solids Contact Units

Suspended-solids contact units were originally used to soften water by the lime-soda ash process. Their use has been extended to the removal of turbidity from water by coagulation and sedimentation. These units combine in a single basin the steps of mixing, coagulation, and sedimentation. Consequently, they are smaller, require less space than conventional sedimentation basins, and are reported to provide treated water at a faster rate than conventional basins.

A suspended-solids contact unit is shown in Fig. 8.2. The chemicals and raw water are introduced into the mixing and reaction zones. The reactions take place in the presence of previously formed solids. The slurry is recirculated with positive return of solids from the separation zone to the primary mixing and reaction zone. A separation of treated water is obtained from the slurry return-flow zone through displacement by raw water. This unit continuously concentrates and withdraws excess solids.

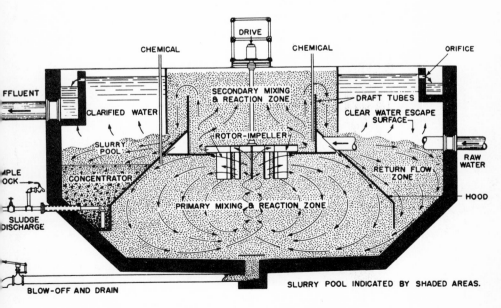

Fig. 8.2. Suspended-Solids Contact Unit. (Courtesy of Infilco.)

There are several suspended-solids contact units available. The units all feature a mixing zone with provisions for flocculation, sedimentation, continuous sludge removal, and removal of the treated water. The American Water Works Association has published a committee report on the capacity and loadings of suspended-solids contact units manufactured by American Well Works, Cochrane Corp., Dorr Co., Graver Water Conditioning Co., Inflico, Inc., Permutit Co., Walker Process Equipment, Inc., and Worthington Pump and Machinery Corp.[11]

Coagulation

When turbid or colored waters are filtered through a granular filter medium, the color and some of the turbidity usually pass through the filter. It is the purpose of coagulation to gather together all of the turbidity, oil, and color into clumps which will settle out during sedimentation or be removed easily by filtration. If water contains a very small amount of objectionable material, such as clay, silt, organic matter, algae, and bacteria which may be removed by slow sand filtration, the use of coagulation may not be necessary. However, when large amounts of objectionable material are present, coagulation reduces the load on the filters significantly.

The coagulation of turbid waters is influenced by several factors. Of these, only the kind of coagulant, quantity of coagulant used, and the time of mixing and flocculation are easily controlled.

1. KIND OF COAGULANT

There are three different groups of coagulants: coagulating agents, coagulating aids, and natural coagulants present in the water. In some waters, natural coagulants are present which will give a floc with the proper treatment. These waters may contain iron or magnesium that will form flocculent precipitates when treated with alkali.

The coagulants generally used in water treatment are compounds of iron or aluminum. Usually, these are sulfates and are acidic in nature. These compounds react with the natural or added alkalinity present in water to form a gelatinous precipitate and magnesium, calcium, or sodium sulfate. Coagulation aids are materials which are not necessarily effective coagulants in themselves but are useful in helping the coagulant to perform its function. Alkalies and acids used to adjust the pH of the flocculating water into the optimum range may be considered coagulating aids. Activated silica and natural or synthetic polyelectrolytes are also effective coagulation aids.

2. pH Value for Coagulation

For any given water, there is an optimum pH value, where good flocculation occurs in the shortest time with the least amount of chemical. The optimum pH value as well as the coagulant dosage will vary for different waters.

For aluminum coagulants, the dosage may vary from less than 5 to above 50 ppm, and the most favorable pH usually ranges between 6 and 7. The dosage ranges between 5 and 50 ppm for ferrous iron coagulants, and the optimum pH above 9.[12] Ferric iron coagulants may be used at pH values as low as 4. However, for actual application of coagulating agents, the dosage and optimum pH range should be determined by coagulation control or a jar test, as described in the Appendix.

3. Mixing

Mixing is the phase of coagulation whereby the coagulant is *quickly* dispersed in the water. This results in the formation of minute floc particles. The chemical reaction involves: (1) neutralization of the negative charge of the impurities, (2) production of positively charged colloidal hydrous oxide flocs which are attracted to negatively charged colloidal impurities, and (3) surface adsorption of impurities by the flocs.

The time required for the reaction to go to completion is influenced by the concentration of the coagulant. When the concentration of the coagulant is *high*, the diffusion time necessary to bring the required amounts of reacting species into contact with each other is shorter than when dilute concentrations are used. However, by the use of a mechanical mixer or a mixing basin, dilute or concentrated solutions of coagulants are rapidly dispersed in the water; consequently, the reacting species are brought into contact with each other and coagulation occurs in a period of seconds.

4. Flocculation

Flocculation is the *second phase* of coagulation. Initially, the precipitate formed in coagulation is gelatinous in nature and evenly dispersed in water in the form of small particles. Flocculation is the agglomeration of these fine particles into larger particles or flocs that will settle more rapidly. The growth of small particles into large flocs depends upon collision and adhesion of the smaller particles. Collision of the particles depends upon physical action or agitation of the water. Adhesion is controlled by chemical or electronic forces.

The agitation necessary for good floc formation should be sufficient to bring the particles into contact but *not so vigorous* as to break up the flocs which have formed. The physical action necessary for flocculation is generally provided by devices called flocculators, or it takes place in mixing basins.

5. QUANTITY OF COAGULANT AND TIME

The coagulation period includes both time of mixing and time of flocculation. It is defined as the period of time between the addition of the coagulant and the termination of the velocity and agitation used to prevent settling. Provided that the alkalinity and pH are in the optimum range, the most important factor influencing the time of coagulation is the quantity of coagulant added to the water.

Generally, the amount of coagulant added is based upon the rapidity with which the floc settles in the basin. The addition of the minimal amount of chemical required for proper coagulation results in a longer period of good floc formation than if a large amount of coagulant is added. This may be illustrated by an example of the coagulation of a fresh water of 10 ppm turbidity. The addition of 6 ppm coagulant may involve a coagulation period of 60 minutes, but if 12 ppm of the same chemical is added, the coagulation period is only 30 minutes. When waters of high turbidity are treated by the addition of considerable quantities of coagulant, the period for coagulation is generally less than that of less turbid waters treated with smaller amounts of coagulant.

6. TEMPERATURE

Temperature influences the coagulation process chiefly by its effect on the time required for satisfactory floc formation. The same amount of coagulant will produce the desired floc faster in warm water than in water at a lower temperature. For example, if the same amount of coagulant is added to two waters, one at 1°C and the other at 20°C, the coagulation period of the warmer water will be from one-third to one-half less than that of the colder water.

Coagulants

The most commonly used coagulants are compounds of iron or aluminum. Usually, the iron flocs are denser and are more rapidly and completely precipitated over a wide pH range than are the aluminum flocs. However, the aluminum compounds are better coagulants for waters containing appreciable organic material. The final choice of a coagulant for a particular water should be based on a coagulation control test and on the over-all economics involved. Oilfield waters are so diverse in mineral characteristics that jar tests are recommended to determine the best coagulant as well as the optimum concentration.

1. Aluminum Sulfate

Aluminum sulfate, $Al_2(SO_4)_3 \cdot 18H_2O$, commonly known as filter alum, alumina sulfate, or papermakers' alum, is widely used as a water coagulant. The commercial product varies in composition from the theoretical 18 moles of water and 15.3 per cent Al_2O_3. The Al_2O_3 ranges from 14.5 to 17.5 per cent, and the water content is usually closer to 14 moles. Aluminum sulfate is available in solution, or as a solid in the form of slabs, lumps, or powder. Both heat and agitation are recommended for dissolving the solid slabs and lumps.

Aluminum sulfate reacts with alkaline substances in the water, according to the reactions shown in Table 8.2. The gelatinous aluminum hydroxide formed in these reactions co-precipitates with and adsorbs turbidity and colloidal matter, resulting in large particles which settle rapidly. Each ppm of aluminum sulfate decreases the alkalinity of the water by 0.45 ppm (as $CaCO_3$) and increases the carbon dioxide by 0.40 ppm. If the water does not contain sufficient alkalinity to react with the aluminum sulfate, the alkalinity can be increased by the addition of an alkaline salt, such as sodium carbonate.

Table 8.2
Some Typical Reactions of Coagulants with Alkaline Substances in Water

Aluminum Sulfate
$$Al_2(SO_4)_3 \cdot 18H_2O + 3Ca(HCO_3)_2 \rightarrow 2Al(OH)_3\downarrow + 3CaSO_4 + 6CO_2 + 18H_2O$$
$$Al_2(SO_4)_3 \cdot 18H_2O + 3Ca(OH)_2 \rightarrow 2Al(OH)_3\downarrow + 3CaSO_4 + 18H_2O$$
Ferric Sulfate
$$Fe_2(SO_4)_3 + 3Ca(HCO_3)_2 \rightarrow 2Fe(OH)_3\downarrow + 3CaSO_4 + 6CO_2$$
$$Fe_2(SO_4)_3 + 3Ca(OH)_2 \rightarrow 2Fe(OH)_3\downarrow + 3CaSO_4$$
Ferrous Sulfate
$$2FeSO_4 \cdot 7H_2O + 2Ca(HCO_3)_2 + \tfrac{1}{2}O_2 \rightarrow 2Fe(OH)_3\downarrow + 2CaSO_4 + 4CO_2 + 13H_2O$$
$$2FeSO_4 \cdot 7H_2O + 2Ca(OH)_2 + \tfrac{1}{2}O_2 \rightarrow 2Fe(OH)_3\downarrow + 2CaSO_4 + 6H_2O$$
Chlorinated Copperas
$$2FeSO_4 \cdot 7H_2O + 3Ca(HCO_3)_2 + Cl_2 \rightarrow 2Fe(OH)_3\downarrow + 2CaSO_4 + CaCl_2 + 6CO_2 + 14H_2O$$
$$2FeSO_4 \cdot 7H_2O + 3Ca(OH)_2 + Cl_2 \rightarrow 2Fe(OH)_3\downarrow + 2CaSO_4 + CaCl_2 + 14H_2O$$
Potash Alum
$$Al_2(SO_4)_3 \cdot K_2SO_4 \cdot 24H_2O + 3Ca(HCO_3)_2 \rightarrow 2Al(OH)_3\downarrow + 3CaSO_4 + K_2SO_4 + 6CO_2 + 24H_2O$$
$$Al_2(SO_4)_3 \cdot K_2SO_4 \cdot 24H_2O + 3Ca(OH)_2 \rightarrow 2Al(OH)_3\downarrow + 3CaSO_4 + K_2SO_4 + 24H_2O$$

The amount of hydrated aluminum sulfate used in coagulation usually falls in the range 5 to 50 ppm. The effective pH range is 5.5 to 8.0 for effective coagulation with aluminum sulfate. Water in the lower part of this range is corrosive to steel, so it may be necessary to raise the pH after coagulation by addition of sodium carbonate or some other alkaline material. The possibility of causing water to become scale-forming by increasing the pH should be considered before any adjustment is made.

2. FERRIC SULFATE

Ferric sulfate, $Fe_2(SO_4)_3$, is applicable to various conditions because of its wide zone of coagulation. It is available in grades with composition varying between 70 and 90 per cent. Ferric sulfate is sold under various trade names. The salt is sold in the granular form and is very soluble in water —one part of ferric sulfate dissolving in two parts warm water. Concentrated solutions are *corrosive*. They should be made up and handled in corrosion-resistant equipment. It is preferable to use concentrated solutions of ferric sulfate to prevent hydrolysis and deposition of ferric hydroxide in the mixing and feeding equipment.

The reactions of ferric sulfate with some alkaline substances present in water are shown in Table 8.2. The reactions show the formation of ferric hydroxide, which functions similarly to the aluminum hydroxide in floc formation. The optimum pH value for coagulation using ferric sulfate differs from that using aluminum sulfate and should be determined from coagulation control tests. Ferric coagulants are effective in the pH range 4.0 to 5.5 and precipitate well at pH values above 9. One ppm of ferric sulfate reduces the alkalinity by 0.68 ppm as $CaCO_3$ and increases the carbon dioxide by 0.30 ppm.

3. FERROUS SULFATE

Copperas is the common name applied to ferrous sulfate, $FeSO_4 \cdot 7H_2O$. The fine crystal or granular form generally used in water treatment is referred to as "sugar sulfate" or "sugar of copperas." In solution, the ferrous ion reacts with the natural alkalinity of the water or with added alkalinity to form ferrous hydroxide, $Fe(OH)_2$. Ferrous hydroxide has a solubility of about 7 ppm in most waters in the neutral pH range.

There are two methods for the use of ferrous sulfate as a coagulant in water treatment. In one method, the ferrous sulfate is added to the water, followed by the addition of lime. The lime raises the pH of the water to a point where ferrous hydroxide is precipitated. At pH values above 7, the precipitated ferrous hydroxide may be oxidized to the less soluble ferric hydroxide by oxygen present in the water. Theoretically, 0.03 ppm of oxygen are required to oxidize each ppm of $FeSO_4 \cdot 7H_2O$.

In the second method, chlorine is used to oxidize ferrous sulfate to ferric sulfate. This method is referred to as chlorinated copperas treatment. This type of oxidation may be accomplished by combining the discharges from a dry-feed copperas machine and a solution-feed chlorination feeder. Theoretically, 0.126 ppm of chlorine are required to oxidize 1 ppm of ferrous sulfate. The feeding ratio should be maintained at 7.8 lb of ferrous sulfate to 1 lb of chlorine.[13] The chemical reactions of both copperas and chlorinated copperas with some alkaline substances are shown in Table 8.2. The gelatinous ferric hydroxide formed in these reactions is responsible for removal of turbid and colloidal matter.

4. POTASH ALUM AND AMMONIA ALUM

Potash alum, $Al_2(SO_4)_3 \cdot K_2SO_4 \cdot 24H_2O$, and ammonia alum, $Al_2(SO_4)_3 \cdot (NH_4)_2SO_4 \cdot 24H_2O$, in the lump or crystal form are the only coagulants that can be used in the crystal-alum pot-type chemical feeder. These coagulants are generally used only in small installations. The reactions of potash alum with some alkaline substances in water are shown in Table 8.2. Reactions of ammonia alum are the same, except that $(NH_4)_2SO_4$ is formed in place of K_2SO_4.

5. SODIUM ALUMINATE

Sodium aluminate, $NaAlO_2$, is used principally for the treatment of boiler water—generally, in conjunction with some other coagulating agent, such as aluminum sulfate. The aluminate is added to the feed water to react with the magnesium hardness and form a floc which absorbs and coagulates finer particles formed by other chemicals. Sodium aluminate is alkaline in its reactions, instead of acid like the other coagulants which have been described. The reaction of sodium aluminate with aluminum sulfate is shown in Eq. (8–5), and with carbon dioxide in Eq. (8–6).

$$6NaAlO_2 + Al_2(SO_4)_3 \cdot 18H_2O \longrightarrow 8Al(OH)_3\downarrow + 3Na_2SO_4 + 6H_2O \qquad (8\text{–}5)$$

$$2NaAlO_2 + CO_2 + 3H_2O \longrightarrow Na_2CO_3 + 2Al(OH)_3\downarrow \qquad (8\text{–}6)$$

Either dry- or wet-type feeders may be used to feed sodium aluminate. It is very soluble in water, having a solubility of 29.5 and 40 parts per 100 parts of water, at 32 and 86°F, respectively. There is *danger of scale formation* from dilute solutions of sodium aluminate, if they are permitted to stand longer than 24 hours.

Some characteristics of various coagulants are shown in Table 8.3.

Table 8.3
CHARACTERISTICS OF SOME COAGULANTS

(From Hamer, Jackson, and Thurston, *Industrial Water Treatment Practice* (Butterworth & Co., London, 1961), p. 368. Used with permission.)

Coagulant	Common name	Purpose	Normal dosage	pH range	Charge	Precipitate produced	Remarks
Aluminium sulfate	filter alum	main coagulant	5–50	5.5–8.0 (optimum: 6–7)	positive	hydrated alumina	Floc is relatively light and will generally not settle against an upward flow greater than about 3 ft/h. Higher rates are obtainable, however, in a sludge-blanket type of plant.
		to assist coagulation with sodium aluminate	2–20				
Sodium aluminate	—	main coagulant	5–15	4.0–7.0	negative	hydrated alumina	Floc formed by double coagulation usually coarser than that from filter alum alone. Aluminate should be added $\frac{1}{2}$–2 min before alum. Sometimes useful as main coagulant for surface waters of variable composition.
		to assist coagulation with aluminium sulphate	2 or 0.1–0.05 of alum dosage				
Ferrous sulfate	copperas	main coagulant	5–50	4.0–11.0	positive*	hydrated ferric oxide	At low pH values oxidation to ferric state may not be complete and treated water may contain residual iron. Floc heavier than that of alumina and settles faster.
Ferric chloride	—	main coagulant	5–50	4.0–11.0	positive*	hydrated ferric oxide	Floc heavier than that of alumina and settles faster.

Ferric chloride/ferric Sulfate	chlorinated copperas	main coagulant	5–50	4.0–11.0	positive*	hydrated ferric oxide	Floc heavier than that of alumina and settles faster. Reagent solution prepared as required by passing chlorine into ferrous sulfate solution.
Activated silica sol	—	to assist coagualtion with aluminium sulfate	1–15 (expressed as silica)	5.5–8.0	negative	hydrated silica	Used as a coagulant aid in conjunction with aluminium sulfate rapidly produces strong, coarse floc which settles quickly. May give effective treatment during periods of spate and at low temperatures.
Bentonite or other clays	—	main coagulant or to assist coagulation with aluminium sulfate	2–12	—	—	—	Increases density of floc formed from filter alum and thus gives faster settling. Should be added to water before filter alum.
Calcium carbonate	chalk	to assist coagulation with aluminium sulfate	—	—	—	—	Increases density of floc formed from filter alum and thus gives faster settling. Should be added to water before filter alum.
Nalco 600	—	main coagulant	1	—	—	—	Cationic polyelectrolyte.

*May be negative at high pH values.

Coagulation Aids

It is generally possible to obtain the desired flocculation by the use of a single coagulation agent. However, there are waters which do not give satisfactory flocculation with the coagulating agents available; in these cases, compounds called coagulation aids are used in conjunction with the coagulation agent. These compounds *are not necessarily* effective coagulants themselves.

1. ACIDS AND ALKALIES

Acids and alkalies, added to the water to adjust the pH, may be considered coagulation aids. Generally, sulfuric or phosphoric acid is used to lower the pH, lime or soda ash to raise it.

2. ACTIVATED SILICA

Activated silica is a term given to a negatively charged colloidal particle formed by the reaction of a dilute sodium silicate ($Na_2Si_4O_9$) solution with a solution of activant. The partial neutralization of sodium silicate solutions with sulfuric acid produces a coagulation aid for water. Activated silica is prepared by diluting a sodium silicate solution to a level of 1.5 per cent SiO_2 and adding enough sulfuric acid to neutralize 85 per cent of the alkalinity. The solution is aged 2 hours before use.

Another method of utilizing activated silica involves the addition of 1 part of a 1 per cent silicate solution to 4 parts of a 1 per cent alum solution and using the mixture immediately as a coagulation aid. Activated silica may also be produced by a process called N-Sol A. This method of producing the colloidal dispersion, called a sol, involves mixing diluted silicate solution and ammonium sulfate solution in equimolar proportions, aging the mixture at a SiO_2 concentration of 2 per cent for 1 hour, and then diluting to 1.3 per cent for storage.[14] Carbon dioxide, sulfur dioxide, sulfur trioxide, chlorine, and acid salts have also been suggested as activants.

The use of colloidal dispersions of activated silica as an aid to coagulation has several advantages. These coagulation aids tend to increase the size, toughness, and density of flocs, and decrease the time required for their formation. This results in more rapid settling, clearer settled and filtered water, and longer filter runs. These colloidal dispersions make possible the use of higher flow rates and coarser filter media. The use of activated silica may reduce the amount of alum or iron coagulating agent required for good coagulation, and thus provide a saving in the cost of chemical. By creating a heavier floc, existing equipment may operate at higher capacities and possibly reduce the need of plant expansion.

As with the coagulants, the proportions of activated silica and other coagulants, the order of addition, and optimum concentration should be determined by coagulation control tests. The concentration of activated silica usually ranges between 1 and 15 ppm. The effectiveness of the alum is destroyed if amounts in excess of the required activated silica concentration are added. In combination with alum, the best results have been obtained when the silica is added immediately after the formation of pinpoint floc.

3. POLYELECTROLYTES

The use of natural substances, such as starch, gelatin, and vegetable gums, as coagulant aids is well-known. Synthetic polyelectrolyte coagulant aids have been introduced in recent years. The term polyelectrolyte is applied to polymers which, by some ion-producing mechanism, can become a polymer molecule having electrical charges along its length. If these polymers are treated with acid or base, depending upon the polymer, the polymer chain *unwinds*, and the charge sites can attract ions or colloids of opposite charge, thus facilitating coagulation.

Polyelectrolytes may be divided into three general classifications: (1) negatively charged compounds called anionic polyelectrolytes; (2) positively charged compounds called cationic polyelectrolytes; and (3) compounds with both positive and negative charges called polyampholytes. Which type of polyelectrolyte to use depends upon the characteristics of the water and should be decided only after the jar test, described in the Appendix, has been performed.

Commercially available polyelectrolyte coagulant aids include polymeric amines, polycationic polymers, products from lignin sulphonic acids, gums, proteins, starches, and carboxymethyl cellulose. Some polyelectrolyte coagulation aids that are commercially available are shown in Table 8.4. Those preparations containing Serapan NP10 are anionic. Nalco 600, listed in Table 8.3, is a commercially available cationic polyelectrolyte.

Polyelectrolytes vary in their effectiveness as coagulant aids in different waters. A coagulant aid should only be selected on the basis of jar tests using the actual water. Concentration of the polyelectrolyte is also important. A large excess of some polyelectrolytes will actually inhibit coagulation. Again, tests should be used in selecting the proper concentration.

Polyelectrolytes are effective coagulant aids and offer many advantages. When used in conjunction with coagulants, they form large and dense flocs

Table 8.4

SOME COAGULANT AIDS*

(From *J. Am. Water Works Assoc.*, **54** (1962), 82.)

Manufacturer	Product	Max. Concentration Recommended by Manufacturer, ppm	Manufacturer	Product	Max. Concentration Recommended by Manufacturer, ppm
Allyn Chemical Co.	Claron	1.5	E. F. Drew & Co., Inc.	Drewfloc	1:8 alum
	Claron No. 207	2			1:20 lime†
North American Mogul Products Co.	Mogul Co-982 (identical to Claron)	1.5	Electric Chemical Co.	Ecco Suspension Catalyzer No. 146	3.5
	Mogul Co-980 (identical to Claron No. 207)	2	Hagan Chemicals and Controls, Inc.	Hagan Coagulant Aids	
				No. 2	1
				No. 7	0.75
American Cyanamid Co.	Superfloc 16	1		No. 11	4
				No. 18	15
				No. 801	6
				No. 952	8
The Burtonite Co.	Burtonite No. 78	5	Hercules Powder Co.	Carboxymethylcellulose	1
Dow Chemical Co.	Separan NP10 potable water grade	1			
Illinois Water Treatment Co.	Purifloc N17	1	Illinois Water Treatment Co.	Illco IFA 313	10

Manufacturer	Trade name		
North American Mogul Products Co.	Mogul CO-983 (identical to Separan NP10 potable water grade)	1	
Kelco Company	Kelgin W		2
	Kelcosol		2
National Aluminate Co.	Nalcolyte No. 110		5
Dearborn Chemical Co.	Aquafloc 422 (identical to Separan NP10 potable water grade)	1	
Ionac Chemical Co. (formerly listed as The Permutit Co.)	Permutit No. 65		2
	Permutit No. 66		2
	Permutit No. 67		4
	Permutit No. 68 discontinued and replaced by Permutit Wisporfloc-20 Coagulant Aid		5
Key Chemicals Inc.	Key-Floc-W (a 4 per cent aqueous solution of Separan NP10 potable water grade)	25	
Stein, Hall X Co., Inc.	Jaguar		0.5

*These aids and concentrations have been approved by USPHS for use with potable water.

†Drewfloc to alum, 1:8; when used simply as an aid in alum coagulation; Drewfloc to lime, 1:20, when used in connection with lime softening.

which settle rapidly and thus reduce flocculation time. Cationic poly-electrolytes rapidly and completely coagulate algae.[15] Coagulation may be obtained with polyelectrolytes alone in some waters; in other waters the addition of a polyelectrolyte may reduce the required amount of inorganic coagulant required.

Certain *precautions should be observed* when polyelectrolytes are used as an aid to alum coagulation. In addition to testing the effectiveness of polyelectrolytes with a particular water, the point of addition in con-junction with alum coagulation must be determined for each water. Polyelectrolytes are added as a very dilute solution, and the maximum effectiveness will be obtained within a narrow concentration range as determined by tests.

The use of polyelectrolytes for coagulating oilfield waters containing small amounts of oil has been proposed.[16] Best results were obtained using both cationic and anionic polyelectrolytes in conjunction with a coagulation aid containing bentonitic clay. In these tests, 30 mg/liter coagulant aid were added first, and then 3 mg/liter polyelectrolyte added to give water of acceptable quality.

Tests have also been made on the effects of a polyelectrolyte as a filter aid.[17] Polyacrylamine, with a molecular weight of approximately 1,000,000, and rapid sand filters were used in these tests. Dosages of 10 to 30 ppb, applied directly to the filters, effectively reduced filtered water turbidity and increased the pressure drop across the filter in proportion to the amount of polyacrylamine added. Polyacrylamine collected on the sand filter was readily removed by backwashing. It was concluded from these tests that polyelectrolytes as filter aids would be limited to emergency use where short filter runs were no problem. It would be to an engineer's advantage to redesign his water clarifying system to improve water quality rather than depend upon the addition of a polyelectrolyte as a filter aid to insure turbidity-free water.

4. CLAY

Clay may be used to broaden the pH range for good coagulation of highly colored waters that are free from turbidity and low in mineral content. The clay should be in the form of a not too fine powder. Since different clays may vary in their effectiveness, coagulation control tests should be performed to determine the proper amount and grade of clay.

Bentonite and other clays are effective coagulant aids for use with aluminum sulfate. Clays are also effective with other coagulants and as "weighting agents." Lighter organic matter flocculated around the clay would give a particle of greater density than the organic matter alone, and would settle more rapidly. Clay also has an absorptive power that aids in floc formation.

References

[1]"Mixing and Sedimentation Basins," *J. Am. Water Works Assoc.*, **47** (1955), 768.

[2]T. R. Camp, "Sedimentation and Design of Settling Tanks," *Trans. A.S.C.E.*, **3** (1946), 895.

[3]"Mixing and Sedimentation Basins," *op. cit.*

[4]*Ibid.*

[5]*Ibid.*

[6]*Ibid.*

[7]P. Hamer, J. Jackson, and E. F. Thurston, *Industrial Water Treatment Practice* (London: Butterworth and Co., Ltd., 1961), p. 375.

[8]*Ibid.*, p. 356.

[9]S. T. Powell, *Water Conditioning for Industry* (New York: McGraw-Hill Book Company, 1954), p. 47.

[10]J. R. Baylis, "Design of Mixing Basins," *Water Sewage Works*, **78** (1931), 117.

[11]"Capacity and Loadings of Suspended Solids Contact Units," *J. Am. Water Works Assoc.*, **43** (1951), 263.

[12]J. M. Cohen, G. A. Rourke, and R. L. Woodward, "Natural and Synthetic Polyelectrolytes as Coagulant Aids," *J. Am. Water Works Assoc.*, **50** (1958), 463.

[13]J. S. Gettrust, "Coagulation with Ferrous Sulfate," *J. Am. Water Works Assoc.*, **44** (1952), 459.

[14]H. R. Hay, "Water Purification Methods Involving Sodium Silicates," *J. Am. Water Works Assoc.*, **36** (1944), 626.

[15]Cohen, Rourke, and Woodward, *op. cit.*

[16]J. V. Slyker, "Recent Developments in the Clarification of Oil Field Waters," *Producers Monthly*, **28**, No. 1 (1964), 8.

[17]N. A. Garnell, "Effects of a Polyelectrolyte as a Filter Aid," *J. Am. Water Works Assoc.*, **55** (1963), 597.

Filtration

9

Water filtration is a process for separating undissolved solids from water by utilizing a porous medium that retains the solid but allows passage of the water. The pressure difference necessary to force the water through the medium may be provided by gravity, vacuum, or fluid pressure. The method of applying pressure depends upon the quantities and properties of the system to be separated, filtering area, filtration time available, and resistance to flow. It is desirable to make the filtration time as short as possible, consistent with good separation and low cost.

Filters are operated at a constant rate of flow and a constant pressure, or with small variations in pressures and rates. Operation of a filter at a constant flow rate requires continually increasing pressure to maintain the rate. When a specified maximum pressure is reached, the filter is back-washed. Filters operated at constant pressure deliver decreasing amounts of water with time, until a specified minimum flow rate is reached and the filter is backwashed. Some filters operate at constant rate initially and, as sediment builds up, change to constant pressure.

Theory of Filtration

The theory of filtration as applied in water treatment is used mainly as a basis for estimating optimum filter size, optimum frequency for back-washing, and the effect of changes in operating procedure. The equation describing the flow through filters in constant-pressure filtration is:

$$\frac{t}{V} = \frac{\mu \alpha r_c V}{2\Delta p A^2} + \frac{\mu r_s L_s}{\Delta p A} \qquad (9\text{--}1)$$

where V = volume of filtrate
  t = filtration time
  Δp = total pressure drop
  A = filtering area
  μ = viscosity of filtrate
 r_c and r_s = specific resistance of filter cake and septum, respectively
  L_s = thickness of septum
  α = volume of cake per unit volume of filtrate

This equation is applicable for steady-state filtration after a filter cake has begun to build up. Under these conditions, the resistance of the septum r_s is very small compared with the resistance of the cake r_c. A plot of t/V or $\Delta t/\Delta V$ against V is linear and permits a solution for r_c, provided the other constants are known. However, since $r_c \gg r_s$, the value of the third term in Eq. (9–1) is negligible and can be dropped in most calculations. If the equation is to be valid, the product r_c must be constant during the filtration.

Values of α are determined using Eq. (9–2) where $(v_s)_s$ is the volume fraction of solids in the slurry and $(v_s)_c$ is the volume fraction of solids in the filter cake.

$$\alpha = \frac{(v_s)_s}{(v_s)_c - (v_s)_s} \qquad (9\text{--}2)$$

These values are determined experimentally. The value of r_c changes with variations in filtration pressure, as shown in Eq. (9–3) where c is the compressibility factor and K is a constant.

$$r_c = K(\Delta p)^c \qquad (9\text{--}3)$$

Values of r_c can be determined at pressures corresponding to those used in the α calculation. A log-log plot of r_c against Δp results in a straight line of slope c. With graphs of r_c against Δp and α against Δp in the same pressure range, the performance of a filter operating in a steady state can be calculated.

An empirical equation has been developed by Hudson[1] for application to sand filters. The loss of head or pressure-drop in a sand filter at normal flow rates is given by:

$$h = KQD \tag{9-4}$$

where h = loss of head through the filter medium

    h_1 = increased loss of head due to filter clogging

    K = a constant

    Q = volume of water filtered per unit area per unit of time

    D = depth of filter medium

    C = concentration of suspended matter in the applied water, expressed in weight per volume of water

    D_1 = depth to which suspended matter penetrates into filter

    R = ratio of void space to volume of filter medium

    w = weight of suspended matter per unit volume as trapped in the filter

    t = time

    m = effective size of particles in filter medium

    v = velocity of flow

The volume available in the sand filter for retention of suspended matter per unit area of filter will be D_1R, and the volume of suspended matter applied to the filter will be QtC/w. If the suspended matter is completely removed, the retention volume filled by suspended matter in time t will be QtC/wD_1R. Since this space will be filled, the space open to passage by water can be given by $1 - (QtC/wD_1R)$, and the rate of flow through this space expressed by Q_1 in the following equation:

$$Q_1 = \frac{Q}{1 - \dfrac{QtC}{wD_1R}} \tag{9-5}$$

The loss of head through the clogged filter area is given by Eq. (9–6) and the total loss of head through the sand filter by Eq. (9–7).

$$h_1 = \frac{KQD_1}{1 - \dfrac{QtC}{wD_1R}} \tag{9-6}$$

$$h = KQ(1 - D_1) + \frac{KQD_1}{1 + \dfrac{QtC}{wD_1R}} \tag{9-7}$$

While the filtered material may compress and increase slightly in density,

w may be considered as constant without introducing an appreciable error. For clean sand, R is practically constant and C, the concentration of suspended matter in the applied water, is generally uniform. The constant K is the reciprocal of the coefficient of permeability and can be determined from the initial loss of head or pressure. The value of D_1 can be calculated from "loss-of-head" data or by measurement of the floc penetration.

Filter Media

The porous mass which retains the suspended solids and allows the fluid to pass through is called the filter medium. Of the many types of porous media available, only a few have been used to any extent in filtration. Filter media are available in several different forms including: rigid, porous plates formed by sintering particles together; loose particles such as sand, anthracite coal or diatomaceous earth; metallic screens; and organic or metallic cloths. Cost, degree of filtration required, and type of filter to be used are the main criteria for selecting a filter medium.

1. ALUMINA

Alumina, fused into Alundum, or Aloxite, forms a rigid, porous, and permeable material, suitable for use as a corrosion-resistant filter medium. Its porosity ranges between 25 and 38 per cent. Different values of porosity, pore size, and permeability are obtained by varying the particle sizes of the fused grains. Fused alumina is used in water filtration both as a direct filter medium and as a support for sand or other loose media. Advantages include portability, temperature and chemical resistance, suitability for use in vertical or horizontal position, and ease of cake removal. The main disadvantage is that small particles tend to penetrate and clog the pores, becoming difficult to remove.

2. POROUS CARBON

Porous carbon plates are sometimes used as filter media. These plates are temperature- and acid-resistant, but because of the bond used for lamination, their caustic resistance is poor. Other advantages and limitations are similar to fused alumina.

3. METALLIC PLATES AND SCREENS

Sintered metals can be made with as much as 50 per cent porosity and tensile strengths of 10,000 psi. Perforated or slotted plates can be used for filtering coarse particles. Because of their smooth surfaces, deposits are readily removed.

Wire made from various metals can be woven in the form of screens or cloths for use as filter media.[2] Generally, wire screens are used for coarse separations or as a support for filter cloths or filter aids. The wire cloth should be made from metal which will resist corrosion; otherwise, corrosion products may form in the openings and produce clogging.

4. SILICA

Silica is the chief constituent of a commercial filter medium called Filtros, which is made by fusing natural sand with a synthetic silicate. The advantages, limitations, and physical properties of Filtros are similar to Alundum. Its porosity ranges from 25 to 40 per cent, and it is chemically inert to most fluids.

5. SAND AND GRAVEL

Silica sand in combination with gravel is the most common filter medium used in water treating. Sand and gravel is a low-cost medium and is easy to clean by backwashing. Although the function of the gravel is to support the sand, gravel is considered part of the filtering medium. The gravel also assists in distributing the water during backwashing.

Filter sands varying over a wide range of sizes have been used. The properties of the untreated water and the requirements of the filtered water should be considered before the grade of sand is selected for a particular filter. The grade of sand is specified on the basis of effective size and uniformity coefficient. The effective size is defined as the diameter of openings in a hypothetical screen that will retain 90 per cent of the sand and pass 10 per cent. The uniformity coefficient is defined as the ratio of the diameter of openings in two hypothetical screens, where one screen will pass 90 per cent of the sand and the other screen 60 per cent.

Some typical specifications for fine, medium, and coarse filter sands are given in Table 9.1. The per cent size refers to the amount of the sample that is smaller than a given grain size. The grading of these sands according to sieve size is shown in Table 9.2. The size of the sand grain is the standard specification, not the sieve size. The size of the grain is defined as the diameter of a sphere of volume equal to that of the grain.

The American Water Works Association offers a convenient method of classifying filter sand.[3] This classification defines the percentage of sand that is to be finer than a stated grain size. For example, the percentage of

Table 9.1

TYPICAL SPECIFICATIONS FOR FILTER SANDS BY PER CENT SIZE

(From *J. Am. Water Works Assoc.*, **41** (1949), 290.)

| Per Cent Size* | Grain Size, mm | | | | | |
| | Fine | | Medium | | Coarse | |
	Min.	Max.	Min.	Max.	Min.	Max.
1	0.26	0.32	0.34	0.39	0.41	0.45
10†	0.35	0.45	0.45	0.55	0.55	0.65
60†	0.53	0.75	0.68	0.91	0.83	1.08
99	0.93	1.50	1.10	1.80	1.46	2.00

*If 1 per cent of the sand sample is finer than 0.34 mm, the sand has a 1 per cent size of 0.34 mm.

†The ratio of the 60 per cent size to 10 per cent size shall not exceed 1.70.

Table 9.2

TYPICAL SPECIFICATIONS FOR FILTER SANDS BY SIEVE SIZE

(From *J. Am. Water Works Assoc.*, **41** (1949), 290.)

A.S.A. Sieve Opening, mm	Grain Size, mm				
	Sieve Number		Fine	Medium	Coarse
	Tyler No.	U.S. No.	0.35–0.45 mm	0.45–0.55 mm	0.55 mm
			Per Cent Passing Sieve		
1.19	14	16	94–100	84–99	68–93
0.84	20	20	71–97	49–84	30–71
0.59	28	30	31–73	14–39	6–31
0.42	35	40	6–25	3–6	0–1
0.30	48	50	0–3	0–1	0

sand finer than 0.26 mm is to fall between 1 and 2 weight per cent of total. If the percentages that correspond to the separation sizes of standard sieves are fixed, the results of a sieve analysis can be used directly.

Filter sand is classified as material less than 2.0 mm in diameter. The sand must be composed of hard, durable grains, and must not contain clay, loam, dirt, or organic matter. A maximum of 1 per cent by weight of flat or micaceous particles is permitted.

It is desirable when using sand as a filter medium to have a grade that prevents floc or other suspended solids from passing through the filter, holds the removed particles as loosely as possible to facilitate backwashing, and holds as large a volume of floc or suspended solids as possible without clogging. A filter sand must be of sufficient size to permit backwashing at a flow rate high enough to remove the retained floc and suspended matter without removing the sand.

Fine sand is used when the following conditions exist:

(1) The complete removal of turbidity is required.

(2) Pretreatment of the water is insufficient to contribute appreciably to the water clarification.

(3) The removal of bacteria is required.

(4) Shorter filter runs and larger amounts of wash water can be tolerated.

(5) The permissible rate of backwash is sufficient only for cleaning fine sand.

(6) Buildup of grain size because of calcium carbonate precipitation is not expected.

Coarse sand is used when the following conditions exist:

(1) Pretreatment of the water coagulates the smaller particles.

(2) A high degree of filtration is not necessary.

(3) Lower water quality is permissible in order to obtain longer filter runs and to reduce the required volume of wash water.

(4) High backwash rates can be used.

Medium sand is used for intermediate conditions. Generally, good pretreatment of the water makes it possible to use coarse sand, with its advantages of high flow rate and ease of backwashing.

Gravel used in filters should consist of hard, rounded stones having a minimum average specific gravity of 2.5 and less than 1 per cent by weight of material with a specific gravity less than 2.25. The amount of thin, flat, or elongated pieces, whose largest dimension is greater than three times the smallest, is restricted to less than 2 per cent by weight.

The porosities of sand and gravel used as filter media can be determined on samples of the material. The procedures used for these measurements are given in the Appendix.

6. ANTHRAFILT

Anthrafilt (crushed and screened anthracite coal) is used extensively as a filter medium. The specific gravity of this material is 1.55, compared with 2.65 for silica sand. Therefore, anthrafilt will produce nearly twice the volume of filter medium as an equal weight of sand. The anthrafilt should have a Moh scale hardness of 3.0 to 3.75, and a specific gravity of not less than 1.55.[4] Anthrafilt particles are classified by the same system as that used for sand.

Because of its lower specific gravity, anthrafilt can be backwashed at a rate about two-thirds of that used for sand, and wash water facilities of lower capacity can be used. The porosity of anthrafilt is larger than that of sand for a given particle size. Also, the surface of the particles has more resistance to some encrustations (especially silicates) which may form on the filter medium.

7. Diatomaceous Earth

Diatomaceous earth, also called kieselguhr, infusorial earth, diatomaceous silica, or diatomite, is also used as a filter medium. The diatomaceous earth, usually called diatomite, is nearly pure silica formed from fossilized one-cell marine plants. Diatomite is lighter than sand and contains more void space. One cubic foot of sand weighs about 100 lb and contains 25 per cent void space, while 100 lb of diatomite occupies more than 5 cu ft and contains 90 per cent void space. Generally, diatomite serves as a filter aid or a precoat.

8. Cloth

Cotton woven into ducks and twills finds use as a filter medium.[5] The cotton cloth is mechanically strong, and the numerous hairlike fibers of the threads help to trap fine particles at the start of filtration. Cotton cloth has the disadvantage that it may be attacked by fungi and bacteria. Many synthetic fibers are available which have some advantages over natural fibers.

9. Other Filter Media

There are many other filter media which find application in filtration. Some of these are glass cloth, hemp, straw, paper, wool, and rubber.

Filtration Rate

The maximum rate of filtration of a sand filter depends upon: (1) the required quality of the effluent, (2) the character of the unfiltered water, (3) the size of sand used in the filter bed, (4) the depth or thickness of the filter bed, and (5) the condition of the filter bed. By application of pressure, water can be forced through a filter at high rates; however, the water is not necessarily filtered, since the suspended matter may be forced into the filter bed and eventually through it. The desired quality of effluent and efficiency of operation can best be obtained by controlling the rate within permissible limits and avoiding rapid or large fluctuations in rate.

1. REQUIRED QUALITY OF FILTERED WATER

The rate of water passed through a given filter is governed in part by the required quality of the effluent. Water of *low* turbidity may be obtained by using moderate filtration rates through a filter, while higher rates may result in carrying some of the smaller particles of suspended solids through the filter, though this is permissible where some turbidity can be tolerated. However, it is generally better to use a filter designed for a given rate of flow, rather than to increase the flow rate beyond the design limit by increasing the pressure drop across the filter.

2. CHARACTER OF APPLIED WATER

The character of water to be filtered has a large bearing on the success of filtration. Filtration is used to clarify water by removing suspended particles. Properly designed and executed filtration operations will do this, provided the water is stable and all chemical reactions occurring within the water have reached completion before the water is filtered.

Filtration of water containing both dissolved iron and oxygen is only partly successful, since the oxidation of iron will continue after filtration, resulting in formation of new deposits. A similar situation exists when waters containing dissolved iron and hydrogen sulfide are filtered. The chemical reaction forming black iron sulfide continues after filtration, producing "black water." Waters unstable with respect to calcium carbonate deposition can show the same phenomena. Postfiltration water will continue to form calcium carbonate. In addition, calcium carbonate will be deposited in the filter, causing cementation of the sand grains, decrease in porosity by plugging, and ineffective filtration.

Filters are frequently condemned as being ineffective when the above postfiltration reactions occur. Actually, the filter is not at fault, but feeding unstable water decreases the effectiveness of the filter. This is a particularly serious problem with oilfield waters, that are frequently unstable because of exposure to air or mixing of different waters.

Oil should be removed from water before it is passed through a sand filter, since it coats the sand grains and generally fouls the filter. Filtered particles of iron oxide, iron sulfide, and other suspended material form a gumlike deposit with the oil that is difficult to remove by backwashing. Oil removal devices and effective coagulation will eliminate oil fouling of sand filters.

By combining good coagulation and effective sedimentation, water turbidities as low as 1 ppm can be obtained before filtration. When treating surface waters, increases in turbidity may result from changes in the raw water quality or in the dissolved mineral content. The principal difficulties in producing filtered water result from changes in the concentration and nature of the settled-water turbidity. The use of a coagulant aid often improves turbidity removal and permits longer filter runs.[6]

Floc characteristics influence the rate of filtration. If the flocculation is *strong* and the suspended matter is such that penetration of coagulated material into the filter bed is small, the limiting condition of filtration is the clogging rate. High filtration rates result in frequent backwashing, but there is no problem of suspended matter in the filtered water. When the floc is *weak* and the suspended matter is colloidal in nature, the limiting condition is the penetration of the particles through the filter bed. Under conditions of weak flocculation, the penetration of floc can be expressed by Eq. (9–8), developed by Hudson:[7]

$$K = \frac{vs^3 \Delta p}{L} \tag{9-8}$$

and, under conditions of strong flocculation, by Eq. (9–9):

$$K = \frac{vs^2 \Delta p}{L} \tag{9-9}$$

In these expressions, K is the index of filterability, v is the approach velocity, Δp is the loss of pressure through a bed of thickness L at a time when a measurable increase in the effluent occurs, and s is the effective size of the bed particles. With either strong or weak flocculation, the penetration of suspended matter into the bed is directly proportional to the filtration rate. Therefore, higher filtration rates can be used with proportionately thicker beds, finer sand, or lower head loss, without diminishing the quality of the filtered water. Some approximate values of filterability index K for various waters and conditions are given in Table 9.3.

Table 9.3

APPROXIMATE VALUES OF FILTERABILITY INDEX FOR VARIOUS
WATERS AND CONDITIONS

(From Hudson, *J. Am. Water Works Assoc.*, **48** (1956), 1138.)

Conditions	Value of K
Raw water difficult to coagulate, average pretreatment facilities and, operation	0.4
Raw water easy to coagulate, average pretreatment facilities and operation	1.0
Average raw water, high-grade pretreatment facilities	2.0
Average raw water, high-grade pretreatment facilities and control, plus activated silica treatment	6.0

3. FILTER BED CONDITION

The maximum rate of filtration cannot be obtained through clogged or fouled filters without the application of excessive pressure which results in an economic loss, as does the probable breakthrough of suspended matter into the filtrate. Filters whose beds crack, mound up, or pull away from the side walls cannot be relied upon to produce clear water. Dirty filters can be cleaned by surface washing and backwashing.

4. EFFECT OF SAND SIZE

The rate of filtration is faster through coarse than fine sand. In constant rate filtration, the pressure necessary to maintain the rate increases as the floc penetrates the filter medium and produces clogging or a breakthrough of particles into the filtered water. An example of the effect of sand size on floc penetration at a constant filtration rate of 2 gal/min per sq ft of bed area is shown in Fig. 9.1. If the amount of permissible head loss is known, it is possible to estimate from a curve of this type the depth of sand of a given mean diameter necessary to prevent the breakthrough of turbidity.

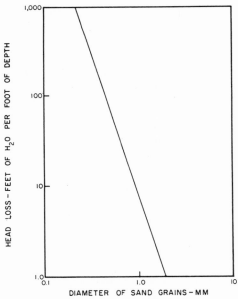

Fig. 9.1. Increase of head loss per unit floc penetration of a sand filter (From Hudson, *J. Am. Water Works Assoc.*, **48** (1956), 1138.)

5. TURBULENT FLOW

Generally, it is assumed that the flow through the filter bed is laminar. However, at high filtration rates through coarse sand or at high terminal losses of head, turbulence may occur.

During filtration through a partially clogged bed, the greatest volume of applied water enters the bed through a small portion of the pores. The pores may terminate or branch within the bed so that the water travels laterally to other larger pores. This results in a different flow pattern than that through a bed of clean sand where nearly all the pore space of the bed is available for flow. Therefore, the velocities within a constant-rate sand filter increase as clogging proceeds. It seems reasonable that the largest volume of water passes through the largest pores and is affected by turbulence in the pores.

The transportation of sediment and dislodgement of particles is greater under turbulent flow than under laminar flow. At high filtration rates, the movement of sediment into the bed is greater than at lower rates. Thus, increased filtration rates which result in turbulence cause a greater penetration of particles into the bed. Fig. 9.2 shows the relation between floc penetration and Reynolds Number for a sand filter.

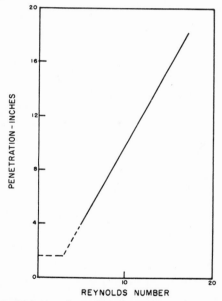

Fig. 9.2. Relation between floc pentration and Reynolds Number for a sand filter. (From Hudson, *J. Am. Water Works Assoc.*, **48** (1956), 1138.)

Washing Filters

During the process of filtration, some of the filtered material penetrates the body of the filter medium, and larger amounts collect on the surface of the filter. As the amount of filtered material builds up, both on the surface and in the body of the filter, the rate of filtration is decreased until it is necessary to clean the filter. In the case of slow sand filters, this material is predominantly on the surface of the filter, which can be cleaned by removing the top few inches of sand and replacing them with clean sand. However, it is not practical to remove sand from rapid sand filters or pressure filters, since the filtration rate is much higher than that of slow sand filters; consequently, the need for cleaning occurs much more frequently. These filters are cleaned by backwashing—forcing clean water in the reverse direction of filtration. The effectiveness of backwashing as a means for cleaning a filter is dependent upon several important factors.

1. DISTRIBUTION AREA

Most troubles which occur in filters originate at the top or the bottom of the filter. Those which start at the bottom of the filter can generally be attributed to a poorly designed distribution area, causing uneven distribution of wash water. Uniform distribution of wash water over the bottom of the filtering area is the most important function of the underdrain and gravel layers. Since the hydraulic requirements for backwashing are more severe than those for collecting the filtered water, an underdrain system which is satisfactory for backwashing is adequate for collecting the filtered water.

There is a wide variety of filter bottoms. Some proven systems are: (1) a header and perforated laterals; (2) a central manifold and laterals, with a secondary distribution system consisting of Wagner precast blocks between the laterals; (3) the Leopold bottom, composed of vitrified tile block with orifices and water passages to take the place of laterals; (4) a false bottom, precast or otherwise, containing inverted pyramids with orifices at the apexes covered with porcelain spheres (a Wheeler bottom) used to support the gravel layer; and (5) porous plates.

The criterion of relating orifice openings in laterals to the area of the filter bed does not necessarily result in adequate design. The change in pressure along the lateral and the variation in orifice coefficients along the manifold must be considered. Because water meets more resistance turning to pass through the orifice when the lateral velocity is high, there is a tendency for the discharge through the orifices to be lower near the inlet to the lateral than near its terminal end. Therefore, there is a systematic variation in the flow through the orifices along each lateral, and the variation is greater for systems having a larger number of orifices. However, in order to insure adequate distribution of wash water, the orifices must be spaced reasonably close together. Both distribution and flow can be aided by using a large number of small-diameter orifices in the laterals. This results in a loss of head, but distribution of the wash water is improved.

During backwashing, the gravel layers serve to distribute the water through the area served by the orifice. Layers of gravel, graded so that the sizes vary only gradually from one level to the next, provide adequate distribution of the backwash water, provided that the underdrain system is properly designed. The top layer of the gravel should be fine enough to support the sand during filtration.

2. VELOCITY OF BACKWASH FLOW

The rate of water flow during backwashing should be sufficient to remove from the surface and within the sand bed all material filtered out during the preceding filter run. The velocity of the water should be high enough to provide adequate expansion of the bed and scouring action, but not high enough to cause mixing of the sand and gravel in the filter bed. The velocity of backwash water depends upon the size and specific gravity of the filter media, the temperature of the water, and the character of the filtered material.

The friction produced by the backwash water flowing past the sand grains produces expansion of the bed, and the velocity of the backwash water governs the amount of friction. Therefore, if more friction is required to clean the sand, the velocity must be increased. Generally, a rate of flow sufficient to give a 50 per cent expansion of the filter bed is satisfactory for cleaning the filter. This means raising a layer of clean sand by 50 per cent of its settled depth.[8] An unnecessarily high flow rate may result in mixing the sand and gravel, and possibly forming channels in the filter bed.

3. VISCOSITY OF WATER

The viscosity of the water affects the amount of bed expansion obtained at a given flow rate. In cold weather, when the water viscosity is high, a 50 per cent bed expansion may be obtained for a given flow rate. But, with higher temperatures and lower water viscosities in the summer, the same flow rate gives less bed expansion. This results from the effect of water viscosity on the friction generated between the flowing water and sand.

In one filter bed having a 0.50 mm average sand size, the wash rate required to give 50 per cent bed expansion at 32°F must be increased 50 per cent to give the same expansion as at 70°F.[9] Therefore, it is better to backwash filters on the basis of per cent bed expansion rather than on the basis of a given flow rate.

4. SIZE AND SHAPE OF SAND

The expansion of the sand bed at a given backwash velocity is affected by the size and shape of the sand. Coarse sand and gravel require higher flow rates than fine sand for adequate expansion because of their smaller surface area per unit volume. Bed expansion is greater with angular sand than with round sand of equal grain size and specific gravity because of the greater surface area of the angular sand. The surface area influences the friction between the water and the particle.

Clean, dry silica sand has a specific gravity of 2.65. When a wash fails to clean a sand surface of gelatinous or organic material, the specific gravity of the sand is reduced by the accumulated layer. This is particularly serious with the particles near the surface of the filters. Here the coated sand particles float higher than the clean sand particles during backwashing and, as the coating builds up, eventually wash out the filter. Reducing the wash velocity only aggravates the situation, since the lower velocity produces less friction and, therefore, less scouring and less cleaning. In an attempt to prevent washing the coated sand from the filter, the velocity can be reduced until it fails to clean the filter.

Although a bed expansion of 50 per cent is sufficient to clean most filters, it is not necessarily best for all filters. The per cent voids or space between sand grains is the same for all sizes of similarly shaped sand at the same percentage expansion. However, the interstitial velocity of wash water for a given bed expansion is much greater through the coarser sands. Consider two sands, one of 0.45 mm size and the other, 0.55 mm. The velocity through the larger size would be 41 per cent higher at the same expansion.[10]

Because of this increased interstitial velocity and the resulting friction, a coarse sand filter washes cleaner than one composed of fine sand. Also, the coarse sand offers a smaller surface area to clean. A cubic yard of 0.45 mm sand has approximately one-third of an acre more surface area than does 0.55 mm sand. At the same expansion, the larger sand will be separated by larger pores than the smaller sand, offering a larger escape route for the trapped dirt, as well as more rapid removal due to the greater wash water velocity. Also, the collisions of coarse sand grains during backwashing is more violent and more abrasive because of the greater energies involved.

Filters of crushed coal or anthracite require lower backwash rates because of the lighter density.[11] The specific gravity of anthracite is only 1.55, compared with 2.65 for sand. Backwash rates for anthracite may be 8 to 10 gal/ft^2, compared with 12 to 15 gal/ft^2 for sand.

5. SURFACE WASH

The filter troubles which start at the top of the filter may not always be remedied by backwashing. Surface troubles are generally caused by compacted, flocculated material which combines with the filter media to produce "mudballs." The mudballs form in the *"schmutzdecke"* or rolling scum that floats on the sand surface during washing. As the velocity of the wash water raises the finer sand, the larger mudballs may sink to levels where their terminal velocity reaches equilibrium with the wash velocity. The mudballs may actually penetrate the body of the filter.

By using a surface wash in conjunction with the backwash, the formation of mudballs may be minimized. The surface wash consists of applying a jet of water at right angles to the backwash flow or parallel to the surface of the sand. This increases the turbulence and friction between the water and sand at the surface. The surface wash is particularly helpful in cleaning filters that are subject to too heavy loading or those in which the material filtered out is very sticky.

Essentially, the surface wash system consists of a piping arrangement that produces jets of water at the surface of the sand bed in a manner designed to break up mudballs when they start to form. A system utilizing fixed jets usually produces more rapid breakup of the mudballs, but revolving jets have also proved effective in some installations. For the purpose of illustration, one fixed-jet system employs a one-eighth inch jet for each square foot of filter area and requires about 2 gal/min per sq ft at 50 psi, while a rotating system applying a high rate of water to only one area at a time has fewer jets and requires about 0.5 gal/min per sq ft under 50 psi pressure.[12]

Cleaner beds result when a surface wash is used in conjunction with a backwash. This increases the length of filter runs, reduces wash water requirements, and provides for shorter wash periods. Both the surface wash and the backwash are started at the same time. A backwash rate that produces a 10 per cent expansion is usually sufficient when used in conjunction with a surface wash.

6. FREQUENCY OF BACKWASH

The frequency of backwashing may vary from a few hours to several days, depending upon the filter and the water being filtered. It is desirable to select a backwashing schedule that will minimize operating costs. When clogged filters are operated too long before backwashing, the rate of output is reduced and may be many times less than that of the clean filter. In the case of constant-rate filters, the consumption of extra power necessary to push water through the filter may be wasteful.

After the filter has been operated for some time, the operator can determine the length of filter run possible before backwashing, and the amount of wash water required. An effective backwash requires about 1 to 5 per cent of the amount of water filtered during a filtration run.

The filtration cycle for maximum filter output can be estimated by constructing a graph of volume of water filtered versus the filtration time in hours.[13] Such a graph is shown in Fig. 9.3. The time necessary to backwash the filter is plotted on the abscissa to the left of zero. A line is then drawn from this point, tangent to the curve. The point of tangency represents the length of filtration cycle for maximum daily capacity. An additional graph may be constructed to show the volume of water obtained per day at several filtration cycles. This graph, as shown in Fig. 9.4, is constructed by reading the volume of water obtained at various filtration times, as shown in Fig.

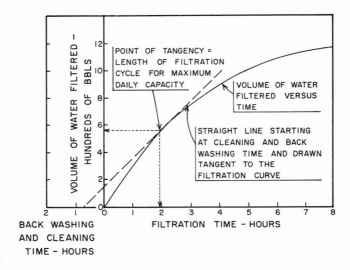

Fig. 9.3. Graph used to determine optimum filtration time. (From Crawford, *Producers Monthly*, **20**, No. 4 (February, 1956), 10.)

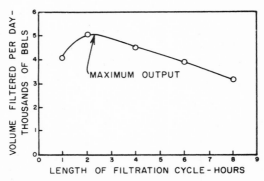

Fig. 9.4. Filter output versus cycle length.

9.3, and then multiplying these volumes by the number of filtration cycles per day. The number of filtration cycles per day is obtained by dividing 24 hours by the filtration plus backwashing time in hours. The volume per day is then plotted against the length of filtration cycles.

The filtration cycle for maximum daily output is not necessarily the optimum from an economic standpoint. If the cost of backwashing the filter is excessive at maximum output, it may be advisable to operate with a longer cycle to reduce costs.

7. PRECAUTIONS IN WASHING

The backwash valve should be opened slowly to prevent damage to the filter. Sand beds expand from the top downward, rather than from the bottom upward. Sand boils can occur if the wash water rushes in at a rate sufficient to lift the sand bed off the gravel, resulting in a layer of water between the sand and gravel. After lifting the sand bed, the water breaks through the sand and produces large boils. The boils can be violent enough to throw some of the gravel above the sand and generally disrupt the filter. If the gravel layer is filled with sand, the entire layer may be lifted by the backwash water.

The backwash velocity should produce enough scouring action to remove any deposited material, but the agitation should not be so great as to disrupt the bed and mix the sand and gravel. A flow rate of 5 to 7 gal/min per sq ft of filter (bed area) is usually required before a bed of 0.50 mm sand starts to expand.[14] As a general rule, a minimum rate for backwashing pressure filters is 12 gal/min per sq ft of bed area. It should be emphasized that this is *actually a minimum*—the bed cannot be cleaned effectively by backwashing at some lower rate for a longer period of time. Better results are usually obtained by using a backwash rate in excess of this minimum. Packing of the bed, gravel hills, and eventual overturning of the bed can be caused by too low a backwash rate, too high a filtration rate, and too high a content of suspended matter. The backwash is usually continued until a specified low turbidity is reached.

Types of Filters

There are several different types of filters. The principles and theories of filtration apply equally well to all types. Sand filters may be classified as slow and rapid sand filters. Rapid sand filters can, in turn, be divided into gravity feed and pressure filters. There are also diatomaceous earth filters, and filters using other media discussed previously. Sand filters find more use in oilfield operations than any other type.

1. Slow Sand Filters

As the name implies, these filters have a slow rate of filtration. In order to compensate for this, the filter area is large, ranging up to an acre in size. The water is passed by gravity downward through the sand, at rates ranging from 0.032 to 0.160 gal/min per sq ft. Concrete structures are generally used to hold the filter media in sand filters. Underdrains are laid on the floor, and three or more layers of graded gravel are used to support from 12 to 18 in. of graded sand. Sand with an effective size of about 0.35 mm and a uniformity coefficient of approximately 1.75 is an adequate filter medium in most cases.

The surface of the sand provides a place for microorganisms to grow. These soon form a mat or film, that helps in the filtration of the water. This is referred to as allowing the bed to "ripen." When putting a clean, slow sand filter into use, it is started at about one-third its normal rate. The rate is increased gradually until after three or four days the filter has ripened and a *"schmutzdecke"* of sediment and bacterial growth has formed. Depending upon the character of the water, the slow sand filter will deliver from 1,200,000 to 9,500,000 barrels per acre of filter area before cleaning is necessary. The filter is cleaned by removing 1 or 2 inches of sand from the top of the filter and replacing it with clean sand.

Slow sand filters are used most successfully for the removal of tastes and odors, and the bacterial purification of naturally clear waters. These filters might also find application for the filtration of small water supplies where the more skilled supervision required for rapid sand filters is not available. Some lake waters may be filtered directly without pretreatment, but coagulation and sedimentation are generally used before the water is passed through the slow sand filter. Slow sand filters are not popular for oilfield use.

2. Rapid Sand Filters

Rapid sand filters differ from slow sand filters in design, construction, operation, and rate of flow. The filter area is much smaller and, consequently, clogs more rapidly, requiring some method of rapid and automatic cleaning such as that discussed in the section on backwashing. The high rate of filtration necessitates the use of coarser and more uniform sand, as well as some pretreatment of the water such as coagulation and sedimentation.

a. Gravity Rapid Sand Filters

Gravity rapid sand filters for commercial or industrial use are made in rectangular or cylindrical forms. Rectangular basins are generally con-

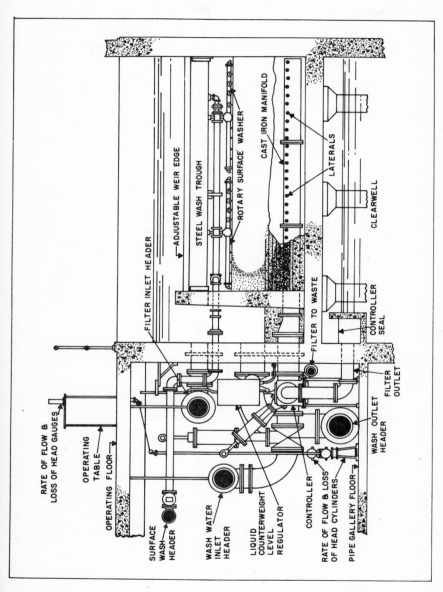

Fig. 9.5. Gravity-feed rapid sand filter. (Courtesy of the Permutit Company, Paramus, N.J.)

structed of concrete, and cylindrical basins of wood, steel, or concrete. In addition to the basin, the gravity filter is equipped with one of the underdrain systems discussed previously, as well as the values and controls necessary to operate the filter. A drawing of a commercially available rapid sand filter is shown in Fig. 9.5. This particular filter is equipped with a cast iron manifold; other noncorrodible underdrain systems are also available with this filter.

Since sand is the most commonly used filter medium, this filter is usually referred to as a sand filter, but anthrafilt can be used in place of sand when silica pickup presents a problem. Some typical specifications for the filter medium to be used in a filter of this type are shown in Table 9.4. For special purposes, somewhat different specifications may be required.

Table 9.4

TYPICAL SPECIFICATIONS FOR FILTER MEDIA USED IN A
GRAVITY-FEED RAPID SAND FILTER

(Courtesy of the Permutit Company, Paramus, N.J.)

48″ Sand & Gravel	48″ Anthrafilt
5″ of $1\frac{1}{2}$″ × 1″ gravel	5″ of No. 6 size $1\frac{5}{8}$″ × $\frac{13}{16}$″
5″ of 1″ × $\frac{1}{2}$″ gravel	5″ of No. 5 size $\frac{13}{16}$″ × $\frac{9}{16}$″
4″ of $\frac{1}{2}$″ × $\frac{1}{4}$″ gravel	4″ of No. 4 size $\frac{9}{16}$″ × $\frac{5}{16}$″
4″ of $\frac{3}{8}$″ × $\frac{3}{32}$″ gravel	4″ of No. 3 size $\frac{5}{16}$″ × $\frac{3}{16}$″
6″ of coarse sand, 0.8 to 1.2 mm effective size	6″ of No. 2 size $\frac{3}{16}$″ × $\frac{3}{32}$″
24″ of fine sand, 0.4 to 0.5 mm effective size	24″ of No. 1 size 0.55 to 0.65 mm effective size
The uniformity coefficient of the sand shall not exceed 1.6. The sand must be round or angular, graded dry, and be practically pure silica, free from appreciable quantities of foreign material. The gravel shall consist of hard rounded pebbles, containing not more than 2% by weight of thin, flat, or elongated pieces, determined by hand-picking, and free of shale, sand, clay, loam, or organic impurities.	The uniformity coefficient of the No. 1 anthracite shall not exceed 1.6. The anthracite shall consist of hard and durable grains, having a hardness of from 3 to 3.75 on the Moh scale; specific gravity approximately 1.57; shall be free from iron sulfides, clay, shale, or extraneous dirt; and not more than 1% shall consist of dust.

These filters can be equipped for manual operation, push-button operation, or fully automatic operation. In automatic operation, the required procedures of backwashing, surface washing (if used), filtering to waste, and return to service are carried out automatically, eliminating the possibility of human error.

Rapid sand filtration can be used to remove turbidity and bacteria and other microorganisms from water. These filters are also used in conjunction with water-softening plants. While the initial cost of a rapid sand filter is less than that of a slow sand filter, operating costs are higher because of coagulation, sedimentation, and backwashing requirements.

The rate of flow through the filter depends upon the size, grading, and depth of sand, type and efficiency of pretreatment, and the required quality of the effluent. For municipal water supplies, gravity-feed rapid sand filters are usually operated at a rate of 2 gal/min per sq ft of bed area. Higher rates can be used for filtering oilfield or plant waters.

b. Pressure Sand Filters

Pressure sand filters are more widely used in industrial applications and in the oil fields than are any other types of filters. They are particularly applicable in closed water-treating systems. Pressure sand filters are based on the same principles as the gravity-feed rapid sand filter, except that the filter media and underdrain system are placed in a cylindrical tank, and the water is passed through the filter under pressure. This has the advantage that the filtered water can be moved without additional pumping. Most pressure sand filters are designed for working pressures of 65 to 75 psig, with the pressure loss through the bed of less than 10 psi.

The position of the pressure filter tank may be either vertical or horizontal. For areas up to 80 sq ft of filtering surface, the filters are usually the vertical type; for larger areas, the horizontal type. Typical vertical and horizontal filters are shown in Fig. 9.6. The horizontal type is generally 8 ft in diameter and ranges in length from 10 to 25 ft. Vertical units range from 1 to 10 ft in diameter. Some typical filter media for use in these filters are given in Table 9.5.

Table 9.5

SOME TYPICAL FILTER MEDIA FOR USE IN PRESSURE-TYPE FILTERS

(From *Betz Handbook on Industrial Water Conditioning* (6th ed) (Philadelphia: Betz Laboratories, Inc., 1962), p. 4.)

Sand	Anthrafilt	
12″ of 0.45 to 0.5 mm effective size	18″ of No. 1	0.7 to 0.8 mm
10″ of 0.8 to 1.2 mm effective size	9″ of No. 2	$\frac{3}{32}$″ to $\frac{3}{16}$″
4″ of $\frac{1}{4}$″ × $\frac{1}{8}$″ gravel	9″ of No. 4	$\frac{5}{16}$″ to $\frac{9}{16}$″
4″ of $\frac{1}{2}$″ × $\frac{1}{4}$″ gravel	4″ of No. 6	$\frac{13}{16}$″ to $1\frac{5}{8}$″
8″ of 1″ × $\frac{1}{2}$″ gravel		
4″ of $1\frac{1}{2}$″ × 1″ gravel		

The rate of flow through the filters depends upon the character and pretreatment of the raw water and the required quality of the filtered water. The flow rates vary upwards of 0.1 bbl/min per sq ft of filter area, but capacities may be as high as 1,000 bbl/hr for the largest horizontal filter. The total filter area to be used in a filter system is determined by the volume and quality of the water to be filtered, the use of the filtered water, and the rate of filtration. The maximum filter area of each individual filter is determined by the space available for installation and the water available for backwashing.

Fig. 9.6. Vertical and horizontal pressure sand filters. (Courtesy Graver Water Conditioning Co.)

A filter unit is generally filtered to waste for a few minutes before a filter run. This is necessary if the wash water is unfiltered. It is desirable even if filtered wash water is used, in order to settle the bed and collect a little floc on the surface of the filter.

Pressure filters offer some advantages over gravity filters. Since they have a higher capacity, pressure filters require less area. Pressure filters also have an advantage where only one pumping of the water is desired. One disadvantage is that the sand bed is not visible, so that the operator cannot observe its condition and see if the backwash is functioning properly.

It is also difficult to clean and replace the filter media or to observe the filtered water. The treatment of water under pressure also complicates mixing, coagulation, and sedimentation of the water to be filtered.

c. Automatic Valveless Gravity Filters

A variation of the gravity rapid-sand filters is the automatic valveless gravity filter. These filters operate without the use of valves, gauges, rate controllers or other mechanical equipment. A siphon is utilized to regulate the filtering and backwashing cycles. Sand is used as the filter medium.

The valveless filter is divided into a filtering section and a backwash storage compartment. An automatic valveless filter, manufactured by the Permutit Co., is shown in Fig. 9.7. The first water filtered is collected in the backwash storage section. After this is filled, the filtered water is taken to service. As a filter cake builds up on the filter, the water level in the backwash pipe rises. When this water fills the siphon, the backwash cycle begins and lasts until the water in the backwash storage section has all passed up through the sand activating the siphon breaker. This ends the backwash cycle, the filter reverses itself, and the filtration cycle begins again.

The difference in elevation between the water level in the backwash storage section and the top of the siphon loop regulates the frequency of washing. The length of the backwash cycle is determined by the position of the siphon breaker. A regulator on the end of the backwash outlet is used to adjust the wash rate. Because of the higher initial water level, the backwash rate is high at first and decreases as the hydrostatic head decreases. With 6 feet differential between backwash water level and top of siphon loop, the average backwash rate is 15 gpm/sq ft.[15]

These filters have the advantage that the backwash cycle begins at a given head loss without the need for automatic instrumentation. The filter provides its own backwash water and does not require separate storage or a pump. A minimum of backwash water is used to prevent wasting water, and no mechanical maintenance is required. These filters can be used as a battery, utilizing a flow-splitting box to divide the feed water between filters.

3. Diatomite Filters

Another type of pressure filter uses diatomaceous earth (usually called diatomite) as a filter aid. Diatomite filters were developed during World War II, primarily for military use; but have since found use for swimming pool, potable, and industrial waters. The filter medium is supported on a fine metal screen, a synthetic fabric, or porous ceramic. The filter is prepared for use by precoating with diatomite and then put into service. The filtration

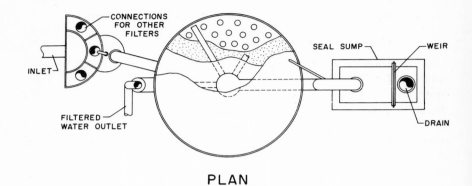

PLAN

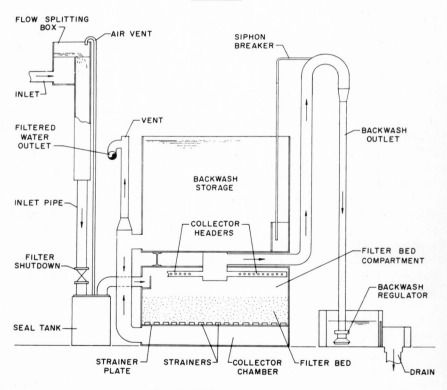

ELEVATION

Fig. 9.7. Automatic valveless gravity filter. (Courtesy of the Permutit Company, Paramus, N.J.)

is actually performed by the deposited diatomite and not the supporting screen or cloth.

Diatomite is the fossilized remains of microscopic one-cell marine plants. It is composed chiefly of silica. In filtration, the diatomite forms a mat or layer which contains about 85 or 90 per cent voids. The major grades of diatomite have an average cake density of 10 lb/cu ft. Figure 9.8 shows some average characteristics of various grades of diatomite processed by the Great Lakes Carbon Corporation.[16]

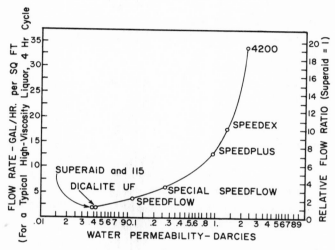

Fig. 9.8. Average characteristics of various grades of dicalite filter aids. (From Allciatore, Harris, and Wallen, *Petrol. Eng.* **27**, No. 5 (1955), B-57. Used with permission.)

Diatomite is suitable for use in pressure or vacuum filters of the drum, disc, plate and frame, tube, or leaf types. A thin coat of diatomite alone or in combination with asbestos fiber is applied to the filter as the first step in the filtration. This step is referred to as the precoat. The precoat liquid is a thin slurry mixed in a separate tank. The slurry volume is about one-third greater than the volume of the filter and lines, and usually contains 10 lb of filter aid per 100 sq ft of filter area. Once the precoat step is started, the liquid flow through the filter must be maintained in order to provide enough pressure to hold the precoat against the cloth or screen. As soon as the water passing through the filter is clear, the precoat application is complete and the main filtration is started. In some instances where the suspended-solids content is low, the filtration is done by means of the precoat alone. In these instances, the filter aid is generally increased to 15 or 25 lb/100 sq ft of filter surface.

Normally, diatomaceous earth filtration requires continuous addition of filter aid by means of a slurry feeder following the precoat step. This "body feed" builds up on the filter throughout the period of filtration and maintains the porosity of the filter cake. The amount of diatomite added to the raw water varies with the nature and quantity of solids to be removed and with operating characteristics of the system. It may range between 0.01 and 0.05 lb/bbl of water to be filtered.

There are certain "optimums" that should be considered in diatomite filtration.[17] These are the optima of body feed, filtration rate, and pressure drop across the filter. The filter cannot necessarily be operated in a manner that will give each of the three optima simultaneously. However, the operation of the filter can be regulated to give one of the optima at a time. Understanding the optima for a particular filter will help achieve more efficient operation of that filter.

The body feed which results in the maximum volume of a specified quality of water for a given filter and diatomite is the economic optimum body feed. This is dependent upon the pressure drop across the filter and the precoat. As a general rule, the optimum body feed decreases with increasing pressure drops and decreasing amounts of precoat. The body feed that produces the maximum volume of acceptable water at a given pressure drop is the optimum pressure-drop body feed. This is a function of the filter cake composition and occurs at higher body feeds than the economic optimum. Operating at a low filtration rate produces the maximum volume of filtered water at a specific pressure drop. High body feeds increase this effect.

Satisfactory results have been obtained in tests using commercial diatomite filters with flow rates ranging from 0.5 to 15 gal/min per sq ft of filter area. However, the higher flow rates require more filter aid and result in shorter filter cycles and more frequent backwashing. For economical operation, most installations are designed for a *maximum* flow rate of about 2 gal/min per sq ft of filter area and are usually operated in the range of 0.5 to 1 gal/min per sq ft. As shown in Fig. 9.8, the permeability of the filter cake is influenced by the grade of diatomite used.

The diatomite filter may be cleaned by backwashing or by the use of high-velocity water jets to remove the cake. Generally, the amount of backwash water necessary is less than that required with sand and anthrafilt filters, because the filter element is cleaned largely by a pressure buildup and sudden release. The diatomite cake and all impurities from the filter elements are flushed to waste by the wash water.

Diatomite filters have the advantages of high flow rates and low space requirements. Waters which contain iron or manganese may prove troublesome because of the precipitation and accumulation of compounds of these elements in the filter screens. Examination of the water will reveal whether it is necessary to pretreat the water to remove these elements or whether they will pass through the filtration process without change. Algae may grow on the surface of the diatomite, unless a proper amount of body feed is maintained throughout the filtration. Chlorination of the water prior to filtration obviates this problem.

When using diatomaceous earth filters to filter oilfield waters, suspended solids in the untreated water should not exceed 30 mg/liter.[18] Small amounts of oil in the water will be removed by these filters. However, if the filter cake becomes oil-saturated, some oil will leak through the filter. Large amounts of oil in the water lead to shortening of filter runs to prevent this oil leakage, and thus increasing the cost of filter runs. The use of oil separators and coagulation will reduce oil droplets in the water going to the filter, and thus lengthen filter runs.

The loss of head through diatomite filters is greater than that through conventional sand filters, so that power requirements for operation will be greater. Some of these filters are operated until the pressure differential cross the filter reaches 35 psi. Above this figure the loss of head *increases so rapidly* that the gain in length of filter run does not compensate for the increased power requirements. Of course, the permissible differential across the filter depends upon the filter—some cannot withstand such a high differential.

The cost and design of a diatomite filter are based on the optimum combination of filtration rate, filter cake terminal-head loss, and rate of body feed that will produce the desired quality water. Baumann and La Frenz[19] have outlined the following procedure for calculating the optimum diatomite filter design:

(1) Select a filtration rate, body feed rate, and head loss.
(2) From laboratory data, determine the length of filter run.
(3) Multiply (2) by filtration rate.
(4) Multiply (3) $\times$ body rate $\times$ 8.345 $\times$ 10^{-6}.
(5) Add precoat + (4).
(6) Divide (4) by (5).
(7) Divide cost of diatomite by (6).
(8) Estimate labor and power costs.
(9) Add diatomite cost + labor cost + power cost.
(10) Repeat (2) through (9) for different head losses and select a minimum cost.
(11) Add minimum operating cost and equipment cost.
(12) Repeat calculations for other body feeds and filtration rates.
(13) For each filtration rate, plot total cost/1,000 bbl against body feed in ppm.

4. VACUUM FILTERS

The basic principles which apply to pressure filtration also apply to vacuum filtration. In vacuum filtration, the liquid is forced through the filter medium by atmospheric pressure rather than an applied pressure. The most commonly used vacuum filter is the rotary drum type. Essentially, this consists of a horizontal drum rotating approximately 50 per cent submerged in the water to be filtered. The inside of the submerged portion of the drum is under vacuum. The surface of the drum is a supported metal screen or cloth, which acts as the filtration septum. Some of these filters employ filter aids, such as diatomite, which are mixed with the water to be filtered. The filter cake is discharged with each turn of the drum. Some of these filters are precoated. During the filtration process, the filterable solids which collect on the surface of the precoat are shaved off by a knife blade.

Vacuum filters have certain advantages. Because the pressure is inward, leaks are not as dangerous to workmen. Also, the relatively low pressure differential tends to produce a porous cake of uniform density. However, vacuum filters are limited to applications which do not require a high-pressure differential for filtration. An additional disadvantage of vacuum filtration is the necessary complexity of the equipment.

5. OTHER TYPES OF FILTERS

There are, of course, many other types of filters. Some of these employ disposable cartridges, others may use perforated metal or porous stone as the filter medium. Filters employing paper sheets are also in use. Generally, these filters are used for special applications or where only small volumes of water are to be filtered.

One application of some of these filters, such as the cartridge filter, are as wellhead or line filters. These are useful for improving injection water quality where the amounts of solids removed are not large and the volume of water filtered small. Large amounts of suspended solids necessitate frequent cartridge changes. Cartridge-type in-line filters are available with a capacity of 20 bbl/hour.

Filter Controls and Gauges

1. RATE-OF-FLOW CONTROLLERS

These controllers operate through the difference in pressure in a Venturi tube placed in the effluent line of the filter unit. The pressure differences operate a control valve, thus regulating filtration rate. With equipment of this type, the filtration rate can usually be controlled to within plus or minus 3 per cent.

2. BACKWASH RATE-OF-FLOW CONTROLLERS

Most filter units are backwashed by means of a backwash pump connected to a clear water well or an elevated tank. Differences in level in the well or in the tank influence the rate of backwashing. A backwash rate-of-flow controller can correct for differences in pump output. Since only one filter is backwashed at a time, one controller is sufficient for a battery of filters. Backwash controllers operate on the same principle as rate-of-flow controllers. Adjustments are made to compensate for the variation in water viscosity with temperature.

3. RATE-OF-FLOW GAUGES

Rate-of-flow gauges may either indicate or record the rate of flow. These gauges not only give a record of filter performance but indicate to the operator the necessity of making adjustments in the filter operation.

4. LOSS-OF-HEAD GAUGES

Since these gauges indicate the end of a filtration run, they are *essential* in operating a filter unit. These gauges are generally either a pressure gauge, connected only to the effluent line, or the differential type of gauge, connected to both the water in the top of the filter and the effluent line.

5. AUTOMATION AND SUPERVISORY CONTROL

In recent years, the use of automatic or remote supervisory controls has increased. The use of automatic controls results in higher quality water, higher production rates, and lower operating costs. These factors compensate for the added initial cost. The use of a central control center to supervise and control filters removed from the water treatment plant gives the engineer or pumper immediate information on all important conditions in the system and at the various stations. Also, a central control center provides "fingertip" control of every component in the system.

However, there are several factors to be considered before installing an automatic or supervisory controlled system. Since the equipment will be *more complex* than manually operated equipment, it will require servicing by trained and able technicians. Also, there is generally an initial period of locating and correcting manufacturing and installation errors, and adjusting the equipment to operating conditions. The engineer should be prepared to allow for this initial period of adjustment.

References

[1]H. E. Hudson, "A Theory of Functioning Filters," *J. Am. Water Works Assoc.*, **40** (1948), 868.

[2]S. Ehlers, "The Selection of Filter Fabrics Re-Examined," *Ind. Eng. Chem.*, **53**, No. 7 (1961), 552.

[3]"Tentative Standard Specifications for Filtering Material," *J. Am. Water Works Assoc.*, **41** (1949), 290.

[4]*Ibid.*

[5]Ehlers, *op. cit.*

[6]G. G. Robeck, K. A. Dostal, and R. L. Woodward, "Studies of Modifications in Water Filtration," *J. Am. Water Works Assoc.*, **56** (1964), 198.

[7]H. E. Hudson, "Factors Affecting Filtration Rates," *J. Am. Water Works Assoc.*, **48** (1956), 1138.

[8]R. Hulbert, "The Filter Backwash-Sand Expansion and Velocity," *J. Am. Water Works Assoc.*, **34** (1942), 1045.

[9]R. Hulbert and F. W. Herring, "Studies on Washing of Rapid Filters," *J. Am. Water Works Assoc.*, **21** (1929), 1445.

[10]*Ibid.*

[11]P. Hamer, J. Jackson, and E. F. Thurston, *Industrial Water Treatment Practice* (London: Butterworth & Co., Ltd., 1961), p. 380.

[12]H. E. Hudson, "Operating Characteristics of Rapid Sand Filters," *J. Am. Water Works Assoc.*, **51** (1959), 114.

[13]J. C. Sharbaugh, "Practical Filtration Formulas," *Chem Eng.*, **69** (December 10, 1962), 153.

[14]J. R. Baylis, "Review of Filter Bed Design and Methods of Washing," *J. Am. Water Works Assoc.*, **51** (1959), 1433.

[15]D. M. McKee, "Automatic Valveless Gravity Filters," *J. Am. Water Works Assoc.*, **54** (1962), 603.

[16]A. F. Alciatore, M. B. Harris, and W. E. Wallen, "Diatomaceous Earth Filtration of Water for Sub-Surface Injection," *Petrol. Eng.*, **27**, No. 5 (1955), B-57.

[17]R. L. LaFrenz and E. R. Baumann, "Optimums in Diatomite Filtrations," *J. Am. Water Works Assoc.*, **54** (1962), 847.

[18]J. V. Slyker, "Recent Developments in the Clarification of Oil Field Waters," *Producers Monthly*, **28**, No. 1 (1964), 8.

[19]E. R. Baumann and R. L. LaFrenz, "Optimum Economical Design for Municipal Diatomite Filter Plants," *J. Am. Water Works Assoc.*, **55** (1963), 56.

Chemical Feeders

10

Chemicals used in water treatment are added by means of devices called chemical feeders. These feeders are classified as wet feeders, dry feeders, and gas feeders. Wet feeders are designed to feed solutions only, or solutions and suspensions. Chemicals in solid form are fed with dry feeders, and gases with gas feeders. These three classes of feeders are divided into proportioning and constant-rate types of feeders. Proportioning chemical feeders add chemicals in proportion to varying flow rates of water; whereas constant-rate feeders feed at a constant rate, and stop or start feeding with the stopping or starting of water flow. Some methods of feeding for chemicals commonly used in water treatment are given in Table 10.1.

Table 10.1

METHODS OF FEEDING FOR COMMON TREATMENT CHEMICALS

(From *Betz Handbook of Industrial Water Conditioning* (6th Ed.) (Philadelphia: Betz Laboratories, 1962), p. 148.)

Chemical	Process Use	Type Feeders	Points of Application
Alum	coagulation color removal	dry pot-type proportional double orifice decanting pumps	Coagulation and sedimentation systems; prior to pressure filters for removal of suspended matter and oil.
Sodium Aluminate	coagulation	dry decanting pumps shot feeders	Usually added with soda ash to softeners; used to some extent for internal boiler water treatment.
Ferric Salts	coagulation color removal oil removal	dry decanting double orifice pumps	Prior to coagulation and filtration systems.
Lime (Hydrated)	pH adjustment softening	dry decanting special pumps (slurry)	Prior to coagulation systems; to softeners; to treated water lines for adjustment of pH.
Soda Ash (Crystalline)	pH adjustment	pot-type proportioning	Prior to pressure filters.
Soda Ash (Anhydrous)	pH and alkalinity adjustment softening	all types of wet and dry feeders	To domestic systems, feed lines, softeners, coagulation and filtration systems; boilers.
Caustic Soda	pH adjustment alkalinity adjustment softening	all types of solution feeders	To softeners; oil removal systems; domesite water systems; boilers.

Material	Purpose	Feeder Type	Application Point
Acid Feed (H$_2$SO$_4$) (H$_3$PO$_4$) (NaHSO$_4$)	pH adjustment reduction of alkalinity	decanting pumps	Treated water lines, prior to degassifiers or de-aerating heaters; H$_3$PO$_4$ to phosphate softeners (for both softening and alkalinity reduction).
Surface Active Phosphates	prevent calcium carbonate deposits eliminate "red water"	all types of proportioning solution feeders	Treated water lines.
Ortho-phosphates (Monosodium Phosphate) (Disodium Phosphate) (Trisodium Phosphate)	prevent scale in boilers	pumps shot feeders	Added continuously to boiler drums; shot-fed to drums or boiler feed line.
Sodium Sulfite	prevent corrosion due to oxygen in boilers, feedlines, economizers	all types continuous solution feeders	Storage section of de-aerating heater; suction or pressure side of boiler feed pumps.
Sodium Nitrate	inhibition of embrittlement	all types of solution feeders	Any point in boiler feed lines or direct to boilers.
Sodium and Potassium Chromates	corrosion inhibitor	all types of solution feeders	To brine systems and various circulating cooling and hot water systems.
Reactive Colloids (Sodium Manuronate)	coagulation	all types of solution feeders	To boiler feed lines; circulating cooling systems.
Protective Colloids (Starches) (Tannins)	particle absorption and adsorption		
Amines and Related Organic Compounds	prevention of return line corrosion	shot feeders pumps	Application depends upon material used. Some materials may be added to boilers and volatilize with steam; others are added to steam line direct, requiring pumps.

Wet-Type Chemical Feeders

1. ELECTRIC-MOTOR CHEMICAL FEEDERS

Electric-motor chemical feeders are also called decanting-type feeders. This feeder operates by lowering a draw-off pipe in the chemical feeding tank at a rate suitable for drawing off the desired amount of solution. The draw-off pipe is attached to a cable drum operated by a constant-speed electric motor. When the motor is actuated, the drum rotates, slowly unwinding the cable and lowering the draw-off pipe. When feeding at a constant rate, the motor operates while the water is flowing. The motor is turned on and off by means of floats set at two levels in the treating tank or basin. For proportional feeding, the draw-off pipe is lowered for a preset period and for a specified volume of water. The constant-speed motor is controlled by a timer operated by a water meter. When a specified amount of water passes through the meter, the timer is activated, starting the constant-speed motor which runs for a preset period. The frequency and dosage of chemical can be readily adjusted.

Either solutions or suspensions can be fed with this type of feeder. For feeding lime, a slaking tank is generally mounted above the feeding tank. The lime can then be slaked before it is admitted to the feeder. When feeding suspensions, the feeder tank should be equipped with an agitator. If both lime and a coagulant or lime and a phosphate are required in the treatment, they are fed from separate feeders.

2. PRESSURE SOLUTION FEEDERS

A diagram of a pressure solution feeder is shown in Fig. 10.1. The soluble chemical is first dissolved, and then admitted to the bottom of the solution tank in such a way that two layers are formed, with the heavier chemical solution on the bottom. The raw-water layer is used as a hydrostatic piston to drive the chemical solution into the line. The chemical solution is fed by a bypass line rather than directly into the raw-water line. Since an orifice is used in the main water line to divert flow through the feeder, its flow is proportional to the mainstream. A needle valve is used to control the flow. An accurate degree of proportional feeding can be obtained using these feeders.

Pressure solution feeders are used for feeding soluble materials, such as sodium carbonate, sodium hydroxide, aluminum sulfate, soluble phosphates, or acids. Special corrosion-resistant materials are necessary for acid service.

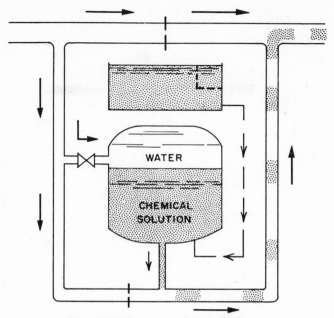

Fig. 10.1. Pressure solution feeder.

When filling the solution tank, care should be exercised to prevent mixing the water-chemical solution layers.

3. POT-TYPE FEEDERS

Pot-type or bypass feeders are used predominantly for slowly dissolving chemicals in lump form, such as alums or condensed phosphates. The chemical to be dissolved, in lump or ball form, is placed in the pot. Water from the high-pressure side of an orifice is bypassed through the pot to the low-pressure side of the orifice. The amount of flow is proportional to the main flow, so that the amount of chemical fed is proportional. The feed can also be regulated to some extent by the inlet valve. A pot-type feeder is shown in Fig. 10.2.

The amount of chemical fed by this type of feeder is primarily governed by the solubility of the chemical and the size of the lumps. This type of feeder is well adapted for feeding a controlled-solubility phosphate to a flow line. The rate of solution is influenced by the amount of surface area of chemical in contact with the water, so that slight changes in concentration of chemical may be affected by altering the size of the lumps.

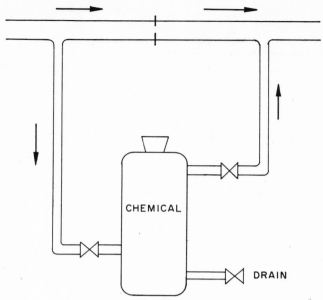

Fig. 10.2. Pot-type feeder.

4. GRAVITY ORIFICE FEEDERS

In this type of feeder, a solution of known concentration is fed to the raw water at constant rate by means of an adjustable orifice. The solution is fed by gravity, using a constant-head device, or a pump. The orifice may be a needle valve. The rate of addition of chemical solution may be measured by collecting the solution in a graduated vessel over a given period of time. A float switch in the treating basin or an electrically operated valve on the orifice discharge line, operating in conjunction with the raw-water pump, may be used for controlling intermittent feeding. This type of feeder *is limited* to solutions—it *will not handle* suspensions.

5. RECIPROCATING-PUMP FEEDERS

A reciprocating pump with an adjustable length of stroke can be used as a chemical feeder. The volume of chemical solution fed is governed by the number of strokes per minute and the volume of the cylinder. The volume can be regulated by adjusting the length of the stroke of the piston. The feeding is accurately controlled, since the volume fed per stroke is uniform. This type of feeder can be used as either a constant rate or a proportional feeder. A reciprocating-pump feeder is best suited for feeding soluble chemicals.

6. DRIP FEEDER

A drip feeder is a very simple constant-rate type of feeder consisting of a tank or reservoir and a bottom take-off valve. The rate of flow from the feeder is regulated by the take-off valve. The rate of feed is not really constant, since it is influenced by the level of liquid in the tank. As the chemical is fed, the liquid level drops, causing a slight pressure decrease that affects the flow through the bottom take-off valve. The feed rate is constant enough for such applications as feeding acid to cooling-tower water. This feeder has the advantage of being easily fabricated.

Dry-Type Chemical Feeders

Dry-type chemical feeders require less space for a given concentration of chemical than do wet types. Dry feeders are used where large quantities of chemicals are required. In order for dry feeders to function properly, the chemical to be fed must be in a granular or powdered form, so as to pass through the control mechanism.

1. VOLUMETRIC FEEDERS

Volumetric-type dry feeders are designed to feed chemicals in granular, lump, or powdered form in a regulated stream or in a succession of small volumes. These feeders can be designed for constant rate or equipped with a meter and timer for proportional feeding. The chemical flows into a mixing chamber, where the water flow is sufficiently high to provide good mixing and prevent settling of the chemical.

2. GRAVIMETRIC FEEDERS

The amount of chemicals fed by gravimetric feeders is weighed. This is accomplished by weighing out unit amounts of chemical at given intervals and discharging them into a mixing basin. Another type of gravimetric feeder operates by releasing a stream of chemical on a traveling belt that is suspended on a balance. The balance acts to control the chemical flow by the weight of chemical on the belt.

Gas Feeders

1. CHLORINE FEEDERS

Chlorine is a water-soluble poisonous gas that is very corrosive in the presence of moisture. Chlorinators are devices used to measure, dissolve, and feed chlorine to the water being treated. Chlorine is used by municipal water companies to disinfect water. It also is used in oilfield operations as a bactericide, algicide, or as an oxidizing agent for small amounts of iron or sulfide.

The amount of chlorine added to the water depends upon the demand. Dosages range from a fraction of a part per million to 10 ppm. After standing from 5 to 30 minutes, the water should show a chlorine residual of 0.1 to 0.2 ppm. "Break-point chlorination" may be used if larger chlorine residuals are required. The "break-point" is found by adding increasing amounts of chlorine to the water and determining the residuals. The residuals will increase, but not in proportion to the amount of chlorine added, until the further addition of chlorine fails to increase the residual. On the continued addition of chlorine, a break-point is reached where the residuals again increase nearly in proportion to the amount of chlorine added.

Chlorine is normally obtained in steel cylinders, containing 105 lb, 150 lb, or 1 ton of the gas. The amount of chlorine added can be determined by mounting the cylinder on a scale. Chlorine leaves the cylinder as a gas and enters the chlorinator. The chlorine is removed from the chlorinator by vacuum produced by an aspirator or hydraulically operated injector. Chlorine is mixed with water at the injector, and the solution fed to the raw water. Chlorine may be fed to water in a flow line or in a treating basin. Chlorine can be fed directly from the cylinder, but when this is done, the chlorine cylinder should be protected against a possible vacuum drawing fluid into the cylinder. A barometric leg, 34 ft high, is used to protect the cylinder. The chlorine delivery tube is run over the top of the leg and down to the feeding point. The chlorine can be diffused, using a chlorine thimble made from high-porosity carborundum.

Chlorine may also be generated in oilfield brines by electrolysis. This method is used to chlorinate the disposal water in the East Texas Oil Field.[1] The feasibility of this method depends upon the amount of chlorine required and the cost of electric power. Chlorine is generated in the East Texas Field for about $0.06 a pound. When small quantities of chlorine are required, they can be obtained from chlorinated lime or calcium hypochlorite. The cost is considerably higher for chlorine in this form than for liquid chlorine.

Chlorine is *very hazardous* and should be *handled with extreme care.* Cylinders of the liquid should be carefully handled without being dropped, and adequately guarded when placed in an upright position. It is preferable to connect the cylinder to the discharge line with approved flexible tube material, using male fittings. Dry chlorine gas is not corrosive and can be handled in iron, steel, or copper lines. However, chlorine in contact with moisture is very corrosive, and equipment lined with rubber or other material designed to withstand the attack of wet chlorine should be used. Graphite should be used if a lubricant is required. Only silver or pure lead solder should be used in contact with the wet gas. If the chlorine cylinder is housed in a building, a ventilating fan should be provided and a gas mask available.

2. CARBON DIOXIDE FEEDERS

In some instances it may be desirable to recarbonate water from cold lime and soda ash softening plants. If flue gas containing a high enough concentration of carbon dioxide is not available, the carbon dioxide may be generated. The necessary equipment for generating carbon dioxide consists of a burner for gas, oil, or solid fuels, a counterflow water scrubber for cooling and purifying the gas, a dryer and compressor, and diffusers in the recarbonation vessel. If only small amounts of carbon dioxide are required, they may be obtained in cylinders and fed directly by the methods used for feeding chlorine. Small quantities of other gases may be fed by the same methods.

Large amounts of carbon dioxide are used in some processes of well stimulation.[2,3] In one variation of these processes, carbon dioxide is fed to the water, giving a highly carbonated water that is then injected. Another variation utilizes slugs of carbon dioxide. Liquid carbon dioxide fed by means of a pump can also be used.[4]

References

[1]*Salt Water Disposal East Texas Oil Field* (2nd ed). (Austin, Tex.: Petroleum Extention Service, 1957), p. 81.

[2]H. J. Ramsay, Jr., and F. R. Small, "Use of Carbon Dioxide for Water Injectivity Improvement," *J. Petrol. Technol.*, **16**, No. 1 (1964), 25.

[3]G. H. Neill, J. B. Dobbs, G. T. Pruitt, and H. R. Crawford, "Field and Laboratory Results of Carbon Dioxide and Nitrogen in Well Stimulation," *J. Petrol Technol.*, **16**, No. 3 (1964), 244.

[4]*Ibid.*

Aeration : Process of Gas Absorption and Release

11

Aeration is a process involving a mass transfer between liquid and gas phases. In treatment of municipal water supplies, it is usually a transfer between water and air. For purposes of treatment of oilfield waters, aeration is not always a mass transfer between water and air but can be between water and carbon dioxide, carbon monoxide, hydrogen sulfide, methane, or nitrogen. The principles of aeration apply for mass transfer between water and all gases.

Use of Aeration in Water Treatment

Aeration is used in water treatment for one of two reasons: (1) to remove undesirable gases from water and (2) to introduce a gas into water for the purpose of causing a chemical reaction. Natural gas or nitrogen can be used to remove dissolved oxygen from water. Carbon monoxide is used to treat some flood waters to remove hydrogen sulfide from the supply water. In these instances, there is no reaction between the gas being absorbed and con-stituents in the water, only physical absorption of one gas and release of the undesirable gas.

Water is aerated to dissolve oxygen for the purpose of reacting with dissolved iron and manganese to affect their removal. This same type of aeration has been used to oxidize dissolved hydrogen sulfide to sulfur, so that it can be removed from the water. Carbon dioxide has been dissolved in water to lower the pH and prevent scale formation after the lime and soda process for water softening.

Theory of Aeration

The process of aeration, or gas absorption and release, is dependent upon the equilibrium between the gas and the water. When a pure gas and water are in equilibrium, there is no change in concentration of dissolved gas in water with time. The solubility of the gas in water influences the ease and degree of aeration.

Henry's law states that the amount of any specific gas dissolved by a given volume of water, at constant temperature, is proportional to the partial pressure of the gas in equilibrium with the solution. It is, of course, also proportional to the solubility of that specific gas in water. Water exposed to air tends to attain equilibrium by dissolving gas from the air or releasing dissolved gas from the water. The partial pressure of oxygen in air is about 0.21 atm, and the partial pressure of carbon dioxide approximately 0.00035 atm. At these partial pressures and at 20°C, pure water saturated with these gases would contain 9.2 ppm oxygen and 0.5 ppm carbon dioxide. (The presence of dissolved salts in the water will influence the solubility of the gases and lower these dissolved-gas concentrations.)

In the process of aeration in water treatment, true equilibrium between the water and the air is seldom attained. However, the equilibrium or saturation concentration of a gas in water at a given temperature and partial pressure is important, because the difference between this concentration and the actual concentration in the water represents the driving force available to cause interchange between the gas and water. The further the system is from equilibrium, the greater the driving force. The function of aeration is to speed up the rate of interchange between gas and water by producing a larger contact surface area.

The interchange between gas and water occurs at the air-water interface. The gas dissolved in water reaches this interface by diffusion, and the rate of diffusion depends upon the concentration gradient. Surface properties of the water influence the interchange between water and air. A water surface film of oriented molecules acts as a barrier to the transfer of gas to or from the water. It is probable that oils, soaps, detergents, and organic acids increase the effect of this film. Increased temperature and turbulence reduce the resistance of this film to gas penetration. A gas film also is present on the air side, but this offers less diffusion resistance than the water film.

The importance of gas and liquid films on absorption and release of gas depends somewhat on the solubility of the gas in water. Gases can be classified as very soluble, slightly soluble, and of intermediate solubility.[1] With a very soluble gas such as hydrogen chloride, the moment the gas contacts the water film it is sucked into solution. The liquid film does not significantly affect the absorption, but absorption is dependent on diffusion of the gas through the gas film.

Gases of low solubility, such as oxygen, have a low rate of absorption, because only small concentration differences can be established across the liquid film. The gas diffuses so slowly through the liquid film that only small concentration differences are required. In this case, the effect of the gas film is negligible. With gases of intermediate solubility, both the liquid and gas films are important in the absorption and release process.

Absorption of a gas is conducted in an atmosphere rich in the gas. If sufficient time is allowed, water absorbs the gas until it is saturated. Conversely, gas release takes place in an atmosphere devoid of the gas. Gas is released from the water until equilibrium is established between water and gas phases. Constantly changing the gas phase insures that equilibrium will not be established and that nearly complete gas release will occur.

The rate of gas transfer is proportional to the difference between the actual and the equilibrium concentration of gas in the water, the exposed area-to-volume ratio, and the gas transfer coefficient. Temperature and pressure influence gas solubility, and thus are important factors in aeration. The amount of gas transferred increases as the period of aeration becomes longer. From the performance data of an aerator under one set of conditions, it is possible to predict the performance of an aerator in absorbing or releasing gas under another set of conditions.

Concentration changes as equilibrium conditions are approached are shown diagrammatically in Fig. 11.1, for conditions of constant pressure and temperature. In this figure, S represents the saturation concentration of the gas in water; C_t, the concentration at time t; and C_o, the initial gas concentration when t is 0. For gas absorption, as t increases $C_t \longrightarrow S$, and $(S - C_t) \longrightarrow 0$. The driving force for gas absorption is represented by $(S - C_t)$ and decreases as $C_t \longrightarrow S$. For gas release or negative absorption, as t becomes greater, $C_t \longrightarrow S$ and $(C_t - S) \longrightarrow 0$. The driving force for this reaction of gas release from a supersaturated solution is represented by $(C_t - S)$ and decreases as $C_t \longrightarrow S$.

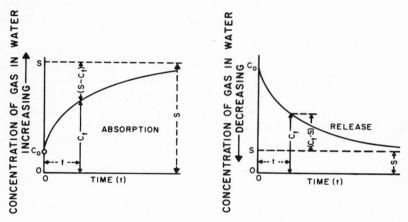

Fig. 11.1. Diagrammatic expression of gas absorption and release. (From Haney, *J. Am. Water Works Assoc.*, **46** (1954), 353.)

The equation for gas absorption at a given pressure and temperature is given by Haney[2] as:

$$\log_{10} \frac{(S - C_t)}{(S - C_o)} = -K(A/V)t \tag{11-1}$$

and the equation for the release of oxygen from water is:

$$\log_{10} \frac{(C_t - S)}{(C_o - S)} = -K(A/V)t \tag{11-2}$$

where S = saturation concentration, g/ml
C_t = concentration in ppm of gas in water at time, t
t = time, hrs
C_o = original concentration of gas in water, g/ml
A = area of gas-water interface, sq cm
V = volume of water, ml
K = constant

For given conditions of temperature, pressure, and gas concentration, the performance of an aerator will remain the same if the effective exposure; $(A/V)t$, remains constant. For example, the size of water sphere undergoing aeration could be increased if t were also increased sufficiently so that the product of (A/V) and t remained the same. Conversely, the time, t, could be decreased if the size of the water sphere were decreased so that the product of (A/V) and t remained constant. Drop-producing spray nozzles can provide aeration faster than a settling pond, because the effective exposure is increased. Tray- and cascade-type aerators provide less water surface exposed to the air than spray nozzles, but the exposure time may be greater. Also, in the operation of the cascade- and tray-type aerators, old water surfaces are continuously destroyed and new ones are formed, facilitating aeration.

Aeration may also be accomplished by passing air through water. Injection aerators inject air, in the form of bubbles, in the bottom of a column of water—as the bubbles rise, they aerate the water. This has an advantage over spray aeration, in that the air bubbles undergo little acceleration and attain a terminal velocity of approximately 1 ft/sec, resulting in an increased time of contact between air and water.

The size of the bubbles formed and the path taken to the surface are

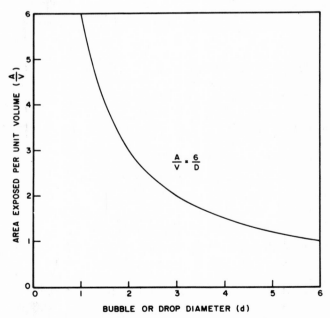

Fig. 11.2. Area-volume ratio vs. diameter of drop or bubble. (From Haney, *J. Am. Water Works Assoc.*, **46** (1954), 353.)

important factors in injection aeration. It is desirable to have bubbles follow a spiral path to the surface because of increased contact time. Generally, orifice plates are used to produce air bubbles, the bubble size being roughly ten times the diameter of the orifice. For a given volume of air: the smaller the bubble, the greater the total surface area exposed, and the more efficient the aeration process. For example, 100 cu ft of air or water in the form of a sphere have a surface area of 104 sq ft. The same volume broken up into spheres 0.1 in. in diameter has an approximate surface area of 72,000 sq ft. However, if this air is formed into bubbles by passing through an orifice plate, which results in the formation of 1 per cent of the bubbles having a diameter of 0.5 in., the efficiency will be greatly reduced, since this 1 per cent will have a volume of 56 cu ft or 56 per cent, but a surface area of only 800 sq ft.[2]

For water drops or air bubbles, the relationship between the area exposed per unit volume, (A/V), and the diameter is shown in Fig. 11.2. This ratio is equal to 6 divided by the diameter of the drop. When the diameter, d, is small, the ratio (A/V) is large and the efficiency of aeration high. Other conditions remaining the same, the efficiency of aeration declines with increasing drop diameter, much as the A/V factor declines in Fig. 11.2.[3]

Number of Plates in Tower for Gas Absorption or Release

If absorption or release is carried out in a bubble-cap or other type of plate tower, the number of plates necessary can be calculated if the interphase transfer on each plate is known. Murphree[4] calculated the vapor efficiency of the cth plate, using Eq. (11–3):

$$E_{MV} = \frac{Y_c - Y_d}{Y_{ec} - Y_d} \qquad (11\text{–}3)$$

where Y_c = average mole fraction of solute in gas leaving cth plate

Y_d = average mole fraction of solute in gas leaving plate below cth and entering cth plate

Y_{ec} = mole fraction of solute in gas, if equilibrium had been established with liquid leaving cth plate

Provided both operating and equilibrium lines are straight and E_{MV} is the same for each plate in the column, the actual number of plates, $N_{p'}$, may be calculated using the equation:[5]

$$N_{p'} = \frac{\ln\left[\left(1 - \frac{mG_M}{L_M}\right)\left(\frac{y_1 - Y_{e2}}{y_2 - Y_{e2}}\right) + \frac{mG_M}{L_M}\right]}{-\ln\left\{1 + E_{MV}\left(\frac{mG_M}{L_M} - 1\right)\right\}} \qquad (11\text{–}4)$$

where m = slope of gas equilibrium curve

  G_M = molar mass velocity of gas in lb moles/hr ft^2

  L_M = water rate in lb moles/hr ft^2 column cross section

  y_1 = mole fraction of solute in gas stream at concentrated end of column

  Y_{e2} = mole fraction of solute in gas at equilibrium, with bulk of liquid at dilute end of column

Oilfield waters vary widely in their compositions and characteristics. Before designing equipment for aeration of a water, tests should be made on a laboratory scale to obtain data specific to the water. Based on the data, the number of plates desired or the time of exposure to gas can be determined and the necessary equipment designed.

Packed Columns for Gas Absorption or Release

Gas absorption and release is also carried out in packed columns. Water is admitted at the top of the column and trickles down the packing, exposing thin films of water to the gas stream flowing from the bottom toward the top of the column. Absorption or release is based on the height of an over-all liquid transfer unit, expressed by Eq. (11–5).[6]

$$H_{OL} = \frac{L_M}{\rho_M K_{La}} \tag{11–5}$$

where H_{OL} = height of over-all liquid transfer unit

  ρ_M = molal density of liquid in lb moles/ft^3

  K_L = over-all coefficient in lb moles/(hr) (ft^2) (unit over-all change in solute concentration in main body)

  a = area of interphase contact in ft^2/ft^3

The number of over-all liquid transfer units is calculated from Eq. (11–6).[7]

$$N_{OL} = \frac{\ln\left[\left(1 - \dfrac{L_M}{mG_M}\right)\left(\dfrac{x_1 - x_{e2}}{x_2 - x_{e2}}\right) + \dfrac{L_M}{mG_M}\right]}{1 - \dfrac{L_M}{mG_M}} \tag{11–6}$$

where x_1 = mole fraction of solute in water at concentrated end of column

  x_2 = mole fraction of solute in water at dilute end of column

  x_{e2} = mole fraction of solute in water at dilute end of column that would be in equilibrium with gas

The reader is referred to a comprehensive discussion of gas absorption and release that has been written by Sherwood and Pigford.[8]

Removal of Oxygen with Natural Gas

Water from rivers and lakes is frequently used for water flooding. Since this water has been exposed to air, it contains dissolved oxygen. This increases the corrosivity of the water, causing damage to equipment and possible plugging of injection wells with corrosion products. Unless the system is completed with corrosion resistant materials, such as plastic-lined pipe or transite pipe, it is advisable to remove the dissolved oxygen from the water. This can be accomplished by aeration, using natural gas for the gas phase.

Oxygen removal by this process will by necessity have to occur in a closed environment, such as a packed column. Both gas absorption and release occur simultaneously. Oxygen from the water is released to the oxygen-poor gas. Any carbon dioxide dissolved in the water will also be released, unless the natural gas contains carbon dioxide. If the natural gas is rich in carbon dioxide, carbon dioxide will be absorbed by the water. Other gases, such as hydrogen sulfide, present in the natural gas will also be absorbed, It is evident from this discussion that the source of natural gas must be selected with care.

The release or absorption of carbon dioxide by water can be an asset or liability. Some fresh waters contain appreciable amounts of dissolved calcium and bicarbonate ions. Removal of dissolved carbon dioxide will cause an increase in pH of the water and result in calcium carbonate scale formation. Absorption of carbon dioxide will lower the pH and decrease the possibility of scale formation. Corrosion could result from too large an absorption of carbon dioxide.

1. OXYGEN REMOVAL FROM OHIO RIVER WATER

One example of the use of natural gas to remove oxygen from water was offered by a water flood in Ohio. In this installation, 1,130 bbl/day of river water were treated with 1,990 ft^3/day of natural gas in a column 20 in. in diameter packed to a depth of 12 ft 7 in.[9] Analysis of the input gas is shown in Table 11.1. At the above gas and liquid input levels, dissolved oxygen was reduced from 11.7 ppm to 0.43 ppm. Because of the 0.7 per cent carbon dioxide in the gas, the pH changed from 7.9 for the input water to 6.9 for the output water, and dissolved carbon dioxide from 3.5 ppm to 7.0 ppm.

Before passing through the packed column, the river water was filtered. Columns of this type have the disadvantage of clogging if suspended matter is not removed from the input water. They are also difficult to clean and usually require repacking, once the column has been clogged.

The removal of oxygen by this method depends on several factors.

Table 11.1

INPUT GAS ANALYSIS

(From Brewster *et al.*, *Producers Monthly*,
19, No. 9 (1955), 18.)

Component	Volume Per Cent
Carbon Dioxide	0.70
Methane	94.33
Ethane	3.75
Propane	0.84
Isobutane	0.13
n-Butane	0.11
C5	0.14
Specific Gravity	0.60

a. Influence of Temperature

The solubility of gases in water is greater at low than at high temperatures. The solubility of oxygen in water at atmospheric temperature is shown in Fig. 11.3. It is apparent that, as the temperature increases, the oxygen solubility decreases and Henry's constant increases.[10] Because of this increased solubility at low temperatures, the effluent from a de-aeration tower will contain more oxygen in cold than in hot weather, if the other factors are the same.

Low temperatures also decrease the rate of diffusion of oxygen through water. This means that oxygen inside a water droplet is less likely to reach the surface of the drop and be removed in cold weather. A tower to be used in the de-aeration of water with natural gas should be designed to reduce the oxygen content of the water to its desired value at the coldest ambient temperature anticipated. It will then function even better in hot weather.

b. Influence of Gas Rates

If other factors remain the same, increasing the rate of gas flow will increase the efficiency of oxygen removal. Carbon dioxide, if present, will also be removed. This may cause a scaling problem and require preventive treatment, depending upon the calcium and carbonate concentration in the water. The gas rate can be increased to such a value that flooding occurs in the tower. At the flooding point, liquid water may be present on top of the packing, with gas bubbling through it.

c. Influence of Water Flow Rate

If some factors remain the same, increasing the water flow rate decreases the efficiency of oxygen removal. When water falls through the packing much

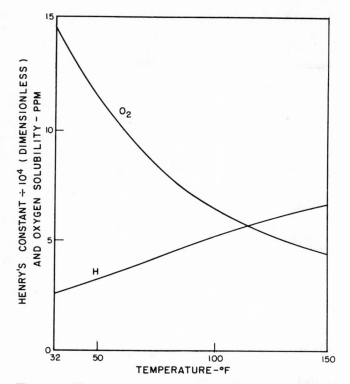

Fig. 11.3. Henry's constant and the solubility of oxygen in water at atmospheric pressure. (From Brewster, Dibble, Jordan, and Neenan, *Producers Monthly*, **19**, No. 9 (1955), 18.)

faster than the gas flow upward, some of the gas containing oxygen may be carried down and contaminate the fresh incoming gas. If it is desirable to increase the rate of water flow, it is generally necessary to increase the height of packing in the tower.

d. Tower Packing

The height and diameter of the tower influence flow rate and oxygen removal. Since the rate of oxygen removal is proportional to the effective surface area, the packing should have a large surface area. Raschig rings or Berl saddles have areas from 30 to 150 sq ft/cu ft, depending upon the size of packing.

The porosity in the tower controls, to some extent, the maximum flow rate of water and gas through the tower. In towers with a small free area, the pressure drop will be large and the rate of water flow low. Such towers flood at lower operating conditions than towers with more free space or porosity.

2. OXYGEN REMOVAL FROM LAKE MARACAIBO WATER

Lake Maracaibo in Venezuela contains brackish water. Dissolved oxygen in this water greatly increases its corrosivity. Before use in a water flood, oxygen was removed from 3,500 bbl/day of this water by passing it down a column 30 ft high and 24 inches in diameter, containing two 5.5 ft packs of one-inch berl saddles.[11] A natural gas flow of 5,250 ft³/day was passed countercurrent to the water to effect oxygen removal.

The oxygen content was 3.85 ml/liter in the input water and 0.05 ml/liter in the output water. The equilibrium curve showing the partial pressure of oxygen in the gas phase corresponding to the dissolved oxygen content is shown in Fig. 11.4. Since the actual concentration of oxygen in the natural gas, as shown by the operating curve, falls below the equilibrium curve, oxygen is released from the water into the natural gas.

Natural gas used in this column contained 5.3 per cent carbon dioxide, which was reduced to 0.6 per cent on passing through the column. The water absorbed 25 ppm carbon dioxide. Fig. 11.5 shows the operating curve above

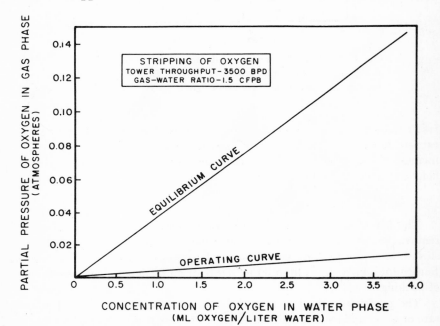

Fig. 11.4. Stripping of oxygen. (From Finley, SPE of AIME, Venezuelan Annual Meeting, 1959.)

the equilibrium curve, which means gas absorption by the water. During the oxygen removal or stripping operation, pH of the water dropped from 8.3 to 6.4 because of carbon dioxide absorption.

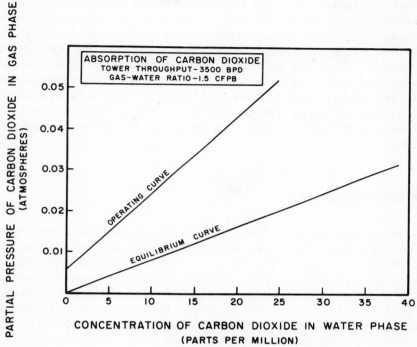

Fig. 11.5. Absorption of carbon dioxide. (From Finley, SPE of AIME, Venezuelan Annual Meeting, 1959.)

Removal of Carbon Dioxide

Carbon dioxide concentrations in water greater than 0.5 ppm can be reduced by aeration. The removal of carbon dioxide may result in a change in the pH of the water. At 80°F, water containing 25 ppm or more bicarbonate alkalinity shows phenolphthalein alkalinity after the carbon dioxide is removed; if the bicarbonate content is 50 ppm or more, 14 per cent of the bicarbonates are converted to carbonates; and if the calcium bicarbonate content is greater than 200 ppm, some calcium carbonate precipitates.[12] Generally, the removal of carbon dioxide by aeration is carried out to a given level, such as 5 to 15 ppm, rather than to equilibrium with the air.

When selecting the type of aerator to be used to remove carbon dioxide, the following factors should be considered: (1) the concentration of free carbon dioxide in the water; (2) the amount of this concentration to be removed; (3) the volumes of water to be handled; (4) the desirability of removing iron or manganese. If it is necessary to reduce the amount of carbon dioxide from water significantly, and if iron and manganese removal is desired, either a coke-tray aerator or a wood-slat aerator is used. An enclosed, forced-draft aerator gives good results, provided iron or manganese removal is not required. Satisfactory results are obtained using a decarbonization tank when small volumes of water are to be aerated for a high degree of carbon dioxide removal. If iron and manganese removal is not a consideration and the amount of carbon dioxide to be removed is small, other types of aerators are satisfactory, such as the spray, step, plate, or riffled-cone types.

Removal of Hydrogen Sulfide

Aeration is also used to remove dissolved hydrogen sulfide from water. The effectiveness of this treatment depends to a large extent upon the characteristics of the water and the amount of carbon dioxide present. Since hydrogen sulfide is nearly three times as soluble in water as is carbon dioxide, carbon dioxide will be removed first during the aeration of waters containing both gases. If water contains bicarbonate alkalinity and no mineral acidity, loss of carbon dioxide results in a pH increase. In acid water, the sulfide is in the form of dissolved hydrogen sulfide gas and can be removed by aeration; however, in alkaline waters the sulfide ion persists and is not effectively removed by aeration. The per cent of total sulfide present as hydrogen sulfide at some pH values is shown in Table 11.2.

For waters containing a low concentration of hydrogen sulfide, aeration may reduce the concentration to the desired level. Some of the sulfide ion

Table 11.2
PER CENT TOTAL SULFIDE EXISTING AS HYDROGEN
SULFIDE AT SOME pH VALUES
(From Pomeroy, *J. Am. Water Works Assoc.*,
33 (1941), 943.)

pH	% $S^=$ as H_2S
5.0	98.0
6.0	86.0
6.5	67.0
7.0	39.0
7.5	17.0
8.0	6.0
9.0	0.6

not removed by aeration may be oxidized to free sulfur by the air, according to the following equation:

$$H_2S + \frac{1}{2} O_2 \rightarrow H_2O + S \qquad (11\text{-}7)$$

This slow oxidation of sulfide by air is noticed when waters containing sulfide are sampled in contact with air and capped. After the water stands for a period of time, oxidized sulfur appears.

If the aeration process does not reduce the sulfide content to the desired level, chlorination may be used to oxidize small residual amounts of sulfide. As shown in the following equation, four molecules of chlorine are required to oxidize one molecule of hydrogen sulfide to sulfate:

$$4\,Cl_2 + 4\,H_2O + H_2S \rightarrow H_2SO_4 + 8\,HCl \qquad (11\text{-}8)$$

Thus, the cost would be prohibitive if large amounts of sulfide were to be oxidized by chlorine. A curve giving the theoretical concentration of chlorine necessary to oxidize a given concentration of hydrogen sulfide is shown in Fig. 11.6. In actual practice, the chlorine required will probably be higher because of the presence of other oxidizable material in the water.

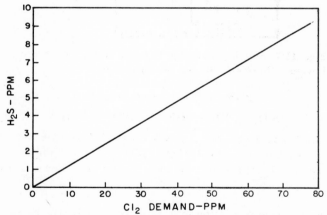

Fig. 11.6. Theoretical amount of chlorine necessary to remove a given amount of hydrogen sulfide. (Modified from Powell and Von Lossberg, *J. Am. Water Works Assoc.*, **44** (1948), 1277.)

1. AIR OXIDATION OF SULFIDE IN PROCESS WATER

Sulfide is removed from some refinery waters by oxidizing it with air.[13] In this process, sulfide-containing water is preheated by heat exchange with the refinery product, mixed with compressed air, and passed through a sulfide oxidation column as shown in Fig. 11.7. The 7-ft diameter column, operated at 200°F, does not contain any packing but is divided into four chambers. The first chamber is 20 ft high and the remaining three, 10 ft each.

Because of the temperature and pressure, most of the sulfide is oxidized to thiosulfate, with 10 per cent being converted to sulfate, as shown in Eqs. (11–9) and (11–10):

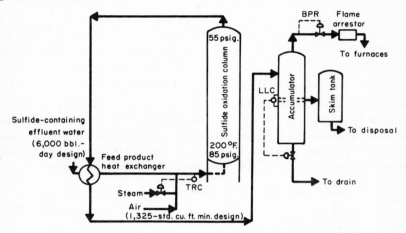

Fig. 11.7. Sulfide oxidation system. (From Martin and Levanas, *Oil Gas J.*, **60**, No. 24 (1962), 184.)

$$2HS^- + 2O_2 \longrightarrow S_2O_3^= + H_2O \tag{11–9}$$

$$S_2O_3^= + 2O_2 + 2OH^- \longrightarrow 2SO_4^= + H_2O \tag{11–10}$$

The column was designed to process 6,000 bbl/day of water containing 8,000 ppm of sulfide. It actually processes only 4,500 bbl/day of water. Performance data for this sulfide oxidation column is shown in Table 11.3.

2. Exhaust Gas for Hydrogen Sulfide Removal

When ordinary aeration does not remove hydrogen sulfide effectively, an atmosphere containing a larger concentration of carbon dioxide may be used in order to maintain a lower pH in the water. Flue gas, available at some industrial plants, contains about 12 per cent carbon dioxide or roughly 300 times more than air. Gas containing carbon dioxide in large concentrations is often available near oil or gas fields.

A two-chambered degasifier is sometimes used when hydrogen sulfide is removed with flue gas. The scrubbed flue gas is blown upward through the upper chamber counter-current to a downward fall of water over superim-

Table 11.3
PERFORMANCE DATA FOR SULFIDE OXIDATION COLUMN
(From Martin and Levanas, *Oil Gas J.*, **60**, No. 24 (1962), 184.)

	Low-Temp.	Operation Normal	High-Temp.
Temperature, °F*	185	203	230
Feed rate, bbl per day	4,500	4,500	4,500
Air rate, std. cu ft per minute	540	530	530
Pressure, psig:			
Bottom	79	82	87
Top	41	40	35
Air-water ratio (approx. inlet conditions), cu ft per cu ft	5.7	5.8	6.0
Pressure drop (typical), psi:			
Over-all column (inlet to top)†	46	49	50
Across distributors	27	30	30
Sulfide concentration, ppm wt:			
Feed	5,505	4,813	4,433
Chamber 1	826	495	471
Chamber 2	70	24	125
Chamber 3	0	0	4
Chamber 4	0	0	0
Sulfide oxidized, tons per day	4.3	3.8	3.5
Sulfide oxidation rate, lb per hour per cu ft	0.35‡	0.37‡	0.37‡
Excess air, % §	54	76	91

*Average temperature in Chamber 1 for a number of tests.
†Includes elevation head.
‡Basis oxidation in Chamber 1 and sulfide concentration of 4,800 ppm in feed.
§Basis oxidation of sulfide to thiosulfate.

posed slat trays. Hydrogen sulfide and flue gas are discharged to the atmosphere through the top of the chamber. In this process the falling water becomes saturated with carbon dioxide at its higher partial pressure in the flue gas, assuring a low pH value and keeping the sulfide as the removable hydrogen sulfide.

Carbon dioxide dissolved in the water during its passage through the upper chamber of the degasifier is removed in the lower chamber, which may be any of the previously mentioned aerators suitable for the removal of carbon dioxide. If a slight residual of sulfide remains in the water, it can be removed by chlorination.

Alternatively, the pH value of water can be lowered by the addition of a mineral acid, such as sulfuric or hydrochloric, prior to aeration to remove hydrogen sulfide.[14] The desirability of this method of pH adjustment depends upon the purpose for which the water is to be used, the alkalinity of the water, the required amount of acid dosage, and the alternative availability of a waste gas containing carbon dioxide.

In one West Texas water flood, 18,000 bbl/day of San Andres water are treated with exhaust gas to remove approximately 335 ppm dissolved hydro-

Table 11.4

Types and Results of Aeration of Waters

(Reprinted from Watkins et al., Bureau of Mines R1 4930 (1952), p. 20.)

	Type Aerator Used	Water Aerated	Dissolved Oxygen, ppm		Free Carbon Dioxide, ppm		Hydrogen Sulfide, ppm		Total Iron, ppm		Dissolved Iron, ppm		pH Value	
			Before	After	Before	After	Before	After	Before	After	Before	After	Before	After
Andrus, Pate & Lavens	tray	Arbuckle	0.0	7.3	162	0	56	0	5.0	3.0	1.5	1.0	7.2	8.0
		produced	3.5		26		0		6.0		1.5		7.6	
Mack C. Colt	tray	lake	4.8	8.6	3	0	0	0	1.0	2.5	0.4	0.4	7.7	7.8
	ramp	produced	1.8		23		0		6.0		0.5		7.5	
Sack-Brundred	tray	Arbuckle	0.0	4.5	54	9	332	0	0.8	3.5	0.3	0.3	7.3	7.8
Producers Development Co.	spray	well	1.9	2.6	25	41	0	0	13.8	11.1	8.5	7.5	7.2	7.2
		produced	0.4		75		0		10.5		11.3		7.2	
White & Duncan	tray	well	0.0	8.1	0	0	0	0	4.0	4.3	3.0	0.5	7.5	7.7
		produced	3.3		0		0		3.3		0.5		7.4	
Cities Service Oil Co.	ramp	Arbuckle	1.8	3.7	63	14	69	0	0.5	0.9	0.0	0.0	6.8	7.5
		produced	0.0		48		5		2.4		2.0		6.7	
Stekoll Petroleum Co.	trough	city	0.1	1.0	14	13	6	2	6.0	6.1	trace	1.3	7.4	7.5
		produced									2.2			

Company	Process	Source												
Sohio Petroleum Co. (Coon)	tray	Arbuckle	0.3	0.0	44	5	51	0	3.3	4.8	2.0	1.7	7.0	7.8
		produced	0.5		55		40		5.0		2.5		7.4	
Kewanee Oil Co.	tray blower	Arbuckle	2.9	6.4	72	10	55	0	4.3	17.0	1.9	1.1	7.0	7.8
		produced	2.0		41		24		1.6		1.1		7.2	
C. C. Harmon	spray	river	7.8	10.8	40	30	0	0	2.0	3.0	1.0	1.8	7.6	7.7
		produced	1.8		78		0		15.0		12.5		7.2	
Sohio Petroleum Co. (Bolton)	tray	Arbuckle	1.7	1.0	309	126	187	5	2.7	6.2	0.9	2.5	6.6	7.4
		produced	1.9		150		1		8.5		5.3		6.8	
Layton Oil Co.	tray	Arbuckle	1.1	2.8	145	16	94	0	0.1	5.7	0.1	1.8	6.8	7.5
		produced	4.3		20		0		7.1		3.2		7.4	
Wellsville Oil Co.	spray	Arbuckle	0.0	0.0	18	13	38	0	9.1	56.0	3.6	3.7	7.3	7.6
		produced	0.0		56		0		38.0		15.0		7.2	
Deep Rock Oil Corp.	tray	Arbuckle Mississippi	1.3	1.1	130	0	135	0	3.8	2.7	0.6	0.2	6.8	7.6
		produced												
The Pure Oil Co.	tray	river	7.8	0.2	0	26	0	0	1.3	14.0	1.0	0.5	7.2	7.5
		produced	0.3		103		31		22.0		1.7		7.2	
Delaware Consolidated Oil Co.	tray blower	Arbuckle	0.4	0.6	212	26	152	1	1.7	1.4	1.4	1.3	6.4	7.1
The Ohio Oil Co.	tray	Arbuckle	0.6	3.0	31	4	28	0	0.9	1.3	0.4	0.5	6.7	7.9
		produced	0.0		29		0		2.7		2.4		7.9	

gen sulfide.[15] An exhaust gas generator burning natural gas under carefully controlled conditions is used to produce an oxygen-free exhaust gas. The hot gas is cooled by blowing the gas into a water contact vessel to permit direct heat exchange with the water. At a gas-to-water ratio of 66.7 scf/bbl, the water temperature is increased 20°F in cooling the gas. Polymetaphosphates are added to the raw water at the producing well to prevent deposition of calcium scales.

The cooled exhaust gas is then transferred to the 25 tray bubble cap column shown in Fig. 11.8. A plate-type column was chosen in preference to a packed column, because it has less tendency to become fouled. This column reduces hydrogen sulfide to a 1.5 ppm residual, that is acceptable in this operation.

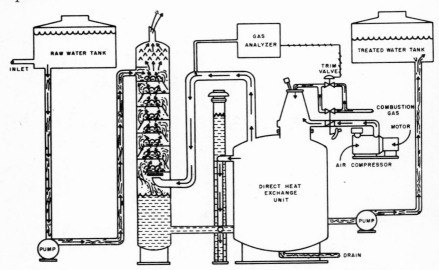

Fig. 11.8. Simplified drawing of hydrogen sulfide removal (with exhaust gas. (From Weeter, *Petrol. Eng.*, **35**, No. 5 (1963), 51.)

Aeration of Secondary Recovery Waters

Aeration of waters to remove undesirable substances is a common practice in the oil field. Results of aeration of water for use in some secondary recovery projects in the mid-continent area are shown in Table 11.4. According to these results, tray-type aerators are more effective in removing hydrogen sulfide and carbon dioxide than are the other aerators listed.[16] Efficiency also depends on design and operation of the aerator. This table also shows that dissolved oxygen and pH were generally increased during aeration.

Other Contaminants Removed by Aeration

Methane is removed readily by aeration. Open-type aerators with ample ventilation, such as the wood-slat tray aerator, are recommended. Most objectionable odors found in water are volatile and can be removed by aeration. However, in the case of drinking water, aeration may not remove the entire amount of objectionable material—it may be necessary to follow aeration by filtration through activated carbon. Spray-type aerators are recommended for odor removal.

Aerators

There are many different aerator designs. Most of these saturate water with air effectively, but they are not equally effective in removing dissolved gases. Aerators that produce thin films or small drops of water and provide long contact time are the most efficient in removing dissolved gases. In the following discussion of various aerators, flow rates are expressed as gal/min per sq ft of horizontal cross-sectional area.

1. Step Aerators

A series of steps over which the water cascades before collecting in a concrete catch basin is called a step aerator. The steps are usually made of concrete, but they can be made of wood. The number of steps varies between three and ten. While the step aerator is satisfactory for introducing air into water, it requires more ground space and drop than wood-slat tray, spray, coke-tray, or forced-draft aerators.

2. Riffled-Cone Aerators

These aerators are in a conical or pyramidal form and usually are only 3 to 5 feet high. They are normally made of wood and have wood cleats or riffles nailed to the sides of the cone or pyramid to create turbulence as the water flows down the sides. The cone should be above the water level of the catch basin so that the water will have some extra fall through air. Because of the thickness of the water flowing over the cone, the small surface area, and insufficient turbulence, this type of aerator is relatively inefficient.

3. PLATE AERATOR

The plate-type aerator is constructed of three or four circular metal trays of different diameters, the smallest diameter mounted on the top and the largest on the bottom. It is more efficient than the riffled-cone aerator because of the several drops through air.

4. COKE-TRAY AERATOR

This aerator is made in both cylindrical and rectangular designs, and is equipped with three or four trays. A desirable flow rate for either the three- or four-tray design is 10 gal/min per sq ft. Generally, the aerator is mounted over a catch basin or reservoir, which is equipped with a float switch to prevent flooding. Incoming water rains down from a distributing tray through the air and through the first coke bed. From the bottom of this bed, the water falls to the next tray, through the coke bed, and again through air to the next tray. From this last coke bed, the water falls into the catch basin and then passes through filters.

Coke-tray aerators are favored for the aeration of iron- and manganese-bearing water. Water detention time in the catch basin should be a *minimum* of 15 minutes for iron removal—30 minutes is preferable. The detention time depends upon the amount of precipitate formed in the water after aeration. If the amount is small, settling is not so important and the precipitate can be removed by the filters. If the amount of precipitate is large, sufficient settling time should be allowed to remove a large fraction of the solid material and thus reduce the load on the filter. Besides requiring a longer settling time than necessary for iron removal, manganese removal usually requires the addition of lime or alkali.

5. WOOD-SLAT TRAY AERATORS

Wood-slat tray aerators are generally rectangular in shape and vary widely in size and number of trays. The slats in the trays are so arranged that water falling over the edges of the slats in one tray will fall on the center of the slats of the next tray. For wood-slat tray aerators of equal height, the one with the shortest water drop and greatest number of trays will be the most efficient. Desirable flow rates range from between 5 and 10 gal/min per sq ft. These aerators are used for the reduction or removal of carbon dioxide, hydrogen sulfide, methane, and often for iron and manganese removal.

6. SPRAY AERATORS

Spray-type aerators function by sweeping the volatile substances out of the water with air. A fine spray results in the most effective air-water interchange; however, fine orifices frequently plug, so that orifices of about 1 inch are generally used. These are mounted above an open basin with the nozzles pointed upward. The nozzles are spaced anywhere from one per 50 sq ft to one per 175 sq ft. The water is sprayed as high as 25 ft into the air. This type of aerator is favored by municipal plants for the removal of odors and tastes.

7. FORCED-DRAFT AERATORS

A forced-draft aerator or degasifier is, in effect, a closed wood-slat tray aerator with a blower arrangement used to force air into the bottom of the tower. The air then flows upward through the aerator, and the water flows downward. An air outlet in the top of the aerator allows the air to escape with its content of removed gas. Aerators of this type are generally constructed of wood and are able to handle corrosive sulfur waters, acid waters, and waters containing large amounts of carbon dioxide.

The forced-draft aerator is very efficient because of its controlled air supply in a counter-current flow of air and water. Also, the action of a large number of slat trays results in fresh water-drop surfaces exposed to air. The recommended flow rate of water is 17.5 gal/min per sq ft. This type of aerator is effective for the removal of carbon dioxide and hydrogen sulfide. The required height of the aerator increases with increasing amounts of free carbon dioxide in the water.

8. DECARBONATION TANKS

Decarbonation tanks, often used to handle small amounts of water from hydrogen ion exchangers, are open tanks containing an air grid in the bottom through which air is released. This type of aerator will decrease the carbon dioxide content of water to any desired value (above an equilibrium value with the air employed) when used on a batch-process basis.

9. PRESSURE AERATORS

The solubility of air in water is proportional to the air pressure. In a pressure aerator, the water is saturated with air under pressure. When pressure-saturated water is exposed to atmospheric pressure, air is released from the water until the equilibrium value at atmospheric pressure is reached. If the pressure-saturated water is mixed with water at atmospheric pressure, this released air will dissolve in the unsaturated water and can cause the entire amount of water to be saturated. In a pressure aerator, one-fifth of the amount of water to be aerated is saturated with air at five times atmospheric pressure. When this water is mixed with the unaerated water, enough dissolved air is available to saturate the entire amount of water.

This type of aerator is sometimes used for iron and manganese removal. The air is supplied by an air compressor. Water enters the top of the pressure chamber and rains down through the tank, mixing with air as it falls. This does not reduce the free carbon dioxide content, since the water is not swept out with air but only saturated.

References

[1]W. K. Lewis and W. G. Whitman, "Principles of Gas Absorption," *Ind. Eng. Chem.*, **16** (1924), 1215.

[2]P. D. Haney, "Theoretical Principles of Aeration," *J. Am. Water Works Assoc.*, **46** (1954), 353.

[3]*Ibid.*

[4]E. V. Murphree, "Rectifying Column Calculations," *Ind. Eng. Chem.*, **17** (1925), 747.

[5]T. K. Sherwood and R. L. Pigford, *Absorption and Extraction* (New York: McGraw-Hill Book Company, 1952), p. 149.

[6]*Ibid.*, p. 133.

[7]*Ibid.*, p. 135.

[8]*Ibid.*

[9]F. M. Brewster, Jr., D. K. Dibble, G. S. Jordan, and A. Neenan, "The Deaeration of Water With Natural Gas," *Producers Monthly*, **19**, No. 9 (1955), 19.

[10]*Ibid.*

[11]H. F. Finley, "Oxygen Stripping for Water Flood Corrosion Control," Society of Petroleum Engineers of AIME, Venezuelan 3rd Annual Meeting, Caracas (1959).

[12]E. Nordell, *Water Treatment for Industrial and Other Uses* (2nd ed) (New York: Reinhold Publishing Corp. 1961), p. 299.

[13]J. D. Martin and L. D. Levanas, "Air Oxidation of Sulfide in Process Water," *Oil Gas J.*, **60**, No. 24 (1962), 184.

[14]W. J. Hart and R. G. Wingate, "Removal of Sulfides from Brine by Aeration with Exhaust Gas from Submerged Combustion," Petroleum Branch AIME, Paper No. 515G (1955).

[15]R. F. Weeter, "Exhaust Gases Strip H_2S from Sour Flood Water," *Petrol. Eng.*, **35**, No. 5 (1963), 51.

[16]J. W. Watkins, F. R. Willett, Jr., and C. E. Arthur, *Conditioning Water for Secondary-Recovery in Midcontinent Oil Fields*, Bureau of Mines Report of Investigation 4930 (Washington, D.C.: U.S. Department of the Interior, Bureau of Mines, 1952), p. 18.

Degasification

12

Aeration, a useful method of removing dissolved gases such as carbon dioxide and hydrogen sulfide, depends upon a mass transfer between the water and gas phases. If the gas phase is air, the water absorbs air and releases the undesirable gas. The water still contains a dissolved gas, even though it is different from the gas originally present. Degasification is the complete removal of dissolved gases from the water, not just an exchange of gases.

The most common use of degasification of water is to remove dissolved oxygen. As discussed in Chapter 4, the presence of dissolved oxygen in water greatly increases its corrosivity and interferes with the action of corrosion inhibitors. Boiler feed waters are frequently degasified, because dissolved oxygen is particularly corrosive at high temperatures. Some water flood waters are degasified to decrease corrosion and prevent the formation of corrosion products that might plug the injection well.

True degasification is a physical process in which all dissolved gases are removed from water. Selective degasification is the removal of a gas by chemical reaction, with a substance added to the water for that specific purpose; for example, the use of hydrazine to remove oxygen from boiler water.

Theory of Degasification

Two laws pertaining to gases govern the removal of gas from water. Dalton's law states that the total pressure of a mixture of gases is equal to the sum of the partial pressures of the individual components in the mixture. This law is expressed in Eq. (12–1):

$$P_{\text{total}} = P_1 + P_2 + P_n \tag{12–1}$$

The partial pressure of an individual gas is the pressure that that gas would exert if it were present in its same concentration in the same volume at the same temperature as the mixture.

The second law, Henry's law, states that the solubility of a gas in a liquid is directly proportional to the pressure of the gas at equilibrium. It is expressed in Eq. (12–2), where C is the concentration, H a constant, and P the pressure of the gas above the liquid:

$$C = HP \tag{12–2}$$

Decreasing the concentration of a dissolved gas in the gas phase will cause the gas to leave the water and establish a new equilibrium concentration. This is the principle used in aeration. In degasification, the chief component in the gas phase is frequently water vapor or steam. When steam is the gas phase, it is the process of aeration without using a gas of a chemical composition different from that of water.

According to Dalton's law, if water in contact with air is heated to boiling in a closed vessel, the pressure of the gas will be equal to the vapor pressure of the water in addition to the air pressure at that temperature. If the vessel is vented to the atmosphere, the pressure is released to atmospheric pressure, which will be equaled by the vapor pressure of water. The steam formed in the boiling process will soon sweep all the air out of the vessel, as the steam escapes. The partial pressure of oxygen in contact with the water will then be very low, so oxygen will leave the water in an effort to establish equilibrium. If the outlet is closed and the vessel suddenly cooled, steam will condense and a partial vacuum will be formed. The only pressure exerted in the vessel will be due to vapor pressure of water and whatever gas has been released from water. This is the principle of steam and vacuum de-aerators.

Solubility of gases is also an important factor in degasification. Gases are less soluble in hot than in cold water. This is readily seen in Table 4.2, where the solubility of oxygen is 14.62 ppm at 0°C and only 5.6 ppm at 50°C. It will be nearly zero at the boiling point of water. A certain amount of degasification occurs from simply heating water near the boiling point.

Open Heaters

Open heaters are used for the de-aeration of feed water for low-pressure boilers not equipped with steel tube economizers. This type of de-aerator will not remove the entire amount of dissolved oxygen, but it will reduce the oxygen content of the feed water to 0.1 to 0.2 cc/liter, depending upon the volume of steam, size of the unit, and the venting of noncondensable gases. This heating also removes dissolved carbon dioxide gas and may break down some of the bicarbonate ions to further reduce the corrosivity of the water.

Essentially, an open heater is a tank or vessel for heating the water by bringing it into contact with steam. The make-up water or condensate-return water enters at the top of the tank and falls downward over trays, thus bringing thin films or drops of water into contact with the steam. The water is sprayed into the tank in some designs. The steam and gas can be vented directly to the atmosphere or passed through a vent condenser, so that heat from the vented steam can be recovered by the incoming water. The heated, de-aerated water is stored in the heater until needed for the boiler.

De-aerating Heaters

Oxygen removal is more complete with de-aerating heaters than with open heaters. In de-aerating heaters the steam is used twice, while it is used only once in open heaters. The steam is used to scrub the hot—but not completely de-aerated—water from the primary heater, and then the steam is used to heat the water in the primary heater. These heaters are capable of reducing the oxygen concentration to 0.005 ml/liter.

In the spray-type de-aerating heater, the water is sprayed into the steam space, where it is de-aerated to less than 0.3 ml/liter dissolved oxygen. This water, heated to within a few degrees of steam temperature, passes into the steam scrubber, where most of the remaining oxygen is removed. The entry of water into the de-aerator is controlled by a float valve in the storage basin.

Some de-aerating heaters utilize a series of trays, much as the slat-type aerators do. The water falls down over the trays and the steam rises up through the water in the counter-flow design de-aerator. Both the water flow and the steam flow are downward in the down-flow design. In the cross-flow design, the steam flows crosswise through the lower trays and upward through the upper set. No matter what the type, it is important that de-aerating heaters be properly vented to keep the partial pressure of air or other gases at a minimum. A tray-type de-aerating heater is shown in Fig. 12.1.

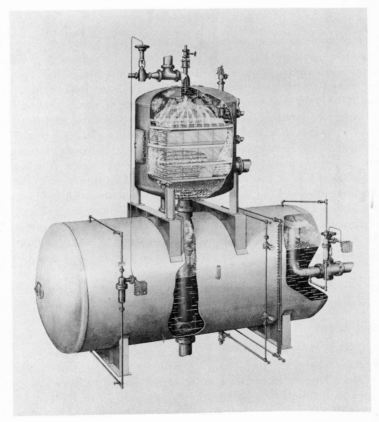

Fig. 12.1. Tray-type deaerating heater. (Courtesy of Graver Water Conditioning Co.)

Vacuum De-aerator

Cold water can be de-aerated by reducing the pressure until the water boils. The reduced pressures at which water boils for various temperatures are shown in Table 12.1. While complete vacuum de-aeration is possible, it is seldom economical. Vacuum de-aeration is often used where a maximum oxygen content of 0.3 ml/liter is permissible. Other dissolved gases would

Table 12.1

BOILING POINTS OF WATER AT REDUCED PRESSURES

Temperature, °F	Pressure, psig
40	0.123
60	0.256
80	0.507
100	0.950
120	1.69
140	2.89
160	4.74
180	7.51
200	11.53
212	14.7

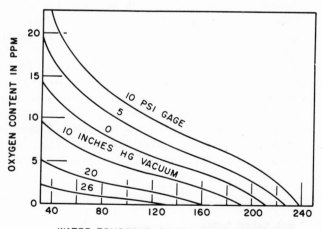

Fig. 12.2. Oxygen solubility vs. temperature at some constant pressures. (From Crawford, *Producers Monthly*, **25**, No. 10 (1961), 10.)

also be removed in vacuum de-aeration. The quantity of oxygen dissolved in water at various air pressures is shown in Fig. 12.2. It is evident from the figure that reducing the pressure and increasing the water temperature simultaneously aids in removing oxygen from water.

The vacuum can be supplied by pumps, but these are bulky and expensive. The vacuum is best obtained by the use of two steam injectors operated in series. A series of superimposed wood-slat trays is mounted in an enclosed steel shell. The heights of the tray stacks depend on the temperature of the water, the degree of de-aeration required, and the ratio of noncondensable gases to water vapor abstracted from the de-aerator. These stacks usually range from 12 to 20 ft. Generally, 100 psig steam is required, but this depends on the water temperature, the degree of aeration, and the height of the tray stack. The water flow rate is usually 40 to 50 gal/min per sq ft of horizontal cross-sectional area.

Chemical Degasification

Chemical methods used to remove a gas from water depend upon a reaction between the gas and a chemical added to the water. This results in the selective removal of a specific gas, rather than using degasification to remove all dissolved gases, as in vacuum de-aeration. The most important application of chemical degasification is for the removal of dissolved oxygen from water. Dissolved carbon dioxide is removed in the lime-soda softening process when calcium hydroxide is added to the water.

All chemical methods used to remove dissolved oxygen from water are based upon the reaction of oxygen with some easily oxidizable substance, the most commonly used being sodium sulfite and hydrazine. These chemical methods are particularly useful for removing small amounts of oxygen from large volumes of water. Both sodium sulfite and hydrazine are used to remove oxygen from boiler feed waters. Sometimes these chemicals are added after physical de-aeration processes to remove last traces of oxygen.

Oxygen Removal with Sodium Sulfite

Sodium sulfite, frequently referred to as an oxygen scavenger, has been used for many years to remove dissolved oxygen from boiler feed water and from oilfield waters used in secondary recovery operations. As shown in Eq. (12–3), dissolved oxygen is removed in the oxidation of sulfite to sulfate:

$$\frac{1}{2}O_2 + Na_2SO_3 \rightarrow Na_2SO_4 \qquad (12\text{--}3)$$

Stoichiometrically, 7.9 ppm of sodium sulfite are required to react with 1 ppm dissolved oxygen, but in actual practice 10 ppm of sodium sulfite are used with 1 ppm dissolved oxygen.

Sodium sulfite reacts slowly with dissolved oxygen at normal atmospheric temperatures. As with other chemical reactions, the rate increases as temperature rises. In applications where immediate oxygen removal is required, sodium sulfite alone is not effective. Fortunately, one can add catalysts that greatly increase the rate of reaction between oxygen and sulfite ion.

Some of the catalysts available are the divalent ions of manganese, copper, cobalt, nickel, and iron. Cobaltous and cupric ions are the most effective of these for catalyzing the oxygen-sulfite reaction. The effect of some catalysts on the rate of this reaction is shown in Fig. 12.3. The great increase in reaction rate achieved by adding a catalyst is readily seen in this figure. Cobaltous ion is more effective than cupric ion, and as little as 0.001 ppm of cobaltous ion will catalyze the reaction.[1] Because of the potential corrosion hazard of adding copper to water, cobalt ions are preferred as catalysts.

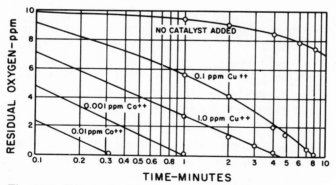

Fig. 12.3. Effect of catalysts on rate of oxygen-sulfite reaction. (From Pye, *J. Am. Water Works Assoc.*, **39** (1947), 1121.)

Since sodium sulfite is a reducing agent, it will react with other oxidizing agents in the water as well as with dissolved oxygen. Chlorine added to the water as a bactericide or dichromate added as corrosion inhibitor will react with sulfite. Usually when both sulfite and chlorine are used in the same system, catalyzed sodium sulfite is added in the amount necessary to remove dissolved oxygen, then chlorine is added at a point located downstream that allows for sufficient oxygen-sulfite reaction time.

Two solubility factors frequently present in oilfield waters make the application of sodium sulfite to scavenge oxygen more difficult than with boiler waters. These are the presence of the sulfide that will form insoluble sulfides with the catalyzing ions, and high concentrations of calcium ions that could precipitate sulfite ions.[2] When catalyzed sodium sulfite is added to water containing small amounts of sulfide ion ($<$ 1 ppm), additional catalyst can be added to compensate for the formation of insoluble metal sulfide. This amounts to sulfide removal by precipitation with heavy metals and would only be practical in very specific applications. It does emphasize that sulfate-reducing bacteria should be prevented from growing in water-handling systems in which sulfite is used to scavenge oxygen.

Precipitation of calcium sulfite is a possibility in waters of high calcium content that require the addition of large amounts of sodium sulfite. Fortunately, situations of this type are rare and when they do exist, laboratory tests can determine if precipitation of calcium sulfite will occur. Usually, if large amounts of dissolved oxygen are present in the water, physical methods of removal are used.

Both catalyzed and uncatalyzed sodium sulfite are readily available as trade-name products from companies specializing in water-treating chemicals. Sodium sulfite without catalyst is also available from chemical supply houses. Because of the low concentration required (0.001 ppm of cobaltous ion in the water), cobaltous hexahydrate may be purchased and fed with the sodium sulfite as a catalyst, without materially increasing the cost of sulfite. Adding the catalyst in the field reduces the cost of treatment about 25 per cent. Chemical cost must be weighed against convenience of treatment when selecting the catalyzed or uncatalyzed chemical.

The sulfite ion can also be formed in water by adding gaseous sulfur dioxide to water as shown in Eq. (12–4):

$$SO_2 + H_2O \longrightarrow H_2SO_3 \tag{12–4}$$

Sulfurous acid formed will tend to reduce the pH of water. When sulfur dioxide is used to produce sulfite ion for oxygen removal in boiler feed waters, the gas or solution of the gas is fed into a dilute sodium hydroxide solution to give a slightly alkaline feed solution.[3] Cobalt solution is fed into this to provide the catalyst.

Oxygen Removal with Hydrazine

As an oxygen scavenger, hydrazine and its hydrates or salts have found their greatest use in boiler feed water applications. Sodium (or potassium) sulfite is generally satisfactory for removing oxygen from boiler water, when used in boilers operating below 650 psi. Above this pressure the temperature of the boiler is sufficiently high to cause decomposition of the sulfite to give corrosive sulfur dioxide. Hydrazine is effective in these high-pressure boilers.

The primary products of the oxygen-hydrazine reaction are nitrogen and water, so hydrazine does not add to the dissolved solids content. Equations (12–5) through (12–8) illustrate the proposed mechanisms for the hydrazine-oxygen reaction:

$$N_2H_4 + O_2 \longrightarrow N_2 + 2H_2O \tag{12-5}$$

$$N_2H_4 + O_2 \longrightarrow [N_2H_4O_2] \longrightarrow N_2 + 2H_2O \tag{12-6}$$

$$6Fe_2O_3 + N_2H_4 \longrightarrow 4Fe_3O_4 + N_2 + 2H_2O \tag{12-7}$$

$$4Fe_3O_4 + O_2 \longrightarrow 6Fe_2O_3 \tag{12-8}$$

Equation (12–5) represents the starting and end products, while Eqs. (12–6) and (12–7) more nearly represent the mechanism. In Eq. (12–6) the reaction occurs on a metal surface. According to Eq. (12–7), iron oxide in a system would be reduced to magnetite by the hydrazine, and oxygen would be removed by oxidizing the magnetite back to hematite as shown by Eq. (12–8). This means that in initiating hydrazine treatment, it would be difficult to maintain an excess until all the hematite is converted to magnetite.[4] Therefore, it would be advisable to add an excess of hydrazine when treatment is initiated.

Hydrogen ion concentration or pH of the water influences the rate of the hydrazine-oxygen reaction. The rate of this reaction increases with increasing pH, reaching a maximum at approximately pH 10.5 and then decreases.[5] At pH 9, the rate of reaction is about half that at pH 10.5.

Temperature influences the rate of the hydrazine-oxygen reaction. The reaction rate is very slow at room temperature, so that hydrazine and oxygen can exist in the same solution.[6] As with other chemical reactions, the rate increases with a rise in temperature. In a series of experiments where hydrazine hydrate was added to boiler feed water at 117°F, 81 per cent of the oxygen was removed before the water entered the boiler, and 94 per cent was removed when the feed water temperature was increased to 203°F.[7]

The reaction rate of the hydrazine-oxygen reaction can be increased somewhat by using catalysts. Catalytic effect of copper and manganese on the reaction at room temperature is illustrated in Table 12.2. Cupric copper ion appears to be a more effective catalyst than manganous ion. Another catalyst is activated charcoal. After hydrazine addition, the water can be passed through an activated charcoal filter to catalyze the reaction. In one experiment using boiler feed water at 150°F, the amount of oxygen removed at a sampling point was increased from 72 to 89 per cent by using charcoal.[8] Even with the use of a catalyst, the rate of hydrazine-oxygen reaction is not increased enough to make the use of hydrazine practical in many water flood applications.

Table 12.2

OXIDATION OF HYDRAZINE IN PRESENCE AND
ABSENCE OF A CATALYST*

(From Baker & Marcy, *Trans. ASME*, **78**, 299 (February 1956).
Used with permission.)

Test No.	N_2H_4 (ppm)	Catalyst (ppm)	N_2H_4 Residual After 45 Minutes (ppm)
1	7.9	none	7.0
2	7.9	0.1 Cu^{++}	2.1
		(added as $CuSO_4 \cdot 5H_2O$)	
3	7.0	0.5 Cu^{++}	0.9
4	7.9	0.1 Mn^{++}	6.9
		(added as $MnSO_4 \cdot H_2O$)	
5	7.9	0.5 Mn^{++}	5.8

*Deionized water samples originally contained 8 ppm dissolved oxygen and had a pH of 8.1.

Hydrazine is a powerful reducing agent and will react with other oxidizing agents besides oxygen that may be present in water. Chlorine and hypochlorous acid rapidly and quantitatively oxidize hydrazine to nitrogen. When adding hydrazine to a water containing chlorine or hypochlorous acid, sufficient quantity must be added to react not only with the oxygen but also with the chlorine or hypochlorous ion. Where 7.8 ppm sodium sulfite are required to scavenge 1 ppm oxygen, only 1 ppm hydrazine is needed. One ppm hydrazine reacts with 2.23 ppm chlorine.

Hydrazine is a hazardous chemical, and certain precautions should be observed in handling it. It is available in the pure liquid form, but it is usually purchased in dilute solutions, since these are less hazardous to handle. The chemical should be stored in a cool place to minimize hazards of fire or explosions from the vapors. Since hydrazine reacts with iron oxides, the feed solution should be prepared in a rust-free container, such as one made from stainless steel. Hydrazine should be added to water in the tank that is used in the make-up of the feed solution. Protective equipment, such as rubber gloves and goggles, should be used to prevent contact with the skin while handling hydrazine. Any area of skin contacted by hydrazine should be washed immediately with soap after flushing with large quantities of water. Spilled hydrazine solution should be immediately diluted with water. Hydrazine vapors are irritating and should not be inhaled. When hydrazine salts are used, they should be kept out of contact with oxidizing agents as a precaution against any chemical reaction from taking place between the two substances.

References

[1]D. J. Pye, "Chemical Fixation of Oxygen," *J. Am. Water Works Assoc.*, **39** (1947), 1121.

[2]C. C. Templeton, S. S. Rushing, and Jane C. Rodgers, "Solubility Factors Accompanying Oxygen Scavenging with Sulfite in Oil Field Brines," *Materials Protection*, **2**, No. 8 (1963), 42.

[3]Pye, *op. cit.*

[4]W. F. Stones, "The Use of Hydrazine as an Oxygen Scavenger in High Pressure Boilers," *Chem. Ind.*, **2**, No. 8 (1963), 42.

[5]A. S. Gordon, "The Reaction Between Hydrazine and Hydrogen Peroxide in the Liquid Phase," Third Symposium on Combustion and Flame and Explosion Phenomena, University of Wisconsin, 1948.

[6]J. Leichester, "The Chemical Deaeration of Boiler Water—The Use of Hydrazine Compounds," *Trans. ASME*, **78** (1956), 273.

[7]*Ibid.*

[8]*Ibid.*

Water for Injection into Subsurface Formations

13

The ease with which water can be injected into the oil reservoir is one of the most important factors affecting the success of a secondary recovery by water-flooding project. When applied to proposed injection waters, either for secondary recovery or for disposal, the purpose of water treatment is to condition the water so that it can be injected with the least amount of pressure. Water treatment should minimize corrosion of equipment in the water injection system, prevent scale deposition on equipment or in the well bore, and improve the efficiency of the water as a flooding medium.

Water that requires no treatment is seldom available for use in secondary recovery projects. If a choice of supply water exists, the one requiring the least degree of treatment but still providing sufficient volume for the flood should be chosen. Treatment should be kept to a minimum that is consistent with required water quality.

Water Sampling and Analysis

Before water-treating facilities and an injection system are designed and constructed, a careful study should be made of all waters involved in the project. The first step in any study involving waters is the determination of the dissolved solids and gases in the waters. It was emphasized in Chapter 2 that obtaining representative samples of water was the most important aspect of a water problem.

Samples of all waters involved should be collected according to the procedures outlined in Chapter 2. These samples should include water present in the oil reservoir, as well as all available sources of potential injection water. Often the only analyses of waters in formations above the oil reservoir that might be considered as supply water are those obtained from a drill-stem test taken during drilling of the oil well. This emphasizes the importance of taking the necessary time and precautions essential to obtaining reliable DST water samples.

All samples collected should be submitted to a reliable laboratory for analyses. These analyses should include determinations for carbonate, bicarbonate, sulfate, chloride, iron, calcium, magnesium, sodium, dissolved oxygen, total dissolved solids, alkalinity, pH, and specific gravity. If the dissolved sulfate is very low, a barium analysis should be included. When the odor of hydrogen sulfide is detected, the water should be analyzed for this gas.

Results of the analyses are used to compare the waters and estimate their compatibilities. From the analyses, the degree and type of water treatment is estimated. Calculations based on the analytical data are used to predict scaling tendencies of the waters. Where more than one water source is available, the source requiring the least treatment is selected, based on comparison of water analyses data and subsequent scaling tendency calculations for individual waters and hypothetical mixtures of the waters.

Some estimate of the corrosivity of the waters can be obtained from the analytical data. Water analyses showing appreciable dissolved solids, dissolved oxygen, and low pH will obviously indicate a corrosive water. In designing the water-handling system and treatment plant, measures for preventing corrosion can be included. This is more effective and less costly than discovering the water is corrosive after the system has been constructed and then trying to modify the system to minimize corrosion.

Throughout the operating life of the system, periodic water analyses should be made. If the injection project is large, these analyses should be made on samples taken simultaneously from different parts of the system. These analyses made every three to six months will enable the operator to detect changes in water composition and often prevent potential problems in the system before they become severe.

Compatibility of Waters

Waters that are compatible can be mixed without producing any undesirable chemical reactions between components dissolved in the individual waters. Undesirable reactions are those that produce insoluble products such as calcium and carbonate ions, forming calcium carbonate or barium, and sulfate ions, forming barium sulfate. Insoluble products produced from these reactions can decrease flow in lines, plug injection wells, or reduce permeability.

Compatibility of waters used in secondary recovery operations is of primary importance in designing and operating water flood systems. It is also important in some waste water disposal systems. Interstitial and injection waters should be compatible to prevent permeability reduction caused by deposited solids.[1] Waters mixed at the surface for injection should be compatible; otherwise, deposited solids can block flow lines or plug injection wells. Produced waters and supply waters are sometimes scale forming. Mixing incompatible waters produces a scale-forming water that could have been avoided if good engineering practices had been observed.

Damage from mixing waters that are not compatible is caused by deposited solids. The amount of solids deposited depends upon the concentrations of reacting ions present in the individual waters and other factors influencing solubility of the compound. The amount of mixing of the two or more waters also influences the magnitude of deposits. If waters are mixed in a tank or flow line before injection, total mixing will occur and the amount of slightly soluble compound formed in excess of the solubility will deposit.

When a water that is not compatible with interstitial water is injected into a reservoir, deposits will form only where the waters make contact and mix. If there is a small degree of mixing, deposits will form in only a small volume of water; conversely, a large degree of mixing will result in deposits forming in a large volume of the water. A breakthrough of injection water into the bore of a producing well would mix large amounts of the incompatible waters and cause severe damage to the well.

When reactions occur between the chemical constituents of incompatible waters to form insoluble products, not all of the reacting ionic species are precipitated—only enough to adjust the product of the reacting ion concentrations to the thermodynamic solubility product or to provide a saturated solution. The amount precipitated represents that in "excess" of the saturated concentration. As shown in Chapter 3, the solubility of a compound is influenced by other ions in the water, temperature, and sometimes pressure. For example, calcium sulfate solubility will vary depending upon temperature and concentration of foreign ions in the water, as shown in Fig. 3.6 and 3.7.

Figure 13.1 shows the amount of deposit formed per 10,000 barrels of incompatible waters versus the excess concentration of ions expressed as

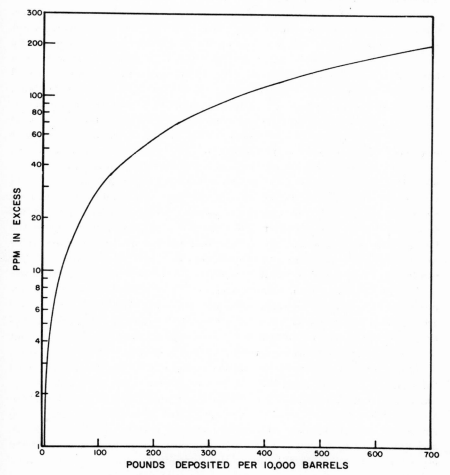

Fig. 13.1. PPM excess constituent vs. weight of deposit per 10,000 barrels. (From Ostroff, *Producers Monthly*, **27**, No. 3 (1963), 2.)

ppm. Based on the density of the various compounds shown in Table 13.1, the amount deposited has been converted to volume in cubic feet. A section of well bore, 6 inches in diameter and 10 feet high, has a volume of approximately 2 cubic feet. Fig. 13.1 and Table 13.1 give an indication of the amount of solids that can form from incompatible waters and the amount that would collect in a water input well if waters were mixed before injection. They also show how much could form as a result of mixing injection and formation water in the formation. However, it is likely that the deposits when mixed in a formation, would only form in the zone of mixing at the injection water-formation water interface.

The volume of water in the mixing zone increases as the injection water-formation water interface moves away from the well bore of the water input well. Assume that, by the ionic diffusion process or by mixing caused by flow, the two incompatible waters are mixed in a zone 1 foot wide in a formation of 25 per cent porosity. Let this mixing zone represent the wall of a hollow cylinder, 10 feet high, of some average radius from the well bore. The formation is 100 per cent saturated with water. Figure 13.2 is a graph of the volume of water in this mixing zone, at an average radius of the zone measured from the well bore. When the injection water-formation water interface is 34 feet from the injection well bore, the volume of water in the mixing zone is 100 barrels. If 100 ppm excess insoluble compound is present when the incompatible waters are mixed, Fig. 13.1 shows 3.5 pounds of solid would be formed. From Table 13.1, we see that this would represent 0.02 cubic foot or less, compared with a total void volume of 100 barrels or 561 cubic feet. It is unlikely that this amount would result in plugging the formation around a water input well. Greater amounts of deposited solids would affect the permeability proportionately. Decreases in permeability would decrease injection rates or necessitate increased injection pressures.

In practice, the mixing zone varies with the distance from the water input well bore. For the case of a 1-to-1 viscosity ratio, the mixing zone growth is proportional to the square root of distance traveled. The hypothetical example of a 1-foot mixing zone is useful in illustrating the amount of deposits that could form in each foot-thick increment of the mixing zone.

Calcium carbonate or calcite can serve as an example of a deposit formed from mixing two incompatible waters or from a single unstable water. Calcium carbonate $(CaCO_3)$ is present in water solution as calcium bicarbonate $(Ca(HCO_3)_2)$. Its solubility is dependent upon ionic strength, calcium ion concentration, bicarbonate ion concentration, pressure of carbon dioxide, and temperature. A change in carbon dioxide pressure or temperature can cause $CaCO_3$ to precipitate. If the solubility product is exceeded, solid $CaCO_3$ will deposit.

When two waters are mixed, the concentration of dissolved ions becomes the average concentration of the respective ions in the two waters. If mixing

Table 13.1

VOLUME OF SCALE VS. WEIGHT DEPOSITED

(From Ostroff, *Producers Monthly*, **27**, No. 3 (1963), 2.)

Pounds Deposited per 10,000 Barrels	Volume (Ft³)							
	$CaSO_4 \cdot 2H_2O$ (Gypsum)	$CaSO_4$ (Anhydrite)	$CaCO_3$ (Aragonite)	$CaCO_3$ (Calcite)	$BaSO_4$ (Barite)	FeS (Troilite)	$FeCO_3$ (Siderite)	Fe_2O_3 (Hematite)
3.5	0.02	0.02	0.02	0.02	0.01	0.01	0.01	0.01
17.5	0.12	0.10	0.10	0.11	0.06	0.06	0.07	0.05
35.0	0.24	0.19	0.19	0.21	0.13	0.12	0.15	0.11
52.5	0.36	0.29	0.29	0.32	0.19	0.17	0.22	0.16
70.0	0.48	0.38	0.38	0.42	0.25	0.23	0.30	0.22
105.0	0.72	0.57	0.58	0.63	0.37	0.35	0.44	0.33
175.0	1.20	0.95	0.96	1.05	0.63	0.58	0.74	0.55
350.0	2.40	1.90	1.92	2.10	1.25	1.16	1.48	1.10
700.0	4.80	3.80	3.84	4.20	2.50	2.32	2.96	2.20
1,400.0	9.60	7.60	7.68	8.40	5.00	4.64	5.92	4.36

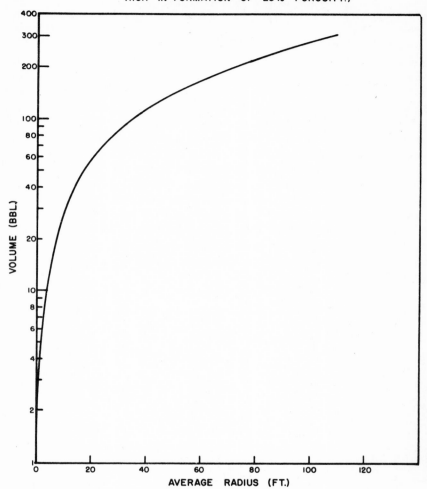

Fig. 13.2. Volume of water in mixing zone* vs. average radius from well bore. (From Ostroff, *Producers Monthly*, **27**, No. 3 (1963), 2.)
*Mixing zone 1 ft wide and 10 ft high in formation of 25% porosity.

the waters produces a concentration of calcium carbonate in excess of the amount permissible on the basis of the solubility product, the water is said to be supersaturated. This condition is adjusted to saturation by precipitation of the excess amount of calcium carbonate. This precipitation may occur rapidly if the excess concentration is large, or require a waiting period if the excess concentration is small. This waiting period, called an induction period, represents the time necessary for the calcium carbonate crystal nuclei to form. Once formed, other calcium carbonate molecules adhere to the nuclei to form a crystal and finally precipitate as a solid.

According to Stümper,[2] the more supersaturated the water is with calcium bicarbonate, the shorter the induction period. This is shown in Fig. 13.3 for solutions agitated with an air stream flowing at the rate of 1,300 cc/minute. The broken line represents a curve drawn through the induction periods. At the end of the induction period, solid calcium carbonate forms and settles out of the water. Its concentration in solution declines, as shown by the curves. If solid calcium carbonate is present, there is no induction period for the formation of crystal nuclei.

Some other salts have an induction period before they precipitate from a supersaturated solution. Both calcium sulfate and barium sulfate show this behavior. It is interesting to note that the amount of supersaturation required to initiate immediate precipitation of very slightly soluble salts, such as calcium carbonate or barium sulfate, is much less than the amount required to initiate immediate precipitation of a more soluble salt, such as calcium sulfate.

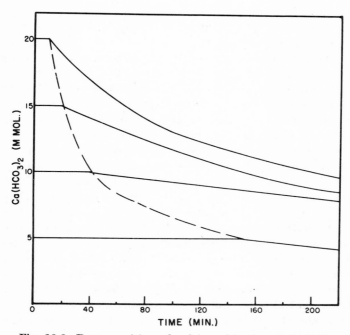

Fig. 13.3. Decomposition of calcium bicarbonate solution agitated with an airstream. (From Stümper, *Angew. Chem.*, **48** (1943), 117.)

Compatibility Tests

Two waters are mixed in definite proportion to test their compatibility. If an induction period is required before salt deposition occurs, it is important that the test be observed for a considerable length of time. If no reaction occurs that produces a deposit, it is advisable to seed the test waters with a crystal of the salt most likely to deposit. From the water analysis data of the individual waters, it is possible to calculate the composition of the mixed water. A prediction of which salt will be most likely to deposit can then be made. A few small crystals of this salt can be used to seed the test mixtures. A procedure for making a compatibility test is found in the Appendix.

Water-Sensitive Formations

Certain reservoir rocks are subject to permeability damage when infiltrated by fresh water. This damage, which is related to rock properties, is caused by swelling of indigenous clays that constrict pores, and the dispersion of indigenous nonswelling particles during fluid flow. Many water injection projects have suffered reduced efficiency because reservoir rock was plugged by clay which swelled when contacted with water. For this reason, when extraneous waters are used, it is advisable to determine the composition and clay content of the reservoir rock before selecting a water source.

The lattice structure of clays is made up of a series of very thin particles, having appreciable length and width, that are stacked one on top of the other. When contacted with water, some clays swell as a result of water adsorption or exchange of basic radicals from foreign water.[3] Montmorillonites, mixed-layer clays, and some illites are the most common swelling clays. It is possible for water to penetrate between the plates of montmorillonite and cause swelling sufficient to separate the plates and disperse the clay particles. The degree of swelling occurring when reservoir clay minerals contact water depends upon the type of clay and the amount of water held by the mineral since sedimentary deposition. Clays which have held the maximum amount of water will not appreciably increase in volume. Clays which are capable of absorbing additional water will increase in volume when contacted by water.

Swelling of clays is also related to salinity of water. Clays susceptible to swelling are more sensitive to fresh water than saline water containing a minimum of 2 to 5 per cent sodium chloride. Clay swelling often results when saline interstitial water is displaced by a relative fresh water. Water sensitivity increases with decreasing salinity.

Permeability reduction can result from mechanical plugging caused by dislodgement and transportation of particles during fluid flow. Clay swelling can contribute to this by loosening the cementation binding the clays and inert particles, so that these particles are more easily removed by the turbulence of fluid flow.

The sensitivity of reservoir rock to water should be determined by using core samples before any injection of water into the reservoir is started. A series of permeability measurements can determine the effect of water salinity on the rock. Analysis of the rock by X-ray diffraction can determine the presence or absence of swelling clays. If swelling clays are present and permeability measurements show a reduction in permeability with reduced water salinity, the cause of the reduction is established. If no swelling clays are present and permeability reduction occurs, then particle mobility and plugging are causing the reduction. To determine adequately the presence, cause, and magnitude of water sensitivity permeability measurements, physical swelling tests, X-ray identification of clay and nonclay minerals, and a microscopic examination should be made of the reservoir rock.[4]

Water Quality

Water quality is a term applied to the suitability of water for injection into an underground reservoir. Standards of water quality vary. The first standards of water quality for potable waters were that it tasted good, looked good, was odorless, and was not toxic. The same type of standards have been established for injection waters; namely, that the water goes in the ground and does not corrode the system. Some attempt has been made to establish more quantitative standards for injection waters, but this has not been universally accepted.[5]

Water quality includes the amount of suspended solids in the water, number of bacteria present, and the corrosivity of the water. All of these factors influence the ease of water injection into a formation. Suspended solids could plug the pore spaces in the formation or build up an impermeable filter cake on the face of the reservoir rock that would impede water injection. Bacteria may contribute to corrosion and corrosion products, resulting in plugging of the injection well. Bacterial growths themselves can sometimes result in plugging. Corrosive water not only damages the system but may produce corrosion products which can plug the well. A common example of this is iron sulfide formed from corrosion by hydrogen sulfide.

The character of the reservoir rock largely influences the quality of water that can be injected. A reservoir rock with small pore sizes and low porosity requires water of very low suspended solids or a high-quality water. Conversely, a high-porosity reservoir having large pores and voids would take water containing a considerable amount of suspended solids. Probably the chief value in defining water quality is in providing a yardstick for comparison between water initially injected into the formation and that which is injected at some date later during the injection program.

1. SUSPENDED SOLIDS

Suspended solids carried by water may be sand grains from the water-sand, corrosion products such as iron sulfide or iron oxide, free sulfur, or bacterial growths. If allowed to enter the injection wells, these materials will either plug the wells completely or cause increases in injection pressures. These materials are often present in water in a finely divided state and in amounts small enough so that their presence is not easily detected by looking at the water. Yet, when large volumes of water are injected, even small amounts of suspended solids can form an appreciable filter cake or deposit in an injection well bore. Figure 13.1 shows that a water carrying only 2 ppm suspended solids would deposit 7 pounds of solids from 10,000 barrels, if the formation were of sufficiently fine pore size of filter this from the water. After 10 days' injection, this would amount to 70 pounds, or from 0.22 to 0.48 cubic feet, as shown in Table 13.1. Larger volumes of water and longer injection periods would produce correspondingly greater amounts of solids and eventually fill the well bore.

It is important to determine the amount and chemical composition of suspended solids in the water. This is accomplished by removing the solids by filtration from a measured volume of water. The solids can then be analyzed. If the chemical composition of the suspended solids is known, it is frequently possible to take corrective measures that will either eliminate the source of the solids or remove them from the water before injection.

One of the best methods of removing these solids from injection water for test purposes is by means of a membrane filter. Membrane filters are cellulose ester or polyethylene discs that have about 80 to 90 per cent porosity. They act like a sieve, so that all solids removed are on the surface of the disc. Since the surfaces are smooth, the solids are easily removed by scraping. Immersion oils render the cellulose ester discs transparent, so that deposited solids can be viewed under a microscope.

These filters are available in a variety of pore sizes. The range for polyethylene filter discs is from 1.5μ to 10μ. The smallest pore size available in the cellulose ester filter is $0.45\mu \pm 0.02\mu$. This is the filter usually used in the petroleum industry for water quality tests.[6,7]

As applied to injection water, membrane filtration is more than just a removal of suspended solids. When the filtration of a specified volume of water is conducted at a given pressure, an estimate of the damage caused by a buildup of suspended particles on the formation face is obtained. The filtration is carried out at 20 psi pressure, and the volume of filtrate is measured as a function of time. From this data the flow rate is calculated and plotted against the cumulative volume. The slope of this line indicates the quality of the water. A horizontal line would indicate a perfect water, while a slope of 1.8 or more would be a poor-quality water. A water quality rating chart, giving values relating line slope and suspended solids to water quality, is shown in Table 13.2. Membrane filtration test instructions and example data curves are found in the Appendix.

The 0.45μ pore size of the membrane filter is smaller than that of the smallest significant pore in formation rock. Obviously, the most suitable test of the tendency of water to plug a formation rock is to use a core in the plugging tests. The disadvantage of this is that cores are not always available, and the test procedure would be cumbersome and inconvenient. Although the membrane filter pores are smaller than those in formation rock, the membrane filter test has proved to be very useful in determining plugging tendencies. Practically all the particles are removed from water by the filter, so that the filtration rate is really that of the filter cake. This is a reliable indication of the effect of filterable solids on the injection pressure and rate.

Membrane filtration tests performed at different locations in a water distribution system will give the engineer a clear picture of the water quality in the system. If he knows the differences in the suspended solids' content at various locations, it will help him locate the problem and differentiate between poor-quality water at its source and poor-quality water caused by conditions within the lines. These conditions may be caused by corrosion of the lines or instability of the water itself, or they may be the result of mixing two waters from different sources.

These tests are applicable in all periods of the life of a water injection project. If possible, membrane filters should be used to determine the suspended solids in potential injection waters before the system is designed. This will permit incorporation of any water treatment facilities required in the original design of the system. If various water sources are available, these tests will be invaluable in selecting the water to be used for injection.

After water injection is started, membrane filtration tests will be useful in monitoring the quality of water or the effectiveness of any treatment designed to remove suspended solids from water. Tests performed at specified periods will provide data that can be used to compare water quality at

Table 13.2

WATER QUALITY RATING CHART

(From Wright, *Oil Gas J.*, **61**, No. 20 (1963), 154.)

	Rating					
	1	2	3	5	10	20
Membrane filter test (0.45μ filter) slope	0–0.09 excellent	0.10–0.29 very good	0.30–0.49 good	0.50–0.99 acceptable	1.00–1.79 fair	1.80+ excessive
Filtered solids mg/liter	0–0.4 negligible	0.5–0.9 very low	1.0–2.4 low	2.5–4.9 moderate	5.0–9.9 large	10.0+ excessive
Total sulfide increases lb/day/1,000 sq ft	0 none	0.001 very low	0.002–4 low	0.005–9 moderate	0.01–0.019 large	0.02+ excessive
Iron-count increases lb/day/1,000 sq ft	0 none	0.001–0.011 very low	0.012–0.11 low	0.12–0.59 moderate	0.60–1.1 large	1.2+ excessive
Sulfate-reducing bacteria colonies/ml	0 none	1–5 very low	6–9 low	10–20 moderate	30–90 large	100+ excessive
Total bacteria count colonies/ml	0 none	1–99 very low	100–999 low	1,000–9,999 moderate	10,000–99,999 large	100,000+ excessive
Corrosion rate (30 days) (insulated coupon) mils/year	0 none	0.01–0.09 very low	0.10–0.99 low	1.00–4.9 moderate	5.0–9.9 high	10.0+ excessive
Pit depth (30 days) (insulated coupon) mils	0 none	1 shallow	2–3 minor	4–5 moderate	6–10 deep	10+ excessive
Pit frequency (30 days) (insulated coupon) pits/sq in.	0 none	1 very low	2 low	3 moderate	4 high	5+ excessive

various times in the life of a flood. This is particularly valuable in detecting small changes in the water that would otherwise escape unnoticed. These changes could be the start of a trend toward deterioration of the water quality, but, if detected early, corrective measures can be taken before noticeable increases in injection pressures occur.

2. CORROSIVITY OF WATER

For water to be of good quality, it must not be very corrosive to metal in the system. It has been emphasized before that corrosion is not only destructive to equipment but often produces corrosion products that plug the injection well. Methods used to measure the corrosion rate of metal or the corrosivity of the water were discussed in Chapter 4. In addition, iron oxide or sulfide particles removed during the membrane filtration tests are an indication that corrosion is present.

The allowable corrosion rate depends upon several factors. From the standpoint of equipment failure, a 5 mpy corrosion rate could be tolerated if it were thinning-type corrosion and the corrosion products were not causing a plugging problem. If the corrosion were of the pitting type and the rate were 5 mpy, the pits would soon perforate the metal. Corrosion rates and iron counts for various water qualities are shown in Table 13.2. The rating also includes values for pit depth and frequency or number of pits per unit area. A combination of moderate corrosion rate, deep pits, and low pitting frequency would be very destructive to the system.

3. MICROBIAL POPULATION

The number and type of bacteria present in injection water affect the quality of the water. Bacteria can contribute to corrosion or produce plugging. Desulfovibrio or sulfate-reducing bacteria utilize oxygen in sulfate ion to oxidize organic compounds. Corrosive hydrogen sulfide is produced in the process. Increases in sulfide content of water within the water-handling system are caused by sulfate reducers. Desulfovibrio are nearly always present, but, when conditions are not right for their growth, they are not a serious problem.

The total bacterial count is indicative of the number of all varieties of bacteria in the water. Large growths of bacteria can result in colonies of the microorganisms plugging the injection well or otherwise fouling equipment. The water quality rating chart shown in Table 13.2 includes arbitrary values for colonies of sulfate reducers and all bacteria. Methods of determining these colonies are discussed in Chapter. 6.

Water Characteristics

Dissolved chemical substances and suspended material give waters their characteristics. The suitability of a water of certain characteristics for use in a secondary recovery project is determined from water analysis, compatibility tests, clay swelling tests, and water quality evaluation. If the water is not suitable for use but is the only supply available, it must be treated to change its characteristics and make it suitable for use.

Water Treatment Plant

The characteristics of the proposed flood or injection water and the required changes in these characteristics determine the water treatment procedures and the plant design. Individual water treatment procedures that have been discussed can be used to alter a specific characteristic of the water. Equipment for one more of these procedures constitutes a water treatment plant. The primary object of the plant is to treat the water, so that it meets the particular requirements for injection into the reservoir. The plant should be as simple as is consistent with obtaining the required water quality.

1. PLANT LOCATION

Location of the water-treating plant is influenced by several factors. Sufficient space must be available for the treating equipment and any retention or water storage facilities required. It is advisable to provide space for future expansion of the plant. Often, an economy in piping costs is realized if the plant is located in the center of the flood area. Location of the plant near the source of supply water may be advantageous.

Contour of the land is an important factor in plant site selection. By taking advantage of natural elevations in the land, gravitation of water throughout the plant, and possibly the flood area, can be accomplished with a minimum number of pumps and pumping costs. This also results in savings in maintenance expense.

Placement of filters with respect to other components of the plant is very important. Filtration is used to remove suspended solids from the water. Once water has been filtered, it is assumed that no suspended solids are present. If water has been softened or aerated to remove calcium carbonate or sulfide, a retention period is required for the reactions to go to completion. Filtration of the water before these reactions are complete only results in removing the solids present at that time. This is frequently accomplished by placing a storage tank or retention pit between the filters and the other components of the plant.

If water is to be pumped long distances after treatment, and small particles such as corrosion products are a problem, it is advantageous to locate the filters nearer the injection wells. Where practical, this often is a simpler solution than trying to prevent any corrosion products from entering the water during transit.

2. Treating Capacity

The water treatment plant is designed to treat the maximum amount of water required for daily injection. Plants are frequently constructed before water injection projects reach full capacity. If only enough of the plant is constructed to treat water sufficient to meet the immediate requirements, the components should be located on the plant site in such a manner that the additional capacity can be added later in an orderly manner in accordance with the master plan.

The plant is designed to treat a certain maximum volume of water to provide water of specified quality. Increasing the volume of water treated over the maximum design volume results in water of lower quality. Therefore, the absolute maximum capacity must be incorporated into the building of the plant, because additional water volumes cannot be obtained without sacrificing water quality.

3. Type of Plant

The type of water treatment plant is selected after consideration of the characteristics of both the injection water and the formation water. Obviously, the supply water must be treated to make it compatible with the formation water and to give it the required quality for injection. Treatment plants have arbitrarily been classified as closed systems or open systems. The choice depends on source of water, water characteristics, and amount of treatment water.

a. Closed Systems

The term closed system is applied to treatment plants that are designed to prevent contact of supply water or injection water with air. It is difficult to prevent air-water contact if the water requires a large amount of treatment, so that closed systems are generally used only when the water requires a minimum amount of treatment. In fact, closed systems are used mostly for water that requires no treatment except the addition of a corrosion or scale inhibitor.

The purpose of closed systems is to keep the water from contacting air and dissolving oxygen, and to minimize the loss of dissolved gases from the water. An alternate purpose in extremely cold climates is to protect the water from freezing. This will aid in minimizing corrosion and prevent oxidation of dissolved iron or sulfide. Generally, closed systems are used only with supply waters taken from deep wells or in projects where produced water is being reinjected. To be effective, all air must be excluded from the system. This means that storage tanks must be closed and protected with a gas blanket or an oil seal on the water.

Water in underground reservoirs is frequently in contact with a gas phase containing carbon dioxide. When this water is raised to the surface and exposed to air, carbon dioxide will be lost from the water. If this water has an appreciable calcium content, loss of carbon dioxide will cause calcium carbonate scale to deposit. Keeping this water in a closed system and not exposing it to air will minimize the loss of carbon dioxide and reduce the scaling tendency. Supply or produced waters in contact with a high-pressure carbon dioxide gas phase will lose dissolved carbon dioxide even in a closed system, since separators or storage tanks cannot be maintained at much over atmospheric pressure.

It is apparent that waters containing no oxygen and requiring minimum treatment can be handled in a closed system, thereby minimizing corrosion and scale problems. If appreciable water treatment is required, it cannot be conveniently adapted to a closed system. Therefore, in planning and designing the system, particular attention must be given to determining the extent of water treatment required before a closed system is chosen.

b. Open System

Open systems are those in which no attempt is made to exclude air-water contact. The treatment plant is open to the atmosphere, and in many of these plants the water is aerated to remove an objectionable gas or introduce oxygen for the purpose of oxidizing ferrous iron or sulfide ion. Supply waters from rivers, lakes, and oceans are already saturated with air and are generally handled in open systems.

The advantage in open systems is that they can be exposed to the atmosphere. Large volumes of water can be stored in open pits or retention ponds. Water thus has the opportunity to stabilize, and suspended particles can settle out, minimizing the load on filters.

The disadvantage is that, with some supply waters, oxygen is introduced into the water. This can be easily compensated for when the system is designed. Steel flow lines and injection tubing can be protected by cement or plastic coatings. Water can be de-aerated after treatment, so that only oxygen-free water is passed through uncoated flow lines and injection tubing.

Water Storage

Facilities should be provided for storing treated water. The type and capacity of storage facility depends upon the use of the treated water and the daily required volume. Storage of water for backwashing filters varies from 2 to 5 per cent of the filtered volume. This water is usually stored in a tank separate from other water storage, unless filters and main water storage are in close proximity to each other.

In water injection projects, a good rule to follow is that treated water storage should hold a minimum of one-fourth the daily injected volume. This is generally sufficient to allow operation to continue for several hours in the event some unit of the treating plant must be shut down for repairs. In many instances, smaller volumes or no water storage is provided. Usually this happens in connection with closed systems in which supply water taken from water wells requires no treatment before injection.

In open systems, storage of large volumes of water is simplified since lined, open earthen pits can be used. This type of storage is cheaper than the use of tanks. Water injected in closed systems cannot be stored in open pits but must be stored in closed tanks that have an oil seal or inert gas blanket. For reasons of economy, storage of treated water in tanks is generally limited to a small percentage of the injected volume in large water flood projects.

Lining earthen storage pits was discussed in Chapter 5. Both wooden and steel tanks are used for water storage. Steel tanks should be protected from corrosion. Tanks should be set on a concrete base coated with tar or on well-drained soil. When tanks are placed directly on the soil, the bottoms should be coated and protected by cathodic protection. Inside surfaces of the tanks should also be coated, and when necessary, cathodically protected.

Control of Microorganisms

The growth of microorganisms is sometimes a problem in water-handling systems. Uncontrolled growth of slime-forming bacteria can plug injection wells and clog equipment. Sulfate-reducing bacteria contribute to corrosion and can cause the formation of iron sulfide in the water. Iron bacteria

Crenothrix and Gallionella precipitate iron from water, forming a red scum that is a potential plugging material.

In any water-handling system it is advisable to guard against the growth of microorganisms. Conditions for their growth and methods of controlling it are discussed in Chapter 6. Water selected for injection should be examined microbiologically to determine the type and number of bacteria present. If this examination indicates that microorganisms will present a problem, provisions should be made to add a suitable bactericide to the water. Periodically during the life of the system, water samples should be examined microbiologically to determine the effectiveness of any bactericide added or to tell whether the water is still relatively free of microbial growth

Some Typical Waters and Treatment Procedures

1. OPEN TREATMENT FOR INJECTION OF PRODUCED BRINE

The classic example of subsurface injection of salt water is the disposal of brines from the East Texas Oil Field. In this field, the East Texas Salt Water Disposal Company collects produced brine from the operators in the field and reinjects it into the Woodbine sand. A cumulative total of 2,349,958,237 barrels was treated and injected during the period 1938–1957.[8]

A mineral analysis of salt water in the East Texas Oil Field is shown in

Table 13.3

MINERAL ANALYSIS OF SALT WATER IN EAST TEXAS OIL FIELD

(From Plummer and Walling, *J. Petrol. Technol.*, **9**
(1946), T.P. 2019.)

Ion	Concentration (ppm)
Carbonate	0
Bicarbonate	525
Sulfate	233
Chloride	37,128
Calcium	1,380
Magnesium	309
Sodium	22,223

Table 13.3. In addition to the ions shown in the analysis, iron is picked up by the water during its passage through corroding tubing and lines. The water has a tendency to deposit calcium carbonate scale and some iron compounds, so that before reinjection, the water requires some treatment.

One factor influencing the choice of an open-type system for treating and handling this water was that the water would be collected from hundreds of leases with different operators, making it very difficult to control water-handling procedures. The large volume of water involved in this disposal project is more easily handled and treated in an open than in a closed system.

The amount and kind of water treatment required was determined from the minimum quality of water that could be injected without seriously damaging the reservoir. Because economics are so important where large volumes of water are to be treated, cost was a prime consideration in improving the water quality. In this particular project, it was decided that the infrequent clean-out of an injection well would be more economical than treating the water to the degree that no well clean-out would ever be required.

Salt water collected from the various leases in the East Texas Field contained varying amounts of suspended or entrained oil. The water is first passed through an oil skimmer to remove the oil. Water from the oil skimmer is then aerated to oxidize iron in the water resulting from corrosion. Aeration also serves to reduce dissolved carbon dioxide and hasten stabilization of the water.

After aeration, the water flows into treating pits, where chemical treatment is applied to the water. Chlorine is added to complete oxidation of iron and to control algae and bacterial growths. Both liquid chlorine purchased in cylinders and chlorine generated *in situ* by electrolysis were used. Approximately 4.4 pounds of chlorine per 1,000 barrels of water were required to complete oxidation of the iron and provide a chlorine residual.

Hydrated lime was added to the water in the treating pit to promote sedimentation and for partial reaction with calcium and magnesium compounds in the salt water. Only 8 to 12 pounds of lime per 1,000 barrels were added, which was not sufficient to soften the water and completely stabilize it with respect to calcium carbonate precipitation. With this treatment, some carbonate precipitates collected on the face of the injection formation.

From 8 to 12 pounds of alum or aluminum sulfate per 1,000 barrels of water were added as a coagulant. The water then underwent a 24-hour retention period before being filtered. Successful flocculation was also obtained, by a combination of 20 ppm alum and 15 ppm sodium aluminate. In 1957, the average cost for chemical treatment of this water with chlorine-alum-lime and sodium aluminate was 0.437 mil/bbl.[9]

After sedimentation, the water was filtered with pressure-type sand or "anthrafilt" filters. Water was then injected through wells completed with cemented-in-place casing, but no tubing.

This treatment does not produce water of the highest quality, but, by balancing treatment costs against an infrequent well clean-out, the treatment proved satisfactory and economical for the purpose.

2. CLOSED SYSTEM FOR INJECTION OF PRODUCED
AND SOURCE WATER

A unit flood in Kansas required injection of 9,000 barrels of water per day, of which 6,500 barrels were produced water and 2,500 barrels were supply water from the Douglas sandstone.[10] Mineral analyses of the two waters, shown in Table 13.4, indicated the waters to be very similar, so the waters were mixed without chemical treatment other than the addition of a bactericide. A flow diagram of the treatment plant is shown in Fig. 13.4.

Table 13.4

Mineral Analyses of Kansas Injection Waters

(From Watkins *et al.*, Bureau of Mines RI 4930 (1952).)

	Douglas Sandstone (ppm)	Produced Water (ppm)
Carbonate	0	0
Bicarbonate	74	84
Sulfate	32	26
Chloride	65,559	66,397
Iron (total)	21	19
Calcium	5,131	5,153
Magnesium	1,389	1,426
Sodium	34,071	34,495
Barium	25	26
TDS	106,296	107,581
Sp. Gr.	1,075	1,075
pH	7.0	7.2
M.O. Alk.	92	111

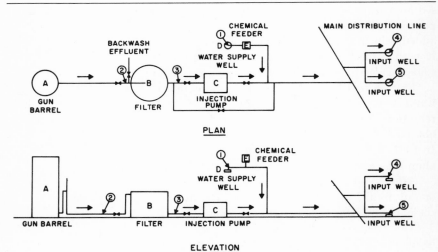

Fig. 13.4. Flow diagram of closed water-treating system. (From Watkins *et al.*, Bureau of Mines RI 4930 (1952).)

Produced water and oil were separated in the gun barrel. The water was then passed through a closed gravity sand filter and through the injection pumps into the distribution line. Water from the supply wells was pumped directly into the distribution line, where it mixed with the produced water.

Corrosion tests, made at points 1 through 5 in Fig. 13.4, all gave low corrosion rates, indicating that the system was effective in excluding air. Water treatment in this system was limited to filtration, which was not sufficient to prevent some plugging of the sand faces in input wells.

3. Treatment of River Water for Injection into a Low-Permeability Formation

A very good illustration of a procedure designed to make source water suitable for injection into a formation was the treatment of North Saskatchewan river water for injection into the Cardium sand.[11] A pilot flood of six injection wells was used to determine the reservoir characteristics pertaining to water injection. Flood water was obtained from wells in a fresh-water sand.

During the operation of the pilot flood, two of the injection wells having the lowest over-all permeability were plugged with bacterial slime and iron compounds. The untreated well water had a turbidity of 3 ppm and an iron content of 0 to 0.4 ppm. No increase in turbidity was noticed as the water flowed from the source well to the injection wells, but the dissolved iron content increased to 2.5 ppm. Experience gained during operation of this pilot flood indicated that only injection water of high quality could be used. Injection water specifications for this flood are shown in Table 13.5, that also gives analyses for North Saskatchewan river water and produced water from the Cardium sand formation. These specifications call for less than 1 ppm iron or dissolved oxygen, less than 2 ppm turbidity, and absence of harmful algae and bacteria as the water leaves the treating plant. The dissolved iron concentration is influenced by the dissolved oxygen and its tendency to oxidize ferrous iron to the insoluble ferric iron.

Because of the limited supply of well water, water from the North Saskatchewan river was used for the main flood. This water was taken from the river by three different methods: directly from the river, by Ranney collector,* and from water wells in the river's sands. The amount of water treatment required varied with the method of collection. Water directly from the river required the most treatment, while that from the Ranney collector and wells was filtered as it passed through the sand and had satisfactory low turbidity.

---

*A Ranney collector is a concrete caisson, set in the river sand, with perforated laterals running out from the caisson under the sand. The sand thus acts as a filter.

Water produced with the oil required reinjection. Compatibility tests of the river water mixed with the formation water indicated that these waters were not compatible over the range 40 to 60 volume per cent produced water. The decision was then made to handle the waters separately. This avoids excessive treatment required to make the produced water compatible in all proportions with the river water.

Table 13.5

COMPARISON OF PRODUCED AND SOURCE WATERS AND INJECTION
WATER SPECIFICATION

(From Messenger, *et al.*, AIME Paper 1225G Rocky Mountain
Regional Meeting, Casper, Wyoming (1959).)

	Produced Water	N. Saskatchewan River*	Injection Water Specifications
Dissolved gases, ppm			
O_2	—	9.65	<1
CO_2	—	—	<10
H_2S	0	0	0
Dissolved solids, ppm			
$CO_3^=$	185	0	—
HCO_3^-	2,075	145	—
$SO_4^=$	53	26	—
Cl^-	4,900	12	—
Fe, total	—	3	1
Ca^{++}	34	43	—
Mg^{++}	14	15	—
Na^+ and K^+	4,060	1	—
TDS (evap)	10,760	224	—
pH	8.6	8.5	6.5–8.5
Undissolved Solids, ppm			
Organic	present	present	—
Suspended	—	2,310	0
Turbidity	8	452	<2
Microbiological, organisms/ml			
Fungi	0	0	0
Algae	0	0	0
Bacteria: nonspore-forming slime	0	220	0
Spore-forming slime	—	0	0
Sulfate-reducing	—	0	0
Iron-depositing	—	0	0
Aerobic-viable	—	1,000	>10,000

*At flood stage.

Potential problems involved in handling the produced water were scale formation, microbiological growth, and suspended silica, alumina, and iron. Produced water was separated from oil in a combination free-water knockout, treater, and separator, and then discharged to an oil skimmer and sedimentation tank. The water was chlorinated to a residual chlorine content of 1 ppm. Water from the skimmer was mixed with treated river water, passed through a wellhead cartridge-type filter, and injected in a single well.

The water treatment plant shown in Fig. 13.5 was constructed to treat the North Saskatchewan river water. River water was collected in the caisson and transferred to the coagulator by turbine pump. A 1,000-barrel tank was used to hold water for backwashing the caisson and feed lines, when they became partially plugged with sand. In the winter, the transferred water was heated to 45°F before it entered the coagulator, where three coagulants were added to the water. At the point of entry, aluminum sulfate was added to the water, bentonitic clay in the center of the agitator, and a polyelectrolyte as the water left the agitator. Settled floc was removed from the coagulator and discharged to the river.

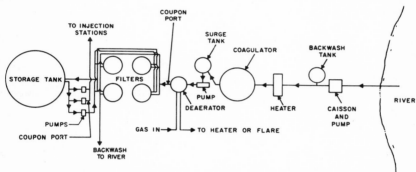

Fig. 13.5. Treating plant for Saskatchewan river water. (From Messenger *et al.*, AIME Paper 1225G (1959).)

In winter, the surface of the river is frozen, and the water contains less turbidity but more hardness. Coagulation was not required during these periods. Instead, sodium hexametaphosphate was added to the water as it passed through the coagulator to overcome the increased hardness. This served to stabilize the water during treatment and injection.

Water flowed from the coagulator into the surge tank. A dosage of sodium pentachlorophenate was added to the surge tank every two weeks to kill any microorganisms growing in the tank and to supplement the quaternary amine treatment. From the surge tank, the water was pumped to a de-aerator, where oxygen content was reduced from about 10 ppm to 0.8 ppm by a countercurrent of natural gas. The water was then filtered and pumped into a clear-water storage tank. A quaternary amine salt was added to the water as it left the clear-water storage tank for injection. The average cost of this treatment was 0.703 cents per barrel for chemicals. Because of oxygen removal and the low dissolved solids content of the water, there was less than 1 mpy corrosion of the system.

References

[1]R. W. Laird and A. F. Cogbill, "Incompatible Waters Can Plug Oil Sands," *World Oil*, **146**, No. 6 (1958), 188.

[2]R. Stümper, "Physicochemical Investigation of the Separation of Calcium Carbonate from Water," *Angew. Chem.*, **48** (1934), 117.

[3]P. D. Torrey, "Preparation of Water for Injection into Oil Reservoirs," *J. Petrol. Technol.*, **7** (1955), 9.

[4]C. H. Hewitt, "Analytical Techniques for Recognizing Water-Sensitive Reservoir Rocks," *J. Petrol. Technol.*, **15**, No. 8 (1963), 813.

[5]C. C. Wright, "Rating Water Quality and Corrosion Control in Water Floods," *Oil Gas J.*, **61**, No. 20 (1963), 154.

[6]T. M. Doscher and L. Weber, "The Use of the Membrane Filter in Determining Quality of Water for Subsurface Injection," *API Drilling and Production Practice* (1957), p. 169.

[7]C. C. Wright, "Water Quality and Corrosion Control for Subsurface Injection," *API Drilling and Production Practice* (1960), p. 134.

[8]*Salt Water Disposal East Texas Oil Field* (2nd ed.) (Austin, Tex.: Petroleum Extension Service, 1957), p. 4.

[9]*Ibid.*, p. 87.

[10]J. W. Watkins, F. R. Willitt, Jr., and C. E. Arthur, *Conditioning Water for Secondary-Recovery in Midcontinent Oil Fields*, Report of Investigation 4930 (Washington, D.C.: U.S. Department of the Interior, Bureau of Mines, 1952), p. 53.

[11]J. U. Messenger, S. W. J. Harper, and A. J. Morris, "Treatment of Source and Produced Water in Pembina," SPE of AIME Rocky Mountain Regional Meeting, Casper, Wyo. (April 2–3, 1959), Paper 1225G.

Boiler and Cooling Water Treatment

14

Small plants, such as gasoline plants and engines using cooling water, are frequently connected with oilfield operations. Some plants use boilers, but boilers are no longer used as a major source of power in drilling operations. Water used by these installations requires treatment. Cost of treatment is, of course, important, but the volumes of water required are smaller than those used in water flooding, and frequently a greater degree of treatment is required. The acceptable cost of treatment of plant waters is normally higher than that of flood waters, but the lowest-cost treatment that provides acceptable water quality is still desired

Boiler Systems and Water

Although there are many different types of boilers, they are all essentially devices for transforming liquid water into steam by heating the water. Boiler operation is stated in terms of pressure, but it is the corresponding temperature that is the important variable in water treatment of boiler feed waters. Boiler feed water treatments vary with the operating pressure of the boiler. An arbitrary classification of boilers lists all boilers operating at pressures up to 200 psi as low-pressure boilers, 200 to 500 psi as intermediate-pressure boilers, and 500 to 2000 psi as high-pressure boilers. Most boilers used in oilfield installations are of the low or intermediate class.

The purpose of boiler feed water treatment is threefold: (1) to prevent scale formation, (2) to minimize or prevent corrosion in the boiler and steam system, (3) to insure steam purity.

1. BOILER DEPOSITS AND SCALE

Deposits and scales in boilers can result in failure of the equipment. Scale forms fastest at points of highest heat input. The thermal conductivity of scale averages about 5 per cent that of steel. The temperature differential between metal and water is greater for scaled boilers than for clean boilers operating at the same rating. If scale deposits become thick enough to cause a metal temperature higher than 900°F where metal creep of boiler steel becomes appreciable, *the metal is likely to fail.*

Boilers vary with respect to the amount of scale they can tolerate. A one-tenth-inch layer of scale, with a thermal conductivity of $K = 0.75$, results in a temperature differential across the scale of 111°F at a heat input of 10,000 BTU/sq ft. This temperature differential increases to 1,110°F differential, when the heat input is 100,000 BTU/sq ft.[1] Scale formation was not nearly as damaging with earlier types of low-pressure boilers as it is with modern high-pressure boilers.

Boiler scale is much more troublesome than sludge. Some scales must be removed by chipping, while sludge can be blown or washed off. The most common scale- and sludge-formers are calcium carbonate, magnesium hydroxide, calcium sulfate, and with some improperly treated waters, calcium hydroxide. Except in unusual cases, silica is not generally a problem. Some other deposits which may form in boilers are shown in Table 3.1.

Scale deposits in boilers also result in some heat losses. These heat losses are undesirable, but the greatest objection to scale buildup is the danger caused by hot spots. Proper treatment of boiler feed water controls scale deposition.

2. Corrosion of Boiler and Steam System

Because of high temperatures existing in boilers, corrosion may progress at accelerated rates. Dissolved oxygen and other corrosive gases are particularly serious. The presence of substances dissolved in feed water which decompose to give corrosive gases at temperatures existing in boilers should be avoided. Corrosive gases will pass with the steam, causing corrosion of steam and condensate lines.

Normally, waters containing hydrogen sulfide or appreciable amounts of carbon dioxide are not used as boiler waters. If used, these gases must be removed along with dissolved oxygen by de-aeration. At boiler temperatures, even pure water may attack the steel. For minimum corrosion, boiler water pH (measured at room temperature) should be adjusted in the range 11–12.[2] Feed water treatment influences corrosion in the boiler, and in steam and condensate lines.

3. Steam Purity

In addition to the presence of other gases in steam, steam purity is affected by carry-over of boiler water and direct solution of substances in high-pressure steam. Boiler carry-over generally refers to the contamination of steam by droplets of water from the boiler. Carry-over is influenced by kind and concentration of dissolved solids in boiler water, suspended solids content of boiler water, design of boiler, and conditions of boiler operation. Except when water treatment influences the dissolved and suspended solids in the boiler feed water, carry-over is governed by boiler operation.

Solids consisting of alkalies, salts, and silica are essentially nonvolatile at boiler temperatures but have some solubility in steam. The solubility of sodium salts is not appreciable in steam at pressures below 2000 psi, but silica solubility may be a problem at pressures as low as 400 psi. Silica solubility in steam is greatest in the presence of solid silica or sodium silicate.

Boiler Feed Water Characteristics

The recommended characteristics of boiler feed water vary with the operating pressure of the boiler. Some boiler feed water characteristics are shown in Table 14.1. Very-high-pressure boilers require practically de-ionized water. The nearer the supply water approaches these boiler feed water characteristics, the less treatment is required.

Table 14.1

Some Boiler Feed Water Characteristics

(Reprinted with permission of the American Society for Testing Materials, Philadelphia, Penna., from *Manual on Industrial Water and Industrial Watse Water* (2nd ed, 1960), p. 24.)

	Turbidity, ppm	Color, ppm	Color + O_2 Consumed, ppm	Dissolved Oxygen, ml per liter	Hardness, ppm	pH	Total Solids, ppm	Al_2O_3, ppm	SiO_2, ppm	CO_3, ppm	HCO_3, ppm	OH, ppm	Na_2SO_4 to Na_2SO_3 Ratio
0 to 150 psi	20	80	100	2	75	8.0+	3,000 to 1000	5	40	200	50	50	1 to 1
150 to 250 psi	10	40	50	0.2	40	8.5+	2,500 to 500	0.5	20	100	30	40	2 to 1
250 psi and over	5	5	10	0	8	9.0+	1,500 to 100	0.05	5	40	5	30	3 to 1

Boiler Feed Water Treatment

Treatment of boiler feed water is designed to make source water suitable for use and to reduce scale deposition and corrosion in the boiler. Boiler feed water treatment is classified as external or internal treatment. External treatment consists of softening and de-aerating the water before it enters the boiler, plus the addition of "conditioning" chemicals to aid in the prevention of scale and corrosion, and removal of the last traces of oxygen. Some degree of internal treatment is, therefore, associated with external treatment. When the water is treated entirely within the system, this is termed internal treatment.

Internal treatment finds its greatest application with small boilers operating at low pressure. It has the advantage over external treatment that a water-softening plant is not required. Except with high-pressure boilers, which require external treatment of feed water, the choice of internal or external treatment is made for economic considerations.

1. EXTERNAL TREATMENT OF BOILER FEED WATER

The capacity of the treating equipment or plant should be sufficient to handle peak demands for boiler water easily. The make-up is estimated from the evaporation and blowdown minus the condensate returns. Evaporation of a boiler is usually given in pounds per hour but can be converted to gallons per hour by multiplication by 0.12.

a. Sodium Cation-Exchange Process

Water softening by sodium-cation exchange process is used for softening boiler feed water; particularly, water for low-pressure boilers. The process has the advantages of relatively low cost, simplicity, and nearly complete reduction of hardness. The disadvantages are that there is no reduction of dissolved solids content of the water or of alkalinity. Sulfuric acid addition is needed to reduce the alkalinity.

b. Hydrogen Cation-Exchange Process

A possible reduction in dissolved solids content to about 50 ppm is possible with the hydrogen cation-exchange process. The process removes hardness and reduces alkalinity. Disadvantages are that the process is more expensive than the sodium cation-exchange process and the possible risk of acidic water. Silica is not removed by this process.

c. Demineralization by Ion Exchange

Demineralization by the ion exchange process is used to treat boiler feed water for high-pressure boilers. The advantages are reduction in dissolved solids content to 5–10 ppm and silica removal if necessary. The chief disadvantage is that the cost is higher than for any other method, with the possible exception of distillation (see Table 7.1).

d. Hot-Lime Soda Softening and Phosphate Process

It is possible to reduce dissolved solids to 80 ppm with this method. Disadvantages of the method are that it is involved, and the treated water is likely to have a high alkalinity (60 to 75 ppm) requiring addition of sulfuric acid.

e. Hot-Lime Softening Followed by Cation-Exchange

This process reduces alkalinity to 25–30 ppm and may make the addition of sodium nitrate or sulfate unnecessary. Some reduction in silica is also possible. Dissolved solids are only reduced approximately to the extent of alkaline hardness less 30 ppm.

f. Distillation

Distillation or evaporation produces a high quality water free of hardness and silica, with a dissolved solids content of 5 ppm or less. This process is more expensive than any of the other softening processes.

Besides being softened, externally treated boiler feed water is generally de-aerated to remove dissolved oxygen and other gases. Last traces of oxygen are removed by addition of catalyzed sodium sulfite or hydrazine to the water as it enters the boiler.

2. INTERNAL TREATMENT OF BOILER WATER

External treatment of boiler water is usually cheaper and more effective than internal treatment. Generally, internal treatment with chemicals is used in conjunction with external treatment to provide insurance against scale formation and corrosion. In some instances, where there is a small plant, a low-pressure boiler, a low make-up, or a good water supply, the cost of an external treating system may not be justified. Under these conditions, internal treatment alone may be satisfactory. Table 14.2 shows some chemicals commonly used for the internal treatment of boiler feed waters.

a. Phosphate Treatment

Because of evaporation, any residual hardness in the boiler feed water or in condensate return tends to concentrate in the boiler. The addition of one of the soluble sodium phosphates precipitates the calcium in a non-adherent deposit and thus prevents hard scale formation. Phosphate treatment is especially applicable to boilers operating at over 200 psi, in which the conversion of sodium carbonate into sodium hydroxide occurs at such a high rate that it is difficult to maintain a sufficient concentration of sodium carbonate to both precipitate calcium and provide a reserve. Phosphate is stable at all boiler temperatures.

Enough phosphate is added to the feed water as mono-, di-, or tri-sodium phosphate to precipitate the calcium noncarbonate hardness and maintain a reserve or excess of 40 ppm $PO_4^{\equiv}$ at pressures up to 750 psi. At higher operating pressures, water quality is usually better and the required excess of

Table 14.2

CHEMICALS USED IN INTERNAL BOILER WATER TREATMENT

(From Powell, *Water Conditioning for Industry* (New York: McGraw-Hill Book Company, 1954), p. 243. Used by Permission.)

Corrective Treatment Required	Type of Chemical
Maintenance of feedwater pH and boiler-water alkalinity for scale and corrosion control	caustic soda soda ash sulfuric acid
Prevention of boiler scale by internal softening of the boiler water	phosphates soda ash sodium aluminate alginates sodium silicate
Conditioning of boiler sludge to prevent adherence to internal boiler surfaces	tannins lignin derivatives starch glucose derivatives
Prevention of scale from hot water in pipelines, stage heaters, economizers, etc.	polyphosphates tannins lignin derivatives glucose derivatives
Prevention of oxygen corrosion by chemical de-aeration of boiler feed water	sulfites tannins ferrous hydroxide glucose derivatives hydrazine
Prevention of corrosion by protective film formation	tannins lignin derivatives glucose derivatives
Prevention of corrosion by condensate	amine compounds ammonia
Prevention of foam in boiler water	polyamides polyalkylene glycols
Inhibition of caustic embrittlement	sodium sulfate phosphates tannins nitrates

phosphate less. With demineralized waters, where introduction of solids is to be avoided, phosphates are not added.

b. Addition of Sodium Carbonate or Hydroxide

Sodium carbonate is added to boiler water to remove those calcium and magnesium salts which are associated with noncarbonate hardness. In the boiler, the calcium and magnesium bicarbonates associated with carbonate hardness are converted to calcium carbonate and magnesium hydroxide, and precipitated. Sodium hydroxide may be added, reacting with the dissolved bicarbonates to form sodium carbonate.

A 300 ppm excess of sodium carbonate (expressed as calcium carbonate) should be present in the boiler water to insure removal of calcium. Only a few ppm excess of sodium hydroxide are required for magnesium removal. A minimum of 150 ppm sodium hydroxide (expressed as $CaCO_3$) should be maintained for corrosion control. If a 300 ppm sodium carbonate excess is maintained in the boiler, it is unnecessary to control the sodium hydroxide content.[3] Sodium hydroxide in boiler water can cause caustic embrittlement, unless precautions are taken.

c. Addition of Oxygen Scavengers

Generally, boiler feed waters are mechanically de-aerated to remove dissolved oxygen. The small amount of oxygen remaining in the water after this process is removed chemically by addition of sodium sulfite or hydrazine (see Chapter 12). To guard against uncontrolled entry of oxygen, a reserve of 20–40 ppm sulfite is usually maintained in the boiler water.[4] Sodium sulfite has the advantage that its reaction product with dissolved oxygen is sodium sulfate, which is used to prevent caustic cracking in boilers.

In high-pressure boilers using demineralized water, addition of sodium sulfite increases the dissolved solids. In addition, the sulfite ion may decompose at high temperatures and give corrosive products. Hydrazine has the advantage that it forms gaseous reaction products with oxygen and, therefore, does not increase the dissolved solids content. It is widely used in boilers to remove dissolved oxygen from the water.[5]

d. Tannins

Tannins are compounds, such as gallotannin, that are extracted from oak, chestnut, and quebracho wood. Tannins prevent the formation of hard scale by plating on the crystal nuclei and distorting the crystal structure. Tannins combine with dissolved iron to form a corrosion-resistant film on the metal. Gallotannin hydrolyzes in boiler water to produce alkaline pyrogallol, which is an oxygen absorber.

The concentration of tannin is best determined by trial. Generally, $\frac{1}{2}$ lb tannin is used with 2 lb of softening salts. One treatment consists of adding a paste mixture of 60 per cent caustic soda and 40 per cent disodium phosphate concentrated in tannin extract, until the final mixture contains 35 per cent tannin. From $\frac{1}{4}$ to $\frac{1}{2}$ lb of this mixture is added per 1000 gal of water.[6]

e. Other Chemical Additives

Lignins are obtained from pulp woods. They are stable at higher temperatures than the tannins and interfere with crystal formation by the same mechanism. Glucose and its chemical derivatives are used for scale control and the dispersion of sludge. Starches are also added to prevent scale buildup. A mixture consisting of 47 per cent anhydrous disodium phosphate, 44 per cent soda ash, and 9 per cent cornstarch has been used as a boiler compound.[7] Seaweed derivatives have also been used as dispersing colloids in preventing adherent scale formation.

Aluminate and silicate compounds have been used to soften boiler feed waters internally. If aluminate is used, the soda ash dose is decreased. The ratio of sodium oxide or potassium oxide to silica should be two to one in any silicates used. The treatment of boiler waters with silicates is a *very delicate* procedure and does not work in all cases. It should be undertaken only by those experienced in the treatment.

f. Antifoam Additives

Foaming results in water being carried from the boiler with steam. It is influenced by several factors, including water level in the boiler and concentrations of dissolved solids and suspended materials. Foaming can be prevented or reduced by boiler blowdown, complete change of boiler water, or the addition of antifoam agents, which permit higher concentrations of dissolved solids in the boiler water. In some applications, antifoam additives have extended the allowable concentration of dissolved solids from 2,000–5,000 ppm to 30,000 ppm.[8]

There are many substances used to prevent foaming in boilers, one of the oldest being castor oil. The dosage may vary with the boiler. In one instance, 8 ppm of castor oil prevented foaming (up to a dissolved salt content of 6,290 ppm), while in another instance, 3 ppm were effective.[9] Too large an excess of castor oil can cause foaming. Gallic and tannic acids, corn oil, cottonseed oil, sperm oil, beeswax, carnauba wax, pyrogallol, tartaric and citric acids, all used in concentrations of 6 to 8 ppm of raw water, have effectively prevented foaming. Fatty acid amides and water-insoluble metallic soaps such as zinc stearate are also used as antifoaming agents.

Boiler Blowdown

Except where demineralization or distillation is used for boiler water treatment, concentration of dissolved solids, in the form of sodium salts, build up in the boiler as a result of chemical treatment. The tolerances of boilers operating at various pressures for dissolved solids are shown in Table 14.3. The concentration of salines in the boiler is controlled by blowing to waste a given amount of the boiler water and replacing it with lower-salinity boiler feed water.

Table 14.3

AMERICAN BOILER AND AFFILIATED INDUSTRIES' LIMITS
FOR BOILER WATER CONCENTRATIONS IN UNITS WITH A
STEAM DRUM

Boiler Pressure (psig)	Total Solids (ppm)	Alkalinity (ppm)	Suspended Solids
0–300	3,500	700	300
301–450	3,000	600	250
451–600	2,500	500	150
601–750	2,000	400	100
751–900	1,500	300	60
901–1,000	1,250	250	40
1,001–1,500	1,000	200	20
1,501–2,000	750	150	10
Over 2,000	500	100	5

The amount of blowdown can be calculated using Eq. (14–1), where A is the blowdown in percentage of make-up water, B is the dissolved solids content in the make-up, and C is the maximum allowable dissolved solids content in the boiler water:[10]

$$A = \frac{B \times 100}{C} \tag{14–1}$$

The blowdown may be intermittent, but modern practice utilizes automatically controlled, continuous blowdown procedures.

Caustic Embrittlement

Stressed boiler metal in contact with concentrated caustic soda solution may fail from intracrystalline cracking, referred to as caustic embrittlement.

The concentrated solutions (10 per cent or more) occur in crevices or cracks where circulation is impaired. The process of evaporation concentrates the caustic soda in the solution held in the crack, where it attacks the grain boundaries of the metal. This is a form of stress-corrosion cracking. Four simultaneous conditions are necessary to produce failure by caustic embrittlement.

(1) Substances capable of causing intracrystalline corrosion of steel, when concentrated, must be present in the boiler water. Generally, hydroxides or sodium carbonate must be present in the boiler water. The presence of silica accelerates the embrittlement.

(2) A joint or seam into which the boiler water can leak must be available.

(3) Concentration of the boiler water must occur within this seam.

(4) The steel exposed to this concentrated solution must be stressed.

The presence of cracks or seams permitting leakage and concentration of boiler water is a mechanical factor. This as well as large residual stresses can be corrected by proper design or maintenance.

The chemical factor can be overcome by addition of certain chemicals to the boiler water. The co-ordinated phosphate method attempts to eliminate caustic cracking by preventing the concentration of alkali from reaching the dangerous level. This is accomplished by adding phosphate in proportions that give a mole ratio of Na_2O to P_2O_5 of slightly less than 3:1. When evaporation of water occurs, precipitation of Na_3PO_4 will prevent a rise in pH.

Another method used in boilers operating in the range of 100–600 psi is the addition of sodium nitrate to the boiler water. The salt is added to obtain a sodium nitrate to total alkalinity (expressed as sodium hydroxide) ratio of at least 0.4.

The sulfate ratio method is also used to minimize the possibility of caustic cracking. With this method, a weight ratio of sodium sulfate to caustic soda greater than 2.5 is maintained in the boiler.

Condensate Returns

The use of condensate returns as boiler feed water has the advantage that the condensate is practically distilled water. However, some mineral impurities may be present, as may carbon dioxide from the boiler, or oxygen from leaks in the condensate lines. If the condensate lines come from engines, oil may be present. The condensate may require some treatment.

1. TREATMENT FOR HARDNESS

In high-pressure boilers, the soluble phosphate treatment will usually take care of the small amounts of hardness present in condensate waters. In low-pressure boilers, any hardness present in the condensate is too small to require special treatment. In the event that condenser leakage is entering the condensate lines, external treatment may be required before the condensate is returned to the boiler.

2. REMOVAL OF CONDENSATE GASES

De-aeration is effective in removing gases dissolved in the condensate. The condensate may be de-aerated with the filtered, softened make-up water.

3. OIL REMOVAL

Oil is *hazardous* in boilers, since it forms a heat-insulating film. The oil may be removed by coagulation with alum and soda ash, followed by filtration through an anthrafilt filter. The water will then require treatment to remove the carbonate.

4. TREATMENT FOR CORROSION

In systems where the condensate is discharged to waste, an effective method is to atomize soluble oil into the steam line ahead of the locations where some condensate occurs. If the condensate is to be used as boiler feed water, the oil must be removed. Film-forming amines can be applied in the same manner as the oil. These amines provide a protective film on the metal surface. Both the oil and the film-forming amine must be applied continuously to maintain a protective coating. Any uncoated areas will be subject to accelerated corrosion.

Some amines, such as cyclohexylamine and morpholine, are stable and volatile enough to be fed with the boiler feed water. These amines condense with the water droplets and give protection in these areas. Carbon dioxide tends to collect in the condensate where it is neutralized by the amine. Amine concentration lost in blow-off or leaks must be made up in the feed water. Ammonia also neutralizes carbon dioxide in condensate, but it has the disadvantage of attacking copper and brass.

Cooling-Water Systems

Cooling waters are used in three general classifications of cooling systems. The "once-through-to-waste" system is sometimes used where a large supply of water is available. Since the water is used only once, any treatment should be very cheap. In another type of system, the water is used once for cooling and then for some other purpose. The water must be treated to satisfy the requirements of a cooling water as well as the requirements of its secondary use.

The third general classification is a recirculating cooling system. Generally, the water circulates through the cooling system and then is cooled through a cooling tower or spray pond. For each 10°F of cooling effected in the cooling tower or spray pond, approximately 1 per cent of the water is evaporated.[11] Water losses are higher in practice because of wind losses and cooling-tower blow-off. After the cooling water is initially treated, only the make-up water has to be treated. This treatment should be based on the character of the raw water and the character of the treated water after it has been concentrated by recycling. Closed recirculating systems, such as those used with diesel or gas engines, require only small amounts of make-up water. The water in these closed systems should be treated initially and whenever make-up water is added.

Scale formation and corrosion are problems commonly encountered with cooling waters. Unless the water is unusually hard, scale formation is not a serious problem in cooling systems where the water is used for only one cycle. However, when the cooling water is recycled using a cooling tower or spray, evaporation causes an increase in concentration of dissolved solids, and scale formation becomes a more serious problem. This increased salt concentration, oxygen content of the water, and high temperatures at the surface of the cooling coil combine to pose a corrosion problem. The objectives of cooling-water treatment are fourfold: (1) to prevent the formation of scale on the cooling surfaces; (2) to prevent corrosion of metal by the cooling water; (3) to prevent fouling of the cooling surfaces and of the cooling tower; (4) to prevent deterioration or corrosion of the cooling-tower materials.

Prevention of Scale Formation

1. SOFTENING THE WATER

Scale deposition from cooling waters can be prevented by removing the scale-forming ions. This can be accomplished by softening or demineralizing the water by the methods discussed in Chapter 7. For economic reasons, these methods are limited to use with recirculating or once-through-and-another-use systems. Softening processes would be too expensive to use with once-through-to-waste systems.

2. ACID TREATMENT

Since the solubility of calcium and magnesium sulfates is much higher than that of the respective carbonates, scale formation can be prevented by adding sulfuric acid to convert the carbonates and bicarbonates to sulfates. This method is effective, provided the concentration of calcium sulfate does not exceed 1,700 ppm, or the product of ppm sulfate times ppm calcium does not exceed 500,000. Hydrochloric acid can also be used, but because

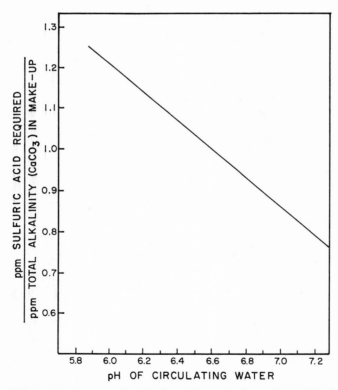

Fig. 14.1. Amount of sulfuric acid required to adjust pH of circulating water. (From McKelvey and Brooke, *The Industrial Cooling Tower* (Amsterdam: Elsevier Publishing Company, 1959), p. 233.)

its cost is higher on an equivalent basis, sulfuric acid is normally used. In a once-through-to-waste system, the amount of acid required is less than that used in a recirculating system, because the carbon dioxide released from the acid-carbonate reaction remains available. Acid treatment is usually the cheapest for once-through-to-waste systems. Depending upon the composition of the water, it may be more or less expensive than lime and soda ash treatment for recirculating cooling waters.

The pH of cooling water should be controlled in the range 6.0 to 6.5 when using acid treatment.[12] The amount of sulfuric acid required to adjust the pH of the circulating water can be estimated from Fig. 14.1. Hardness and pH limit the degree the circulating water can be concentrated. When cooling water is being treated with phosphate, the hardness value at which precipitation takes place at a given pH is shown in Fig. 14.2. The 70 per cent line is usually the limit to which the hardness value is carried for circulating waters. At values lower than pH 6, the effectiveness of the inhibitor in phosphate-treated waters is reduced, until it has no effect at pH 4.5 and the synergistic effect is reversed at pH 2.0.

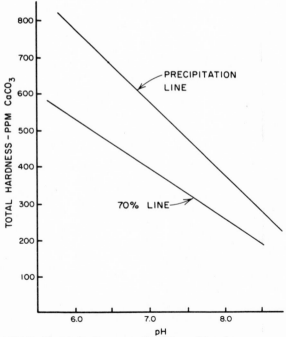

Fig. 14.2. Precipitation as a function of hardness versus pH in phosphate-treated cooling water. (From McKelvey and Brooke, *The Industrial Cooling Tower* (Amsterdam: Elsevier Publishing Company, 1959), p. 234.)

3. Use of Chemicals To Prevent Scale Formation

Polymetaphosphates have found use in the threshold treatment of cooling waters. A slowly soluble granular type, called Micromet, is sometimes used in the threshold treatment. In a once-through cooling system using brackish water of 10,000 ppm dissolved solids, 1 to 2 ppm Calgon (sodium hexametaphosphate) gives adequate scale control.[13] In a recirculating cooling system where the temperature does not exceed 100°F, 5 ppm Calgon is used to prevent scale formation.

When polymetaphosphates such as Calgon are dissolved in water, reversion to the orthophosphate occurs (see "Condensed Phosphates," Chapter 3). The time the metaphosphate stays in the system can be decreased by large and frequent blowdowns. This will help to decrease the amount of metaphosphate reversion. For stabilization of cooling water with metaphosphate, the bicarbonate hardness should not exceed 300 ppm in relatively high-temperature systems such as oil refineries.[14]

Corrosion Inhibition of Cooling Systems

1. Use of Polymetaphosphates

Cooling waters cooled by recirculation through spray- or tray-type towers use higher concentrations of polymetaphosphates for corrosion inhibition than for scale prevention. There are several variations in the treatment for corrosion. The choice depends upon the water and conditions in the system. One variation involves using acid to lower the pH of the cooling water to about 6.5. This reduces pitting by spreading the corrosion more evenly. To reduce this corrosion, 10 to 20 ppm polymetaphosphate are then added.[14] An initial "shock dose" of 100 ppm polymetaphosphate may be used to provide a protective film. Another variation is to adjust the pH of the water by the addition of an alkali until the water is nearly scale-forming. To *prevent* scale deposition, 2 to 5 ppm of polymetaphosphate are then added.[15]

The main disadvantage of condensed phosphates as corrosion inhibitors is their dependence upon the working conditions of the system. Generally, condensed phosphates are only effective as corrosion inhibitors in moving water. Pitting may also occur if underdoses of condensed phosphates are used in slightly alkaline waters.[16] Reversion of the polymetaphosphate may cause the formation of calcium phosphate scales on hot surfaces.

2. Use of Chromates

Hexavalent chromium compounds are used extensively as corrosion inhibitors in cooling waters. These compounds function as inhibitors by increasing the polarization of the local anodes on a metal surface. When chromate is used as a corrosion inhibitor, it is important that the concentration be maintained at a level high enough to maintain anode polarization—otherwise, pitting may occur. The minimum permissible chromate concentration is dependent upon temperature, anion concentration and type, flow velocity, ratio of metal surface to liquid volume, salinity, and pH. Excess chromate results in effective inhibition, comparable to that obtained by cathodic polarization.

Frequently, chromate is added to the cooling water as sodium dichromate ($Na_2Cr_2O_7 \cdot 2H_2O$) and converted to sodium chromate (Na_2CrO_4) by adjusting the pH with the addition of sodium hydroxide. It normally requires the addition of about 27 ppm sodium hydroxide per 100 ppm sodium dichromate to adjust the pH, but this varies with different waters. The pH of a 1,000 ppm sodium dichromate solution is 4.5, while a sodium chromate solution of the same concentration has a pH of about 8.5. For satisfactory inhibition, the pH of chromate solutions should range between 7.5 and 9.5. Sodium chromate can be added initially, but it is cheaper to add the dichromate and adjust the pH with sodium hydroxide. In humid atmospheres it might be advantageous to use potassium dichromate, since it does not hydrate and cake up as much as the sodium dichromate.

Depending upon conditions existing in the system, the concentration of chromate necessary to obtain effective protection may range from 50 to 5,000 ppm (expressed as $Na_2Cr_2O_7 \cdot 2H_2O$). The chloride content of the water influences the amount of chromate consumed in corrosion protection. Chromate consumption increases with chloride concentration, thus requiring more chromate to give adequate protection.[17] Systems of low circulation that contain stagnant volumes require higher chromate concentrations than do rapidly circulating systems because of chromate depletion.[18] The amount of aeration is not important, but the metal to be protected influences the minimum chromate concentration. The minimum chromate concentration necessary for inhibition is higher initially than it is after the protective film has formed on the metal. If dissimilar metals in contact with one another are to be protected, the necessary chromate concentration will depend upon the temperature, salinity and pH of the water, and upon the metals.

The concentration of hexavalent chromate added as an inhibitor may be diminished in the system. During the formation and maintenance of a protective film, the hexavalent chromium is reduced to the trivalent state. In protecting steel, the rate of chromate reduction decreases with time. The rate is dependent on the initial chromate concentration and is greater at high water temperatures and in water of high chloride content. Chromate may be reduced by reducing agents in the raw water. In open cooling systems, reducing gases from the atmosphere may dissolve in the water and reduce the chromate to the trivalent form. Mechanical losses such as leakage, windage, or draw-off may decrease the chromate content unless compensated for by the addition of more chemical. These factors indicate that a careful investigation must be made of an unknown system before the optimum chromate concentration can be determined.

a. Some Typical Chromate Cooling-Water Treatments[19]

(1) Air Conditioning: Begin initially with 500 ppm sodium dichromate and adjust the pH to 7.5. After a protective film on the metal is established, a chromate concentration of 200 to 300 ppm should be maintained.

(2) Ammonia Absorption Systems: Maintain a 2,000 to 4,000 ppm concentration of sodium dichromate.

(3) Automobile Radiators: In systems using fresh water, add 2 ounces of sodium chromate to a cooling system of 4- to 6-gallon capacity. This *should be flushed out* before adding antifreeze, since chromates and antifreezes are not compatible. In climates not requiring the use of antifreeze, maintain a sodium chromate concentration of 1,000 to 3,000 ppm by adding 1 ounce of sodium chromate about once a year.

(4) Bimetallic Systems: The chromate concentration necessary for inhibition of bimetallic systems depends upon the metals involved, pH, salinity, and temperature. As a guide, the results of a laboratory study showed that in a quiescent nonaerated system of pH 8, containing 1,000 ppm of chromate, the following couples were protected: iron and brass, iron and copper, iron and galvanized iron, galvanized iron and brass, aluminum and brass, and aluminum and iron.[20] An aluminum and copper couple was not protected.

(5) Cooling Towers: The treatment of cooling towers with chromate is usually initiated with about 500 ppm. This concentration is maintained until old rust is loosened and removed from the system, and the water is clear and light yellow in color. The concentration is then maintained at about 250 ppm. Sufficient chromate is added to the raw make-up water to compensate for blowdown and windage losses. Some systems may be adequately inhibited by as little as 100 ppm, but the minimum amount should not be used before a protective film has formed in the system. If there is little loss of water from the sys-

tem, a saving can be obtained by maintaining the concentration at 500 ppm, because the consumption of chromate in the chemical protection of the metal surfaces is lowest at this or higher concentrations. (6) Diesel and Gas Engines: If the cooling water circulated through the engine jackets is cooled by passing through a cooling tower or evaporative condenser, the chromate treatment is similar to that described for cooling towers. If the system is closed and the jacket water cooled by passing through a heat exchanger, the chromate treatment is slightly different. For treating this cooling water, 400 to 1,000 ppm of chromate are used with the alkalinity adjusted to pH 7.5 to 9.5. If some water is lost during the cooling process, additional chromate should be added to the make-up water to maintain the proper concentration.

b. Disadvantages of Chromate Inhibitors

Chromates as corrosion inhibitors have the *disadvantage* that they may cause *pitting* if the concentration falls below the minimum value for protection. Chromates are reduced to chromic (Cr^{+++}) salts, which have no value as inhibitors. The use of chromates in the presence of reducing substances is not economical.

Hexavalent chromium compounds are *toxic*. Water treated with chromates should *never be permitted* to enter drinking-water supplies. Chromates are *poisonous* to humans, animals, and fish. This sometimes presents a problem of disposal of cooling-tower blow-off or other waters containing chromate. The hexavalent chromium compounds can cause *skin disorders*, so care should be exercised in handling the chemical.

3. DIANODIC TREATMENT

Both phosphates and chromates, used in concentrations insufficient to control corrosive attack, cause *pitting*. Both are *anodic* inhibitors. When chromate and phosphate are used together at low concentrations and moderate pH, they reduce pitting and tuberculations. This is called the dianodic method or treatment. A phosphate-chromate treatment using 40 ppm polyphosphate and 20 ppm sodium dichromate, with the pH adjusted in the range 6.0 to 6.5, has been successful in some applications.[21]

4. CONTROLLED CALCIUM CARBONATE SCALE DEPOSITION

Corrosion of metal surfaces can be prevented by depositing a thin, even layer of hard calcium carbonate scale. The scale must be thin, so that it will not appreciably decrease heat transfer on heat exchanger surfaces or decrease the rate of flow through pipes. Scale deposition is controlled by water treatment and predicted according to methods discussed in Chapter 3 under calcium carbonate scale.

Corrosion protection by means of calcium carbonate scale formation has been widely used. However, the method *has disadvantages* in some cooling systems. The water is adjusted to equilibrium with respect to scale formation at a definite temperature. In cooling systems that have heat exchanger surfaces at widely different temperatures, the behavior of the water may vary in different parts of the system. Because of these temperature differences, it is possible that the water may be in equilibrium in one part of the system, corrosive in another, and scale-forming in still another part.

Prevention of Cooling-Tower Fouling

Scaling is the formation of deposits from material carried in solution, while fouling is the formation of deposits from material carried by the water in suspension. Suspended material may enter cooling-tower water by several different ways. Some silt or suspended solids may enter as part of the raw make-up water. Fine dust particles may be carried by air into the cooling tower and become suspended in the water. There may be some leakage, such as oil, from the process being cooled. Biological growths may occur within the cooling tower, or material may be present from the deterioration of the cooling tower itself.

1. SUSPENDED MATERIALS

Suspended material, particularly silt, may settle out on areas of metal and cause corrosion by the mechanism of "oxygen starvation." These deposits may also prevent corrosion inhibitors from reaching the metal. Suspended matter in the incoming raw water can be removed by sedimentation, flocculation, or filtration before the raw water enters the tower. Proper maintenance can prevent oil or other processed material from entering the water. In the spring or summer, dead insects may collect in the cooling water around the bottom of the tower. A coarse screen over the pump suction will help to keep the insects out of the system.

It is more difficult to prevent air-borne material from entering the cooling-tower water. In areas subject to dust storms, a considerable amount of suspended material is likely to enter the water from the air. The buildup of suspended solids in the cooling-tower water can be prevented with a side-stream or slip-stream filter. A small portion of the cooling water is taken from the system and passed through a filter (either pressure or gavity type) and returned to the system. The rate of side-stream filtration should be in the range 0.1 to 1.0 per cent of the circulation rate in the cooling tower.

The required side-stream filtration rate is dependent upon the solids removed and the amount of blowdown. The filtration rate may be calculated using Eq. (14–2), where F is the filtration rate in gal/min, R is the per cent removal of suspended solids, and B is the blowdown rate in gal/min:[22]

$$F = \left(\frac{100}{100 - R} - 1 \right) B \qquad (14\text{--}2)$$

Using this equation, it would be necessary to filter 600 gal/min of the cooling water, in a system having a 200 gal/min blowdown rate, to reduce the suspended solids from 20 to 5 ppm.

2. SLIME PREVENTION

Slime growths in piping and exchangers are usually caused by bacterial action. Masses of slime can reduce the flow of cooling water and interfere with the transfer of heat. The formation or growth of these masses in the form of a semipermeable membrane on a metal surface can result in oxygen concentration cells and subsequent corrosion. There are a number of chemicals commonly used to combat these growths.

a. Copper Salts

Copper sulfate, a toxic chemical, is used widely as an algicide in circulating water, cooling-tower installations, and in reservoir water. The toxicity is due to the copper ion. The concentration of copper necessary to kill algae varies with the specie. When using copper sulfate solutions as algicides, it is necessary to take precautions to prevent corrosion of feeding equipment.

The bactericidal effect of copper sulfate is *nullified* in waters of high pH because of the precipitation of the copper ion as copper hydroxide. The addition of an aliphatic hydroxy acid, such as citric acid, will complex the copper ion so that it will stay in solution. The organic acid should be mixed with the copper sulfate, the mixture dissolved in water, and the solution fed to the cooling water. The amount of organic acid needed to complex copper sulfate is shown in Fig. 14.3, and the effectiveness of these acids in keeping copper in alkaline solutions is shown in Fig. 14.4.[22] The concentrations of copper sulfate required to kill Crenothrix, Chlorophycea, Cyanophycea, and Diatomacea algae are shown in Table 14.4.

Copper sulfate may be fed intermittently or continuously. The frequency of treatment varies with temperature and conditions of the system. It is

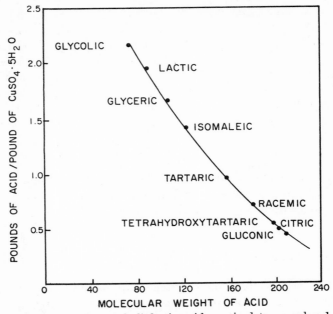

Fig. 14.3. Amount of aliphatic acid required to complex 1 pound of copper sulfate pentahydrate. (From Brooke, *Hydrocarbon Process. Petrol. Refiner*, **36**, No. 2 (1957), 142. Copyright 1957 by Gulf Publishing Company, Houston, *Tex.*)

preferable to feed the copper sulfate to circulating cooling-tower water as it returns to the tower. This is effective in killing growths in the top of the tower, and it provides enough time for the precipitation of any insoluble copper carbonate. The copper carbonate can then settle out in the cooling-tower basin and will not be circulated through the tower.

Table 14.4

LETHAL DOSAGES FOR SOME ORGANISMS

(From McKelvey and Brooke, *The Industrial Cooling Tower* (Amsterdam: Elsevier Publishing Comapny, 1959), p. 242.)

Organism	Trichlorophenate (ppm)	Pentachlorophenate (ppm)	Chlorine (ppm)	Copper Sulfate (ppm)
Aerobacter cloacae	100	50		
Aerobacter aerogenes	30	50		
Escherichia coli	100	50		
Bacillus subtilis	100	50		
Crenothrix			0.5	0.3
Chlorophyceae			0.7	0.5
Cyanophyceae			1.0	0.4
Diatomaceae			2.0	0.5

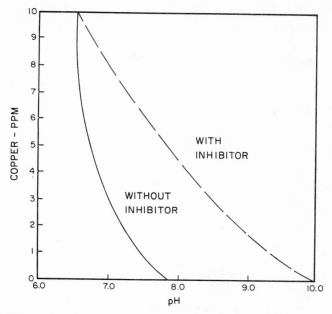

Fig. 14.4. Effectiveness of aliphatic hydroxy acids in retaining copper in alkaline solution. (From Brooke, *Hydrocarbon Process. Petrol. Refiner*, **36**, No. 2 (1957), 142. Copyright 1957 by Gulf Publishing Company, Houston, Tex.)

b. Mercury Compounds

Salts of mercury and its organo-metallic compounds are very toxic to algae and slime as well as to humans. Because of the toxicity of mercury to humans, compounds of mercury have not been widely used in cooling towers, where the spray may be blown or otherwise come in contact with people.

c. Potassium Permanganate

In addition to being a strong oxidizing agent, potassium permanganate is *toxic* to many microorganisms. However, it has the disadvantage that manganese dioxide is precipitated as a result of the reduction of permanganate by reducing substances present in the water. Also, dead as well as live microorganisms consume permanganate as a result of reduction of the permanganate ion by the dead organisms.

d. Quaternary Ammonium Compounds

Quaternary ammonium compounds are *good* bactericides and are *toxic* to slime and algae growths. When used in cooling towers, some of these compounds volatilize and their effectiveness is lost. The effectiveness of some quaternary ammonium compounds is reduced by absorption by organic matter or by high salt concentrations in the water.

e. Phenolic Compounds

Sodium pentachlorophenate and sodium trichlorophenate are used as algicides in cooling-tower waters. The compounds are soluble and stable in alkaline waters. These compounds can be fed with less costly equipment than that required for feeding chlorine. The compounds are *relatively expensive* —high-spray losses or blowdown rates may make their use uneconomical in large cooling towers.

Sodium pentachlorophenate is frequently applied by slug feeding. The slug should be large enough to establish a concentration of 200 ppm of pentachlorophenate in the water. The frequency of the slug treatment depends upon the results and rate of growth of the bacteria or algae. While not as effective as continuous feeding, slug feeding is more economical. Normally, when the concentration of pentachlorophenate has decreased to 50 ppm, a slug is added to return the concentration to 200 ppm. The frequency of treatment may be calculated using Eq. (14–3), where t is the time (in days) between treatments, B is the blowdown rate in gal/day, V is the volume (gallons) of cooling water in the system, C_i is the concentration of algicides obtained with the initial slug, and C_f is the final reduced concentration of algaecide.[22]

$$t = \frac{2.309\,V\,(\log C_i/C_f)}{B} \qquad (14\text{–}3)$$

The concentrations of sodium trichlorophenate and sodium pentachlorophenate necessary to kill some organisms are given in Table 14.4. Slug-feeding 60 to 100 ppm of a mixture of chlorinated phenols and copper has proved an effective algaecide.

f. Chlorine

A chlorine residual of 0.5 ppm is sufficient to kill most microorganisms. These microorganisms do not build up an immunity to chlorine. Small quantities of chlorine may be fed to a system in the form of sodium hypochlorite, but large amounts are fed as liquid chlorine. This is more fully discussed in Chapter 6. Intermittent feeding of chlorine is less expensive than continuous feeding but has the disadvantage that growths may build up between feedings and slough off immediately after feeding, resulting in additional fouling material in the tower.

The concentration of chlorine necessary to kill some algae is shown in Table 14.4. It should be remembered that chlorine is a strong oxidizing agent, and the water demand (organic and other material in the water available for oxidation) must be satisfied before the required residual concentration can be attained.

Prevention of Deterioration of Wooden Cooling Towers

In recent years, transite, plastics, and aluminum have been advocated as construction materials for cooling towers. However, the largest number of cooling towers are made of wood. Redwood is the most popular wood for this use, but cypress, yellow pine, Douglas fir, white oak, southern pine, and cedar are sometimes used. The deterioration of cooling-tower lumber may structurally weaken the tower until it collapses. There are three general types of cooling-tower lumber deterioration: (1) erosion caused by the falling water, (2) chemical deterioration, (3) decay caused by fungi attack.

1. Erosion of Cooling-Tower Lumber

The erosion of cooling-tower lumber by the impingement of falling water is negligible compared with the other forms of attack.

2. Chemical Deterioration

The chemical deterioration or dilignification of cooling-tower wood is caused by the removal of lignin by alkaline chemicals such as sodium carbonate. Lignin acts as a cement in holding the cellulose fibers together. As a result of this attack, the cellulose fibers are exposed and eventually washed away. This attack is increased by strong oxidizing agents, such as chlorine, and by higher temperatures.

Fortunately, it is comparatively easy to control this type of attack by regulating the pH of the water between 6.5 and 7.5. If chlorine is used as an algicide, the chlorine residual should be maintained below 1 ppm. The attack can also be minimized by periodically washing deposits of sodium salts from the wood.

3. Preventing Fungi Attack

Fungi destroy cooling-tower wood by attacking the cellulose. There are two types of microbiological attack. In one type, the attack occurs on the inside of the wood and cannot readily be recognized by visual inspection. This is best detected by probing the wood with an ice pick. Once through the wood surface, the probe will easily penetrate areas of decay. Hitting the wood with the ball end of a ball peen hammer produces a cracking sound if fungus attack is present. This type of attack usually occurs in portions of the cooling tower that are wet but not totally immersed in water. The second type of attack occurs on the surface and can be detected from the checkered appearance of the surface.

It is extremely difficult to control fungus attack of cooling-tower wood. Because decay occurs in sections of the tower not totally immersed in water, bactericides and fungicides added to the cooling water are not successful. At best, the attack can be minimized by adjusting the water to pH 7 and maintaining a low chloride residual. This is also recommended to minimize chemical deterioration.

a. Creosoted Wood

The use of impregnated wood in the construction of cooling towers will prolong the life of the tower. One effective treatment consists of pressure-impregnating wood to a retention of 8 pounds of creosote per cubic foot of wood.

b. Double-Diffusion Treatment

The double-diffusion treatment consists of impregnating the wood with a solution of a salt, followed by impregnation with a solution of a different salt that will form a precipitate with the initial salt solution. One or both of the salts should have toxic properties. The precipitation of the slightly insoluble toxic salt in the wood fibers offers protection against attack by microorganisms. This treatment can be applied to towers by spraying the solutions on the wood and letting them soak in.

One treatment consists of impregnating the wood with copper sulfate solution, followed by sodium chromate solution. Toxic copper chromate is precipitated in the wood fibers. It is claimed that a retention of 0.3 lb/cu ft can be obtained by spraying these solutions on wood.[23] Another double diffusion treatment is applied by first spraying the wood with a solution of 6 per cent by weight zinc sulfate and 1 per cent arsenious acid. When the wood appears dry, it is sprayed with a 6 per cent solution of sodium chromate and allowed to dry.

When the cooling tower is returned to service, the cooling water will dissolve some of these salts, but a substantial residual will remain in the wood. Since the presence of copper in solution is corrosive to steel, the copper sulfate diffusion treatment finds limited application. Because of the presence of these toxic materials in the water, care should be used in disposing of the cooling-tower blowdown.

c. Treatment with Chlorinated Phenols

In this treatment, the water is batch-treated periodically with high concentrations of chlorinated phenols to inhibit microbiological attack in the flooded sections. Portions of the tower that are wet but not totally immersed in water are sprayed with a stronger solution of chlorinated phenols at intervals of three to six months.[24] This treatment may control the attack, but the chlorinated phenols are water-soluble and leach from the wood, thus the treatment must be repeated frequently.

d. Other Treatments

Among the other treatments is a single diffusion treatment. A solution of cupric hydroxide, arsenic trioxide, ammonia, and acetic acid is applied to the wood. The salts are soluble in the presence of ammonia, but precipitate when the ammonia evaporates. The Green Salt or Erdalith treatment impregnates the wood with 0.8 lb of chromated copper arsenate per cu ft.

Treatment of cooling-tower lumber already badly deteriorated with fungus attack will not stop the deterioration process. The infected wood should be removed and replaced with good wood. The tower should then be treated to prevent attack by fungus.

Cooling-Tower Operating Factors that Influence Chemical Treatment

1. DRIFT, WINDAGE LOSS, OR CARRY-OVER

This is the water that is entrained as fine droplets in the circulating air and is carried from the tower. Usually, it is expressed as a percentage of the make-up water. Loss of water by entrainment does not concentrate the dissolved solids, since they are removed with the water droplets. Drift, windage loss, or carry-over may be considered as part of the blowdown.

2. BLOWDOWN

Blowdown is the continuous or intermittent removal of some of the circulating water. Its purpose is to control the buildup of solids in the circulating water. Blowdown can be expressed as a volume per minute or as a percentage of the make-up water and circulating water. In Eq. (14–4), it is calculated on the basis of chloride ion concentration:

$$\text{percentage blowdown} = \frac{\text{ppm chloride ion in make-up}}{\text{ppm chloride ion in circulating water}} \times 100$$

$$(14\text{–}4)$$

3. CYCLES OF CONCENTRATION

The cycles of concentration indicate the number of times the make-up water has been concentrated as circulating water. The higher the number of cycles, the greater the utilization of the cooling water. A knowledge of cycles of concentration, as calculated in the following equation, is useful in calculating dosages of treatment chemicals:

$$\text{cycles} = \frac{\text{ppm chlorides in the circulating water}}{\text{ppm chlorides in make-up}} \qquad (14\text{–}5)$$

4. EVAPORATION RATE

Cooling towers function by the evaporation of water. Depending upon the temperature, it requires approximately 1,000 BTUs to evaporate 1 pound of water. This is equivalent to the amount of heat required to raise the temperature of 100 pounds of water 10°F. Therefore, for each temperature drop of 10°F through the tower, the evaporation rate is 1 per cent of the circulation rate. The evaporation rate, usually expressed in volume per minute, is calculated using Eq. (14–6)[25]:

$$\text{evaporation rate} = \frac{\text{temperature range}}{10} \times \frac{\text{circulation rate}}{100} \qquad (14\text{–}6)$$

Estimating Treatment Dosage

The following example may be helpful in estimating the acid treatment dosage for a cooling-tower water.[26] The make-up water has a total hardness of 120 ppm and total alkalinity of 174 ppm, both expressed as calcium carbonate. The chlorine demand of the water is 7 ppm, and the pH is controlled at 6.3. From Fig. 14.2, it is seen that the cooling-tower water can be concentrated to a hardness of 500 ppm. The cycles of concentration are 500/120 = 4.2. If it is desirable to maintain 60 ppm corrosion inhibitor in the circulating water, it is necessary to add 60/4.2 = 14.3 ppm to the feed water. From Fig. 14.1, the amount of acid necessary to control the pH at 6.3 is shown to be 1.1 ppm per ppm of total alkalinity. This amounts to 1.1 × 174 = 191 ppm of sulfuric acid added to the make-up water. The make-up water will require 7.5 ppm chlorine to give a 0.5 ppm residual.

Engine Cooling-Water Conditioning

Engines operating oilfield equipment are sometimes located in remote areas where constant overseeing is not practical. In these instances, it is advantageous to use distilled or demineralized water as cooling water. This minimizes corrosion and eliminates scale formation. The disadvantage is that this water will normally have to be hauled to the engine, but in closed cooling systems only small volumes are required after the original filling.

References

[1]E. Nordell, *Water Treatment for Industrial and Other Uses* (2nd ed.) (New York: Reinhold Publishing Corp. 1961), p. 249.

[2]R. F. Anders, "Corrosion in the Boiler," *Ind. Eng. Chem.*, **46** (1954), 990.

[3]P. Hamer, J. Jackson, and E. F. Thurston, *Industrial Water Treatment Practice* (London: Butterworth & Co., Ltd., 1961), p. 279.

[4]J. Arthurs, J. A. Robins, and T. B. Whitefoot, "The Treatment of Water for an Industrial High-Pressure Boiler Plant," *Trans. Instn. Chem. Engrs.* (London), **37** (1959), 72.

[5]M. D. Baker and V. M. Marcy, "Hydrazine as an Oxygen Scavenger—A Progress Report on Tests at Springdale Station," *Trans. ASME*, **78** (1956), 299.

[6]F. J. Matthews, *Boiler Feed Water Treatment* (New York: Chemical Publishing Co., 1951), p. 56.

[7]S. T. Powell, *Water Conditioning for Industry* (New York: McGraw-Hill Book Company, 1954), p. 258.

[8]Hamer, Jackson, and Thurston, *op. cit.* p. 293.

[9]Matthews, *op. cit.*, p. 145.

[10]Nordell, *op. cit.*, p. 273.

[11]W. F. Denman, "Maximum Re-Use of Cooling Water," *Ind. Eng. Chem.*, **53** (1961), 817.

[12]K. K. McKelvey and M. Brooke, *The Industrial Cooling Tower* (Amsterdam: Elsevier Publishing Company, 1959), p. 233.

[13]"Prevention of Scale and Corrosion with Phosphates and Filming Amines," *Corrosion Technol.* 5 (1958), 363.

[14]J. P. Kleber, "Chemical Conditioning of Cooling Waters," *Combustion*, **22** (1951), 45.

[15]R. S. Thornhill, "Prevention of Corrosion by Means of Inhibitors," *Research* (*London*), **5** (1952), 324.

[16]M. Cohen, "Sodium Hexametaphosphate as a Corrosion Inhibitor for Ottawa Tap Water," *J. Electrochem. Soc.*, **89** (1946), 105.

[17]M. Darrin, "Chromate Corrosion Inhibitors in Chloride Systems," *Ind. Eng. Chem.*, **38** (1946), 368.

[18]R. B. Roethelli and G. L. Cox, "Prevention of Corrosion of Metals by Sodium Dichromate as Affected by Salt Concentration and Temperature," *Ind. Eng. Chem.*, **23** (1931), 1084.

[19]M. J. Udy, *Chromium*, I (New York: Reinhold Publishing Corporation, 1956), 348.

[20]M. Darrin, "Chromate Corrosion Inhibitors in Bimetallic Systems," *Ind. Eng. Chem.*, **37** (1945), 741.

[21]H. L. Kahler and P. J. Gaughan, "Protection of Metals Against Pitting, Tuberculation, and General Corrosion," *Ind. Eng. Chem.*, **44** (1952), 1770.

[22]M. Brooke, "Cooling Water Treatment—A Review," *Hydrocarbon Process. Petrol. Refiner*, **36**, No. 2 (1957), 142.

[23]F. C. Reisenfield and C. L. Blohm, "Proper Materials Selection Can Prevent Cooling Tower Corrosion Problems," *Petrol. Eng*, **28**, No. 3 (1956), D-64.

[24]P. G. Ketchem, "Cooling Water Treatment," *Chem. Eng.*, **66**, No. 20 (1959), 168.

[25]McKelvey and Brooke, *op. cit.*, p. 63.

[26]*Ibid.* p. 247.

Appendix

Sample Calculations

1. LANGELIER SATURATION INDEX

Example calculations are given for a water at 30°C (86°F), having the composition shown below.

FORT UNION FORMATION WATER

Component	ppm	Moles/Liter
$CO_2^=$	—	—
HCO_2^-	781	0.0128
$SO_4^=$	150	0.0015
Cl^-	70	0.0020
Ca^{++}	19	0.0005
Mg^{++}	5	0.0002
Na^+	380	0.0165
pH = 8.2		

The saturation index SI is given by:

$$SI = pH - pH_s = pH - [(pK_2' - pK_s') + p\text{Ca}^{++} + p\text{Alk}] \quad (3\text{--}6)$$

where pH is the actual pH of the water, pH_s is the pH at saturation, pK_2' and pK_s' are empirical constants, $p\text{Ca}^{++}$ is the negative logarithm of the calcium ion concentration in moles per liter, and $p\text{Alk}$ is the negative logarithm of the total alkalinity titrated to the methyl orange end-point and expressed in equivalents per liter.

To solve Eq. (3–6), it is first necessary to calculate the ionic strength μ, using the following equation where C is the concentration in moles per 1,000 grams of water (essentially equal to moles per liter for this water because of low salt content), and z is the valence of the individual ions:

$$\mu = \frac{1}{2}(C_1 Z_1^2 + C_2 Z_2^2 \ldots + C_n Z_n^2) \quad (A\text{--}1)$$

$$\mu = \frac{1}{2}[(0.0128)(1)^2 + (0.0015)(2)^2 + (0.002)(1)^2 + (0.0005)(2)^2$$
$$+ (0.0002)(2)^2 + (0.0165)(1)^2] = 0.02$$

Then from Table A.1, the value of $(pK_2' - pK_s')$ at an ionic strength of 0.20 and a temperature of 30°C is 2.34. Next, the values of $p\text{Ca}^{++}$ and $p\text{Alk}$ are calculated.

$$p\text{Ca}^{++} = -\log 0.0005 = \log \frac{1}{0.0005} = \log 2,000 = 3.301$$

$$p\text{Alk} = p[\text{HCO}_3^-] = -\log 0.0128 = \log \frac{1}{0.0128} = \log 78 = 1.892$$

Substituting in Eq. (3–6), we have:

$$SI = 8.2 - [2.34 + 3.301 + 1.892] = +0.67$$

The positive value of the saturation index indicates that the water is oversaturated with respect to calcium carbonate.

2. LARSON AND BUSWELL SATURATION INDEX

The following example illustrates the calculation of the Larson and Buswell saturation index on the Fort Union water. Their saturation index I is given by:

$$I = pH + \log(\text{Ca}^{++}) + \log(Alky) - (pK_2' - pK_s')$$
$$- 9.30 - \frac{2.5\sqrt{\mu}}{1 + 5.3\sqrt{\mu} + 5.5\mu} \quad (3\text{--}7)$$

where all symbols have the same meaning as the previous examples, except (Ca^{++}) and $(Alky)$ which are expressed in ppm as calcium and calcium carbonate, respectively.

The $(Alky)$ value is calculated as follows by converting the HCO_3 (ppm) to CaCO_3 (ppm), using the proper conversion factor from Table 2.7:

Table A.1
Values of pK'_2 and pK'_s at 25°C for Various Ionic Strengths and the Difference $(pK'_2 - pK'_s)$ for Various Temperatures

(From Larson and Buswell, *J. Am. Water Works Assoc.*, **34** (1942), 1667.)

Ionic Strength	Total Dis-solved Solids (ppm)	25°C			$(pK'_2 - pK'_s)$									
		pK_2	pK'_s	$pK'_2 - pK'_s$	0°C	10°C	20°C	30°C	40°C	50°C	60°C	70°C	80°C	90°C
0.0000		10.26	8.32	1.94	2.45	2.23	2.02	1.86	1.68	1.52	1.36	1.23	1.08	0.95
0.0005	20	10.26	8.23	2.03	2.54	2.32	2.11	1.95	1.77	1.61	1.45	1.32	1.17	1.04
0.001	40	10.26	8.19	2.07	2.58	2.36	2.15	1.99	1.81	1.65	1.49	1.36	1.21	1.08
0.002	80	10.25	8.14	2.11	2.62	2.40	2.19	2.03	1.85	1.69	1.53	1.40	1.25	1.12
0.003	120	10.25	8.10	2.15	2.66	2.44	2.23	2.07	1.89	1.73	1.57	1.44	1.29	1.16
0.004	160	10.24	8.07	2.17	2.68	2.46	2.25	2.09	1.91	1.75	1.59	1.46	1.31	1.18
0.005	200	10.24	8.04	2.20	2.71	2.49	2.28	2.12	1.94	1.78	1.62	1.49	1.34	1.21
0.006	240	10.24	8.01	2.23	2.74	2.52	2.31	2.15	1.97	1.81	1.65	1.52	1.37	1.24
0.007	280	10.23	7.98	2.25	2.76	2.54	2.33	2.17	1.99	1.83	1.67	1.54	1.39	1.26
0.008	320	10.23	7.96	2.27	2.78	2.56	2.35	2.19	2.01	1.85	1.69	1.56	1.41	1.28
0.009	360	10.22	7.94	2.28	2.79	2.57	2.36	2.20	2.02	1.86	1.70	1.57	1.42	1.29
0.010	400	10.22	7.92	2.30	2.81	2.59	2.38	2.22	2.04	1.88	1.72	1.59	1.44	1.31
0.011	440	10.22	7.90	2.32	2.83	2.61	2.40	2.24	2.06	1.90	1.74	1.61	1.46	1.33
0.012	480	10.21	7.88	2.33	2.84	2.62	2.41	2.25	2.07	1.91	1.75	1.62	1.47	1.34
0.013	520	10.21	7.86	2.35	2.86	2.64	2.43	2.27	2.09	1.93	1.77	1.64	1.49	1.36
0.014	560	10.20	7.85	2.36	2.87	2.65	2.44	2.28	2.10	1.94	1.78	1.65	1.50	1.37
0.015	600	10.20	7.83	2.37	2.88	2.66	2.45	2.29	2.11	1.95	1.79	1.66	1.51	1.38
0.016	640	10.20	7.81	2.39	2.90	2.68	2.47	2.31	2.13	1.97	1.81	1.68	1.53	1.40
0.017	680	10.19	7.80	2.40	2.91	2.69	2.48	2.32	2.14	1.98	1.82	1.69	1.54	1.41
0.018	720	10.19	7.78	2.41	2.92	2.70	2.49	2.33	2.15	1.99	1.83	1.70	1.55	1.42
0.019	760	10.18	7.77	2.41	2.92	2.70	2.49	2.33	2.15	1.99	1.83	1.70	1.55	1.42
0.020	800	10.18	7.76	2.42	2.93	2.71	2.50	2.34	2.16	2.00	1.84	1.71	1.56	1.43

$$(Alky) = \frac{781}{1.22} = 640$$

Substituting in Eq. (8–10) we have

$$I = 8.2 + \log(19) + \log(640) - (2.34) - 9.30$$
$$- \frac{2.5\sqrt{0.02}}{1 + 5.3\sqrt{0.02} + 5.5(0.02)}$$
$$= 8.2 + 1.28 + 2.81 - 2.34 - 9.30 - 0.19 = +0.46$$

The positive value of I again indicates that the water is oversaturated with calcium carbonate and has scale-forming tendencies.

3. Ryznar Stability Index

The Ryznar stability index is given by:

$$\text{stability index} = 2\left[(pK_2' - pK_s') - \log(Ca^{++}) - \log(Alky) \right.$$
$$\left. + 9.30 + \frac{2.5\sqrt{\mu}}{1 + 5.3\sqrt{\mu} + 5.5\mu} \right] - \text{pH} \qquad (3\text{–}8)$$

where all terms correspond to those used in Eq. (3–7).

Substituting the values obtained in the previous example, the stability index for the Fort Union water is calculated as follows:

$$\text{stability index} = 2[(2.34) - (1.28) - (2.81) + (9.30) + (0.19)] - 8.2$$
$$= 15.48 - 8.2 = +7.28$$

This indicates a very slight scale-forming tendency at 86°F.

4. Stiff and Davis Stability Index

The Langelier method has been extended by Stiff and Davis to give a saturation index SI that is applicable to oilfield brines. The Stiff and Davis method is illustrated by example calculations on Water Analysis No. 2036 (Table 2.8).

From the water analysis, the concentration C of each ion in moles per 1,000 grams of water is calculated using the relationship:

$$C = \frac{epm}{z\left(1,000\, Sp\, Gr - \dfrac{TDS}{1,000}\right)} \qquad (A\text{–}2)$$

where epm = concentration of the ion, epm
  z = valence of the ion
  $Sp\, Gr$ = specific gravity of the brine
  TDS = total dissolved solids, ppm

This gives the following results:

Component	epm	Moles/1,000 gm
Carbonate ($CO_3^=$)	—	—
Bicarbonate (HCO_3^-)	0.7	0.001
Sulfate ($SO_4^=$)	158	0.083
Chloride (Cl^-)	2472	2.599
Iron (Fe^{++})	0.4	0.000
Calcium (Ca^{++})	428	0.225
Magnesium (Mg^{++})	231	0.121
Sodium (Na^+)	1965	2.066

Using these molalities, the ionic strength μ is calculated.

$$\mu = \frac{1}{2}(C_1 Z_1^2 + C_2 Z_2^2 \ldots C_n Z_n^2)$$

$$= \frac{1}{2}[(0.001)(1) + (0.083)(4) + (2.599)(1) + (0.225)(4)$$

$$+ (0.121)(4) + (2.066)(1)] = 3.19$$

Then, from Fig. A.1, the value of k, at $\mu = 3.19$ and at the analysis temperature of 77°F (25°C), is found to be 2.96.

The next step is to enter the ppm $Ca^{++} = 8,570$ and ppm $HCO_3^- = 46$ (obtained from the water analysis) as the ordinate of Fig. A.2. Reading the abscissa, the pCa of 0.67 and the pAlk is 3.12.

Then, substituting in Eq. (3–9), the stability index is calculated as follows:

$$SI = pH - K - pCa - pAlk = 6.1 - 2.96 - 0.67 - 3.12 = -0.65$$

This indicates that the water is corrosive and also undersaturated with respect to calcium carbonate.

5. ESTIMATION OF BARIUM SULFATE PRECIPITATED FROM WATER

This calculation is based on the solubility data shown in Table 3.3 and is only valid for waters that contain predominantly sodium and chloride ions and very little magnesium or calcium ions. The sample calculation is made on a water of the composition shown below.

ANALYSIS OF WATER

Component	ppm	Molal Concentration
Bicarbonate	377	0.006
Sulfate	9	0.00009
Chloride	48,656	1.372
Barium	66	0.0005
Iron (dissolved)	0	0
Calcium	934	0.023
Magnesium	157	0.007
Sodium	30,990	1.348

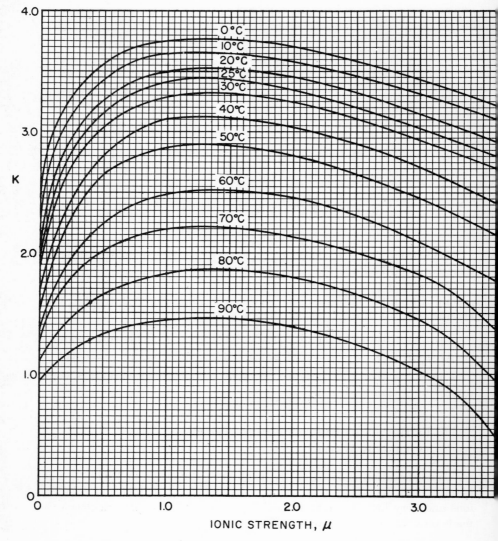

Fig. A.1. Values of K at various ionic strengths. (From Stiff and Davis, *Trans. AIME*, **195** (1952), 213.)

(1) Assume the above water is 1.37 molal sodium chloride solution. From Table 3.3, K' values are obtained for 1.0 and 1.5 molal sodium chloride solution at 25°C. Interpolation between these values, 9.22×10^{-9} and 12.54×10^{-9} respectively, gives a K' of 11.69×10^{-9} for a 1.37 molal sodium chloride solution.

(2) Use the expression

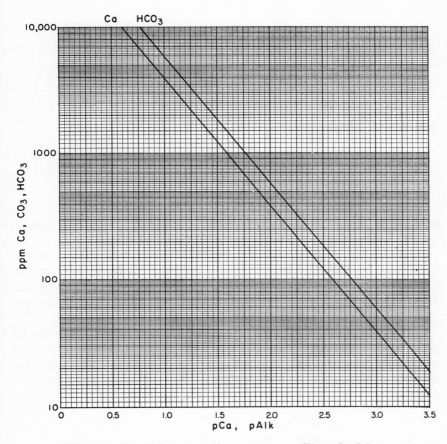

Fig. A.2. Graph for converting parts per million of calcium and alkalinity into pCa and pAlk. (From Stiff and Davis, *Trans. AIME*, **195** (1952), 213.)

$$([Ba^{++}] - x)([SO_4^=] - x) = K' = 11.69 \times 10^{-9}$$

where $x =$ the molal amount of barium sulfate precipitated.

Substituting barium and sulfate values from the water analysis,

$$([5 \times 10^{-4}] - x)([9 \times 10^{-5}] - x) = 11.69 \times 10^{-9}$$

then multiply

$$45 \times 10^{-9} - 5.9 \times 10^{-4}x + x^2 = 11.69 \times 10^{-9}$$

rearrange to

$$x^2 - 5.9 \times 10^{-4}x + 33.3 \times 10^{-9} = 0$$

(3) Using the quadratic equation and solving

$$x = \frac{-b \pm \sqrt{b^2 - 4ac}}{2a}$$

gives x equal to 6.3×10^{-5} molal, or 15 ppm barium sulfate deposited from the water at 25°C.

Scale Analysis Outline

1. SAMPLE PREPARATION AND PRELIMINARY TESTS

A representative portion of the scale sample should be freed from water by being dried for 2 hours at 105°C. Any oil adhering to the sample should be removed by extraction with $CHCl_3$. The amount and nature of the extracted material should be recorded. The dried material should be ground in a mortar and quartered down to about 15 gm. This quartered sample should be further prepared by grinding to pass a 100-mesh sieve and thoroughly mixed. Portions of this prepared sample are used for the chemical analyses as outlined.

Preliminary tests on some of the scale (not the portion set aside for chemical analysis) may shorten the analysis by showing the presence or absence of some elements or compounds. These tests may be made using spot testing methods, spectrographic equipment, or X-ray diffraction equipment.

2. LOSS ON IGNITION

(1) Use 0.5 gm of prepared sample.
(2) Heat in an open crucible at 400°C for 1 hr.
(3) Cool, weigh, and record weight.
(4) Reheat to 900° to 1,000°C for 1 hr.
(5) Cool, weigh, and record weight.
(6) Report % wt loss at 400°C and 900° to 1000°C.

3. WATER-SOLUBLE MATERIALS

(1) Use 0.5 gm of prepared sample.
(2) Add sample to 100 ml distilled water and stir for 1 hr.
(3) Filter through a weighed filter crucible and air-dry.
(4) Weigh crucible and calculate % water-soluble material.
(5) Report % water-soluble.

4. Sulfide Determination

(1) Use 0.5 gm of prepared sample.

(2) Use evolution method for sulfide determination.[1]

5. Carbonates and Bicarbonates Determination

(1) Use 0.5 gm of prepared sample.

(2) Use the procedure for the determination of CO_2 in carbonates.[2,3]

6. Solution of Sample and Silica Determination

(1) Use 1.0 gm of prepared sample.

(2) Add 10 to 20 ml of distilled water to the sample.

(3) To this slowly add 50 ml HCl.

(4) Digest on a water bath for 15 min.

(5) Add 20 ml HNO_3 and evaporate to dryness.

(6) Wash the filter with a hot solution of 5 ml HCl and 95 ml H_2O.

(7) Save the residue, filtrate, and washings.

(8) Combine the filtrate and washings. Evaporate to dryness.

(9) Dehydrate the residue from step (8) at 105° to 110°C for 2 hrs.

(10) Cool residue and add 10 ml HCl. Cover and heat on a water bath for 10 min.

(11) Dilute with 50 ml cold water and filter immediately.

(12) Save the filtrate.

(13) Combine the filter papers from steps (7) and (11).

(14) Determine silica in the combined residues.[4]

(15) Add 5 gm Na_2CO_3 to the residue of step (14). Mix intimately and heat gradually in a covered platinum crucible until complete fusion results. Then heat for 20 min in the full flame of a Meker burner.

(16) After cooling, digest the fused mass with hot distilled H_2O to remove any soluble sulfates. Filter, and wash the residue and crucible clean of sulfates with dilute ammonia water. Collect filtrate and washings for sulfate analysis.

(17) Wash the carbonates off of the paper into a beaker. Use 1:1 HCl to dissolve any carbonates clinging to the filter paper. Cautiously add this extract to the main carbonate mass. Completely dissolve the carbonate mass by the cautious addition of 1:1 HCl. Transfer to a 250 ml volumetric flask and make up to volume.

(18) Combine the filtrate from step (12) with the filtrate of step (16) in a 250 ml volumetric flask and make up to volume.

(19) Pipette 50 ml from the 250 ml solution of step (17) into a test tube. Add 50 ml from the 250 ml solution of step (18). Mix thoroughly and let stand overnight. If no turbidity or precipitate forms, combine the solutions of steps (17) and (18) and use this for the analysis. If turbidity or a precipitate forms, solutions from steps (17) and (18) must be analyzed separately. The solution from step (17) need only be analyzed for Ba, Ca, and Mg.

7. SULFATE DETERMINATION

(1) Use 50 ml of the solution from step (6–18) or those combined in step (6–19).

(2) Determine sulfate as $BaSO_4$.[5,6,7]

8. IRON DETERMINATION

(1) Use the solution from step (6–18) or those combined in step (6–19).

(2) Determine iron colorimetrically, using the Phenanthroline or 2, 2', 2'' Tripyridyl procedure.[8]

9. BARIUM DETERMINATION

(1) Use solution from step (6–17) or if combined (6–19).

(2) Determine barium as $BaSO_4$.[9]

(3) Save filtrate and washings for Ca and Mg determinations.

10. CALCIUM DETERMINATION

(1) Neutralize the solution of step (9–3) with NH_4OH.

(2) Acidify with citric acid.

(3) Determine calcium, using the procedure in *Standard Methods*.[10]

(4) Save the filtrate for Mg determination.

(5) If the solutions were not combined in step (6–19), calcium should be determined on the solution of step (6–18).

11. MAGNESIUM DETERMINATION

(1) Use the filtrate from the calcium determination.

(2) Determine magnesium, using the procedure in *Standard Methods*.[11]

(3) If the solutions were not combined in step (6–19), magnesium should be determined on the filtrates from the calcium determinations of solutions from steps (6–17) and (6–18).

12. Scale Analysis Flow Sheet

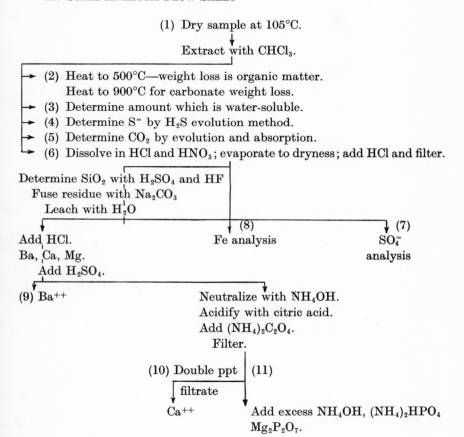

(1) Dry sample at 105°C.

Extract with CHCl₃.

(2) Heat to 500°C—weight loss is organic matter.
    Heat to 900°C for carbonate weight loss.
(3) Determine amount which is water-soluble.
(4) Determine S⁼ by H₂S evolution method.
(5) Determine CO₂ by evolution and absorption.
(6) Dissolve in HCl and HNO₃; evaporate to dryness; add HCl and filter.

Determine SiO₂ with H₂SO₄ and HF
  Fuse residue with Na₂CO₃
    Leach with H₂O

Add HCl.   (8)   (7)
Ba, Ca, Mg.   Fe analysis   SO₄⁼
  Add H₂SO₄.   analysis

(9) Ba⁺⁺   Neutralize with NH₄OH.
                        Acidify with citric acid.
                        Add (NH₄)₂C₂O₄.
                          Filter.

                (10) Double ppt │ (11)

                      │ filtrate
                    Ca⁺⁺   Add excess NH₄OH, (NH₄)₂HPO₄
                                      Mg₂P₂O₇.

Procedure for Evaluation of Corrosion Weight-Loss Specimens

1. New Specimens

(1) Remove grease from specimen, using carbon tetrachloride or trichloroethane.

(2) Remove rust and scale by dipping specimen in dilute (1:1 or 6N) HCl containing 2 per cent Polyrad 1110A as corrosion inhibitor.

(3) Using a surgeon's brush and water, scrub specimen thoroughly with Alconox powder.

(4) Wash specimen in flowing water.

(5) Dip specimen in C.P. dry acetone or C.P. dry methyl alcohol.

(6) Dry specimen under vacuum in a desiccator.

(7) Weigh specimen on analytical balance to 0.1 mg and replace in desiccator.

(8) Using a dry box, or on a very low humidity day ($<$25%), package specimen by heat-sealing in 6-mil polyethylene tape or use of Miracle tape or equivalent. (If a pressure-sensitive tape is used, the specimen must be wrapped in thin polyethylene before the tape is used.)

2. Exposed Specimens

(1) Using dilute (1:1 or 6N containing 2% Polyrad 1110A inhibitor) HCl, spot-test scale on surface of specimen for $S^=$ or $CO_3^=$. Use extreme care to prevent the acid from attacking the metal itself.

(2) Using a surgical brush, clean the specimen by scrubbing with Alconox. If this fails to clean the specimen, it may be cleaned by an electrochemical method. The specimen is made the cathode and treated for 3 min at 74°C in 5% H_2SO_4, using 7 ml Rodine 67 corrosion inhibitor in 1,000 ml of the pickling solution. A current density of 20 amp/sq dm is used.

(3) Wash specimen in water.

(4) Dip specimen in C.P. dry acetone or C.P. dry methyl alcohol.

(5) Dry specimen under vacuum in a desiccator.

(6) Weight on analytical balance to 0.1 mg.

(7) Calculate corrosion rate in *mpy* using the formula:

$$mpy = \frac{(\text{weight loss in grams})(365,000)}{A\rho t} \tag{A-3}$$

where A = coupon area, sq in.

ρ = metal density, g per cu in. (= 128.8 for iron)

t = time, days

(8) Measure pits, using a reliable pit depth gauge.

(9) Report maximum penetration; average penetration; in mils and *mpy*.

(10) Place clean coupons in a tightly sealed jar containing a silica gel packet and return to the laboratory.

Jar Test[12]

1. APPARATUS

Tests may be made in 1- or 2-quart glass jars. Variable speed, multiple stirrers should be used to provide agitation during the tests. A light source to provide illumination for watching floc formation is also necessary.

2. SOLUTIONS

Solutions of coagulants or other chemicals are made up so that 1 ml added to the sample results in a concentration of 1 ppm. Suspensions of lime or clay of known concentration should also be made. These suspensions can be measured by shaking vigorously and quickly measuring the desired amount before the suspended material settles.

3. PROCEDURE

(1) A 1- or 2-liter sample of known concentration of suspended material is prepared by adding some of the prepared lime or clay suspensions to water. The actual water may also be used.

(2) Solution of the coagulating agent is added to the sample.

(3) Flash-mix the sample. The stirring rate is then decreased to a rate low enough to condition the floc. The period of floc conditioning should not exceed the plant mixing time.

(4) Stop the agitation and note the time necessary for the floc to settle. The percentage of the floc settled in 5-minute periods (or other appropriate time periods) can be estimated.

(5) Plot the data.

Estimation of the percentage settled is subject to human error. Experience will usually enable the operator to obtain usable data. Also, there is a large difference between good and poor coagulation and rapid settling. First tests generally show the approximate concentrations and proper pH range for good coagulation. Additional tests will show the required amount of coagulant and optimum pH for best results. Several tests can be run at one time. Care should be used to keep all conditions the same.

Determination of Sand Porosity[13]

1. APPARATUS

A Jackson turbidimeter tube, 750 mm long, is required.

2. PROCEDURE

(1) Fill the Jackson turbidimeter tube approximately half-full of water.

(2) Add a weighed sample w of approximately 150 gm of sand to the tube.

(3) Shake the tube to remove air entrained in the sand.

(4) Decant any water that appears above the sand, being careful not to lose any sand. Shake again to be sure all the air is removed.

(5) Fill the tube with water and stopper. Be sure no air space is left.

(6) Invert the tube so that all the sand rests on the stopper. Turn the tube right side up and immediately clamp in position. This should be accomplished before the first sand grains reach the bottom of the tube.

(7) As soon as the sand has settled, read the volume v.

(8) The per cent porosity of silica sand is then calculated:

$$\text{per cent porosity} = \frac{v - \dfrac{w}{2.65}}{v} \times 100 \tag{A–4}$$

Water Compatibility Test

Two waters are mixed in definite proportions to test their compatibility. If an induction period is required before salt deposition occurs, it is important that the test be observed for a considerable length of time. If no reaction occurs that produces a deposit, it is advisable to seed the test waters with a crystal of the salt most likely to deposit. From water analysis data, it is possible to calculate the composition of the mixed water. A prediction can then be made of which salt will be most likely to deposit, and a few small crystals of it can be used to seed the test mixtures.

The water used in the compatibility test should be freshly sampled according to approved sampling techniques. If necessary, the water should be filtered to remove any entrained or suspended solids. The water must be clear and free of solids before the test.

For testing the compatibility of two waters, A and B, the following procedure is used. Seven clean culture tubes are set in the rack and numbered one through seven. Waters A and B are added to the tubes in the amounts shown in the succeeding tabulation. The tubes are then capped and agitated by turning end-over-end several times. After standing for 24 hours, the tubes are inspected visually for the formation of deposits.

Tube No.	1	2	3	4	5	6	7
Water A, ml	50	45	35	25	15	5	0
Water B, ml	0	5	15	25	35	45	50

If tubes one and seven remain free of deposits, and any or all of the tubes two through six have deposits, the waters are unstable when mixed in the indicated proportions. For example, if tubes two and three had deposits but not four, five, and six, mixtures of more than 50 per cent A and less than 50 per cent B would be incompatible.

If tubes one and seven remain clear and free of deposits, it means that the sample water is stable during the test period; otherwise, sample instability under the test conditions is indicated. In the case of unstable waters, it is advisable to send filtered or clear deposit-free samples (at the time of sampling) to the laboratory for a mineral analysis and predictions of compatibility based on calculations.

Membrane Filtration Test Instructions

This test is intended to determine the tendency of solids suspended in field waters to reduce the filtration rate, when the waters are filtered through special filter membranes of known pore size. The amount and composition of the solids can be determined by further laboratory tests. A preferred and two alternate procedures that differ in the manner of collecting the samples and the filtration pressures are given. Comparison of data obtained from membrane filtration tests should only be made with data obtained by the same procedure and at the same pressure.

1. APPARATUS

The following apparatus and materials are required:

(1) Membrane filter holder of 47 millimeter filter disc—available from Custom Fabrication Corp., 2711 Dawson Road, Tulsa, Okla.; approximate cost, $75.

(2) Graduated filtration sample reservoir, 20 psig, 4 liter—available from Custom Fabrication Corp., 2711 Dawson Road, Tulsa, Okla.; approximate cost, $35. (Note: Required for first alternate test procedure only.)

(3) Membrane filter discs—two types of membranes are available. The cellulose disc (item *a*) is the standard and is recommended for use where precision is required; the polyethylene solvent resistant disc (item *b*) can be used if less precision is desired, with systems containing oil, or if the particles being filtered are large.

(a) Cellulose filter membranes, 47 millimeter (mm) diameter, 0.47 microns (μ) $\pm$ 0.02 pore size, MF type, HA white with grid—available from Millipore Filter Corp., Bedford, Mass., approximate cost, $18 per hundred.

(b) Special polyethylene solvent resistant filter membranes, 47 mm diameter, $1.5\mu \pm 0.5$ pore size, MF type, OH with grid—available from Millipore Filter Corp., Bedford, Mass., approximate cost, $27 per hundred.

(4) Pressure gauge, graduated cylinder, and miscellaneous valves, tubing and fittings necessary to attach the membrane holder to the flow line or other water reservoir.

(5) Weighed membrane filter discs—when determining the amount of suspended solids in the water, the membrane filter discs (3*a* and *b*) should be weighed before and after use. After use, the membrane and collected solids should be carefully replaced in the holder and returned to the laboratory for reweighing and analysis, if required.

2. Procedures

(1) Preferred Membrane Filtration Test

(a) Place a membrane filter disc in the holder. Use a weighed disc if the amount of suspended solids is to be determined.

(b) Attach the filter holder to the system as shown in Fig. A.3. The use of flexible tubing will facilitate movement of the attached filter holder. Open the valve before attaching the filter and flow until any sludge or deposits that may have accumulated in the valve have been removed.

(c) Open the valve and slowly fill the membrane filter holder with water. Any air trapped in the filter should be removed by loosening a thumb screw on the filter holder that serves as a bleed-off valve. When the filter is filled with water, the filtration is started. The pressure drop across the filter should be adjusted and maintained at 20 psig for the filtration. Greater

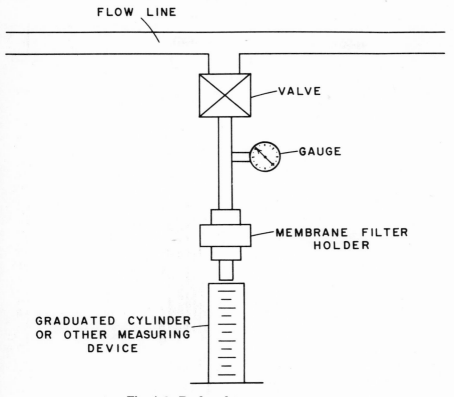

Fig. A.3. Preferred test system.

pressures may injure the membrane. Lesser pressures are permissible, but only data taken at the same pressure may be compared.

(d) The time of filtration should be started with the first drop through the filter when the pressure differential across the filter is 20 psig (less, if this pressure is not available).

(e) The measurement of filtrate volume should coincide with the start of timing. A definite volume of filtrate should be collected (250 milliliters is suggested), and the time necessary for this volume to pass through the filter recorded. Both time and volume are recorded as cumulative values. The time is recorded each time 250 ml of water are filtered.

(f) A minimum of 4 liters of water should be filtered unless the rate of filtration decreases rapidly. This would be all the indication necessary of poor water quality. In all instances where a solids analysis is desired, the

Table A.3

MEMBRANE FILTRATION DATA

Cumulative Volume (liter)	Differential Cumulative Volume (liter)	Cumulative Time (sec)	Differential Cumulative Time (sec)	Flow Rate (ml/sec)
		Water *A*		
0.50	0.50	40	40	12.4
1.00	0.50	82	42	11.8
1.50	0.50	126	44	11.4
2.00	0.50	171	45	11.0
2.50	0.50	217	46	10.9
3.00	0.50	263	46	10.9
3.50	0.50	309	46	10.9
4.00	0.50	355	46	10.9
		Water *B*		
0.25	0.25	26.4	26.4	9.5
0.50	0.25	72.8	46.4	5.4
0.75	0.25	137.0	64.2	3.9
1.00	0.25	215.2	78.2	3.2
1.25	0.25	311.3	96.1	2.6
1.50	0.25	425.3	114.0	2.2
1.75	0.25	447.3	132.0	1.9
2.00	0.25	713.3	156.0	1.6
2.25	0.25	892.3	179.0	1.4
2.50	0.25	1084.3	192.0	1.3
2.75	0.25	1292.3	208.0	1.2
3.00	0.25	1520.3	228.0	1.1
3.25	0.25	3070.3	250.0	1.0
3.50	0.25	3320.3	250.0	1.0

volume filtered must be large enough to provide a sufficient amount of solids for analysis.

(g) A table similar to Table A.2 should be made. The field data is collected as cumulative volume and time. The differential cumulative volume and time can then be obtained and the filtration rate calculated.

(h) The data is plotted on graph paper as shown in Fig. A.4. Curve *A* represents a good-quality water and definitely better than the quality of water represented by Curve *B*.

(i) If the amount and composition of the solid is desired at the conclusion of the filtration, the weighed filter membrane is carefully removed from the holder and replaced in its plastic case for return to the laboratory.

(2) FIRST ALTERNATE MEMBRANE FILTRATION TEST PROCEDURE

(a) While the system is flowing, collect 4 liters of water in the lucite reservoir. The reservoir is then pressured to 20 psi with nitrogen gas from a cylinder.

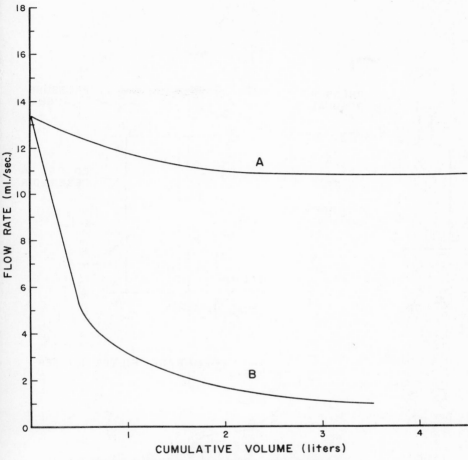

Fig. A.4. Graphic presentation of filtration data.

(b) Proceed with steps (a) through (i), outlined under the preferred method. Figure A.5 is a diagram showing the first alternate test system.

(3) SECOND ALTERNATE MEMBRANE FILTRATION TEST PROCEDURE

(a) While the system is flowing, collect 4 liters of water in a glass jug. Place the jug 4 feet vertically above the membrane filter holder. Siphon the water from the jug to the filter. This will provide a nearly constant filtration pressure.

(b) Repeat steps (a) and (c) through (i), outlined under the preferred method. Figure A.6 is a diagram showing the second alternate test system.

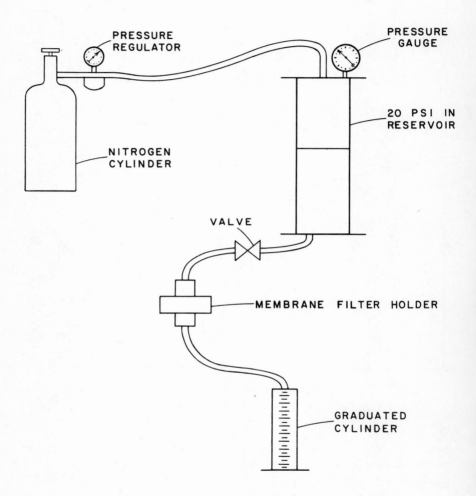

Fig. A.5. First alternate test system.

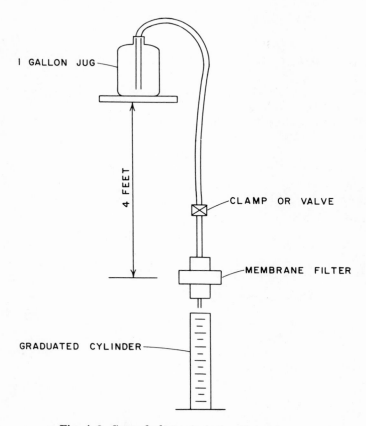

Fig. A.6. Second alternate test system.

References

[1]W. W. Scott, *Standard Methods of Chemical Analysis*, **1** (6th ed.), ed. N. H. Furman (Princeton, N.J.: D. Van Nostrand Company, 1962), p. 1031.

[2]*Ibid.*, p. 298.

[3]*Manual on Industrial Water and Industrial Waste Water* (2nd ed.) (Philadelphia, Pa.: American Society for Testing Materials, 1960), p. 227.

[4]Scott, *op. cit.*, p. 974.

[5]*Ibid.*, p. 1007.

[6]*Manual on Industrial Water, op. cit.*, p. 246.

[7]*Standard Methods for the Examination of Water and Wastewater* (11th ed.) (New York: American Public Health Association, Inc., 1960), p. 237.

[8]*Ibid.*, p. 139.

[9]Scott, *op. cit.*, p. 148.

[10]*Standard Methods for the Examination of Water, op. cit.*, 67.

[11]*Ibid.*, p. 151.

[12]*Water Quality and Treatment* (2nd ed.) (New York: The American Water Works Association, 1951), p. 157.

[13]"Specifications for Filtering Material," *Am. Water Works Assoc.*, **41** (1949), p. 290.

Appendix

API Recommended Practice for Biological Analysis of Water-Flood Injection Waters*

FOREWORD

This recommended practice has been developed by the Mid-Continent District Study Committee on Biological Analysis of Water To Be Used for Waterflood Purposes, in cooperation with research laboratories of operating and chemical companies, and university biology departments.

The objective of the study committee was to set up standard methods of test for determination of the effectiveness of chemicals for treating injection waters to prevent the growth of sulfate-reducing bacteria and to develop procedures for the biological analysis of injection waters.

*Reproduced with permission of the American Petroleum Institute from RP38 (First Edition) (May 1959).

It is believed that these methods will help eliminate some of the confusion concerning biological analysis of injection waters. The use of the standard procedures will allow evaluation of analyses from various waterfloods in order to determine the extent of biological problems in secondary-recovery operations.

1. EXAMINATION FOR MICROORGANISMS

a. Scope

A knowledge of the microbial population of an injection water is necessary to determine whether or not a biological problem exists. This knowledge is also necessary to follow the effectiveness of a chemical treatment.

These procedures are intended to show, in a general way, the number and types of microorganisms present in a particular water sample.

b. Purity of Reagents

Unless otherwise indicated, all chemical reagents shall meet American Chemical Society specifications. Bacteriological grades of beef extract, yeast extract, tryptone, and agar shall also be used.

c. Special Apparatus

(1) Bacteria-colony counter.
(2) Cover glasses—round or square.
(3) Incubator—constant-temperature.
(4) Microscope—capable of providing magnification from 100 to 1,000 diameters
(5) Petri dishes—standard 100 × 15 mm.
(6) Pipettes—bacteriological or serological 1- and 10-ml.
(7) Slides—standard and hanging drop.
(8) Sterilizer—stream.
(9) Test tubes—bacteriological, 150 × 16 mm, without flare or with screw caps.
(10) Water bath—constant temperature.

d. Sampling Methods

(1) A clean sterile bottle will be used.
(2) All taps should be allowed to flow at least 3 min prior to taking the sample.
(3) The bottle should be rinsed at least 3 times in the water to be sampled prior to actually taking the sample.

(4)   The sample should be taken in such a manner as to preclude contamination from external sources.

(5)   The time, date, temperature, and appearance of the water should be recorded at the time of sampling and this information included with the sample. If possible, the total solids and/or salt content of the water should also be included.

(6)   The maximum time between sampling the examination should be 24 hours.

(7)   If an examination cannot be initiated within the 24-hour period, the transportation time should always be reported with the results. The following statement should also be included in the report: "These results do not necessarily represent the actual microbial content of the water at the time of sampling."

e. Microscopic Examination of Water

Microscopic examination makes possible the detection of significant numbers of microbes which are not easily cultivated on ordinary laboratory media. In addition, it may permit an estimation of the numbers of bacteria present, which may be used as a guide in making plate counts.

Probably the best method of examination is by the use of the *phase* type microscope. In this manner one can more easily view the microorganisms "in vivo" and also avoid the distorting tendencies of some of the staining techniques.

The examination should include identification of microorganisms as follows:

(1) Algae and Protozoa
  (a) flagellates
  (b) ciliates
  (c) diatoms
  (d) filamentous
(2) Bacteria
  (a) iron bacteria—describe the type, i.e., sheath or ribbon
  (b) sulfur bacteria
  (c) bacterial slime
(3) Fungi

The microscopic count of each type shall be reported as none, present, present in large numbers. If large numbers of any type are present, a more complete description of this type should be given.

The membrane filter has been found very useful in the detection and enumeration of iron bacteria, algae, and protozoa. A quantity of the water under examination can be filtered through the membrane filter. The filter should be dried, then cut into small squares and placed on microscope slides.

The filter squares can be rendered transparent by a drop of immersion oil, then subjected to the usual microscopic examination.

f. General Bacterial Counts of Injection Waters

The following medium shall be used for making bacterial counts on waters containing less than 20,000 ppm total solids.

Beef extract, grams	3.0
Tryptone, grams	5.0
Dextrose, grams	1.0
Agar, grams	15.0
Distilled water, milliliters	1,000

Adjust pH to 7.0 with sodium hydroxide (NaOH) and sterilize at 15 lb steam pressure for 15 min.

This medium may be purchased in the dehydrated form as Tryptone Glucose Extract Agar.

The sulfate-reducer medium (Par. g) shall be used for making plate counts on waters containing over 20,000 ppm total solids.

Pour plates are more desirable than spread plates because of minimization of surface spreading colonies. Dilutions and plate counts are to be made in the manner prescribed by the latest edition of *Standard Methods for the Examination of Water, Sewage, and Industrial Wastes.*

Plates shall be incubated under aerobic conditions and within 5°C of the recorded temperature of the water when sampled.

Plates should be read at the end of 5 days and at the end of 10 days.

For untreated waters, bacterial counts of less than 10,000 organisms per milliliter are generally of little significance. The significance of counts above 10,000 per milliliter will depend upon additional evidence such as loss of injectivity, increased wellhead pressure, or filter plugging.

g. Sulfate-reducing Bacteria Counts

A medium of the following composition shall be used for counting sulfate-reducing bacteria.

Sodium lactate, USP, milliliters.	4.0
Yeast extract, grams	1.0
Ascorbic acid, grams	0.1
$MgSO_4 \cdot 7H_2O$, grams	0.2
K_2HPO_4 (anhydrous), grams	0.01
$Fe(SO_4)_2(NH_4)_2 \cdot 6H_2O$, grams	0.1
NaCl, grams	10.0
Agar, grams	15.0
Distilled water, milliliters	1000

The ingredients should be dissolved with gentle heating. The pH should then be adjusted to 7.5 with NaOH. If excessive precipitation occurs, the medium should be discarded. The medium is dispensed into test tubes (9 ml per tube), which are then autoclaved for 10 min at 15 psi steam pressure. Screw caps or rubber stoppers should be used to seal the tubes to prevent dehydration of the medium.

After autoclaving, the tubes are cooled to 45° C in a water bath. A series of tubes are inoculated from the sample, to be counted by dilution to extinction. One milliliter of the water sample is transferred to the first tube. The tube is stoppered and flowed back and forth four times to mix the inoculum. One milliliter from this tube is then transferred to a second tube and mixed as before. Continue this serial transfer until a dilution of 1 to 10,000 is reached. After the inoculum has been transferred from each tube, the tube should. be cooled rapidly to solidify the agar. To prevent solidification of agar in the transfer pipettes, warm pipettes (near 45°C) should be used for this operation.

All work is done in duplicate and tubes are incubated at a temperature within 5°C of the recorded temperature of the water at the time of sampling.

All tubes should be held a minimum of 3 weeks. The tubes should be examined daily for the appearance of sulfate-reducing bacteria, as indicated by intense black colonies.

The presence of any number of sulfate-reducing bacteria is considered to represent a potential problem. The extent of the problem will depend upon additional evidence, such as black water of increased iron sulfide content of the injection water.

2. Evaluation of Chemicals for Control of Sulfate-Reducing Bacteria

a. Scope

This procedure is intended to be used to evaluate chemicals as microbial-control agents in water-injection systems where sulfate-reducing bacteria are a problem, and where it is believed that chemical control measures can be expected to yield a desirable end result.

The method is designed to be used for screening purposes in the laboratory. Application to specific sulfate-reducer control problems may require modification of these techniques (see last section).

b. Purity of Reagents

Unless otherwise indicated, all chemical reagents shall meet ACS specifications. Bacteriological grades of agar and yeast extract shall also be used.

c. Special Aparatus

(1) Bottles—1- or 2-oz clear round.

(2)   Bottle screw caps—liners of aluminum foil or Teflon.

(3)   Filter paper—Whatman No. 1 or No. 2, or equivalent.

(4)   Incubator—constant-temperature.

(5)   Pipettes—bacteriological or serological 1 and 10 ml.

(6)   Sterilizer—steam.

(7)   Test tubes—bacteriological, 150 × 16 mm, without flare or with screw caps.

d. Screening Methods-Bacteriostatic Test

The composition of the sulfate-reducer medium for the bacteriostatic test is as follows:

Sodium lactate, USP, milliliters	4.0
Yeast extract, grams	1.0
Ascorbic acid, grams	0.1
$MgSO_4 \cdot 7H_2O$, grams	0.2
K_2HPO_4 (anhydrous), grams	0.01
$Fe(SO_4)_2(NH_4)_2 \cdot 6H_2O*$, grams	0.1
NaCl, grams	10.0
Distilled water, milliliters	1000

The ingredients are dissolved by gentle heating with constant stirring. After dissolution has occurred, the pH of the medium should be adjusted to 7.5 with NaOH. If necessary, the medium is then filtered through Whatman No. 1 or No. 2 filter paper. Following filtration the medium is autoclaved at 15 lb steam pressure for 10 min. After autoclaving the medium is allowed to cool slightly and the iron salt added. The pH is then checked and readjusted if necessary. The medium is now cooled to room temperature as rapidly as possible, without agitation.

After cooling, the medium is inoculated. The inoculum should be from the third successive 24-hour transfer of an actively growing culture of sulfate-reducing bacteria. An actively growing culture is defined as "a liquid culture which turns black within 24 hours after inoculation." Ten milliliters of inoculum are added to each liter of medium.

From stock solutions of the chemical to be screened, sufficient amounts of the compound should be added to 1- or 2-oz clear bottles so that when the containers are filled, the desired concentrations of chemical are present. The amount of stock solution added should not exceed 10 percent of the volume of the test bottle. After addition of the chemical, the bottles are completely filled with the inoculated medium. The bottles are then capped with plastic caps containing cork and aluminum foil or teflon liners and incubated at 35°C ±2°C.

All work is done in duplicate with at least three controls for each series. The controls consist of bottles filled with inoculated medium only. Growth of

*Added after sterilization.

sulfate reducers in the bottles is indicated by an intense blackening of the medium, whereas containers having sufficient chemical to inhibit growth will remain clear. Bottles with no sulfate-reducer growth are observed for a period of 30 days after the controls have blackened.

If the compound under test is effective at less than 50 ppm, the end point should be reported to within 5 ppm (such as 10-15 ppm). If the compound is effective at a concentration range above 50 ppm, the end point should be reported to within 10 ppm (such as 70-80 ppm).

Test cultures of sulfate-reducing bacteria should be used for no more than one month. After this period of time a new test culture must be obtained from the stock culture.

Stock cultures should be transferred every 6 months. Stocks can be carried on sulfate-reducer counting medium (see Section "g.") which contains only 0.3 percent agar.

Mid-Continent Strain *A** has been designated as the test culture of sulfate-reducing bacteria to be used for comparative screening of chemicals. This culture is available from the Department of Bacteriology, University of Texas, Austin, Tex. The university charges a small fee for transfer of this culture.

e. Screening Methods—Other Evaluation Procedures

Usually the final evaluation of a compound for use in a particular injection water will involve some variation of the time-kill technique. This type of test involves exposing sulfate-reducing bacteria to chemical agents and, at various time intervals, determining the number of surviving organisms. A tentative time-kill test procedure is given in the next section.

3. Tentative Time—Kill Test

The test medium is artificial sea water, the composition and instructions for preparation of which are given in Section 5. One-ounce clear dropping bottles with the dropper graduated to deliver 0.5 and 1.0 ml are used as test containers.

From stock solutions of the chemical to be screened, sufficient amounts of the compound should be added to the 1-oz dropping bottles so that the desired concentration of chemical will be reached when a total of 25 ml of fluid is present in each bottle. The amount of stock solution added should not exceed 2.5 ml. The brine solution (pH 7.2) is then added to the bottles in amounts calculated to give a total of 25 ml of fluid in each bottle.

The dropping bottles are then placed in a 30°C water bath, brought to temperature and inoculated. The inoculum shall be 0.25 ml of a 1 to 100

*This culture was isolated in Texaco, Inc., bacteriological laboratory.

dilution of a broth culture of sulfate-reducing bacteria. The culture used for the inoculation should be from the third successive 24-hour transfer of an actively growing culture.

One hour after inoculation 1-ml aliquots are removed from each bottle and placed in tubes containing 9 ml of sulfate-reducer medium (listed above) which have been maintained at 45°C. From these tubes dilutions of 1-10 and 1-100 are made in additional tubes of sulfate-reducer media. For the controls, dilutions are carried through 1-1,000. Following inoculation the tubes are either capped or stoppered with rubber stoppers and flowed back and forth four times. The tubes are then cooled rapidly and placed in an incubator set at 35°C $\pm$ 2°C. The tubes are observed for a period of 3 weeks and sulfate reducers are determined by counting the number of black colonies present in the tubes. All work should be done in duplicate.

Results are reported in terms of the bactericide concentrations which give a 99 percent or better kill. If the effective concentration is less than 50 ppm, the concentration range should be reported to within 5 ppm. If the effective concentration is above 50 ppm, the concentration range should be reported to within 10 ppm.

4. APPLICATION OF TIME-KILL PROCEDURE

One application of the time-kill test procedure is as follows:

Injection waters known to be infected with sulfate-reducing bacteria are exposed to various concentrations of the chemical under consideration. At specific time intervals aliquots are removed and placed in tubes of sulfate-reducer medium. The tubes are then incubated and observed for the appearance of black colonies. The test and incubation can be carried out at the temperature of the water in the field. In the time-kill test the exposure time to the bactericide should be the same as that to be used in the field, i.e., the time it takes the water to travel from the point of bactericide injection to the injection well.

5. SPECIFICATION FOR SUBSTITUTE OCEAN WATER*

a. Purity of Reagents

Reagent-grade chemicals shall be used in all solutions. Unless otherwise indicated, it is intended that all reagents shall conform to the specifications of the Committee on Analytical Reagents of the American Chemical Society, from which such specifications are available. Other grades may be

*ASTM Designation D1141–50T, modified to give a pH of 7.2.

used, provided it is first ascertained that the reagent is of sufficiently high purity to permit its use without lessening the purity of the solution.

b. Reagents

Stock Solution No. 1: Dissolve the indicated amounts of the following salts in distilled water and dilute to a total volume of 7.0 liters. Store in well-stoppered glass containers.

$MgCl_2 \cdot 6H_2O$	3889.0 grams
$CaCl_2$ (anhydrous)	405.6
$SrCl_2 \cdot 6H_2O$	14.8

Stock Solution No. 2: Dissolve the indicated amounts of the following salts in distilled water and dilute to a total volume of 7.0 liters. Store in well-stoppered glass containers.

KCl	486.0 grams
$NaHCO_3$	140.7
KBr	70.4
H_3BO_3	19.0
NaF	2.1

c. Preparation of Substitute Ocean Water

Dissolve 245.34 g of NaCl and 40.94 g of anhydrous Na_2SO_4 in 8 to 9 liters of distilled water. Add slowly with vigorous stirring, 200 ml of Stock Solution No. 1 and then 100 ml of Stock Solution No. 2. Dilute to 10.0 liters. Adjust the pH to 7.2 with 0.1 N NaOH solution. Only a few milliliters of NaOH solution should be required.

NOTE: The solution should be prepared and the pH adjusted immediately prior to use.

Index